McGraw-Hill
Mathematics

Transition
Handbook

Bridge the Gaps!

**What Do I Need
to Know?**

Skill Builder

Challenge

Teacher Guide
4

**McGraw-Hill
School Division**

New York   Farmington

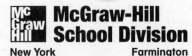

McGraw-Hill School Division ⊗

A Division of The McGraw-Hill Companies

Copyright © McGraw-Hill School Division,
a Division of the Educational and Professional Publishing Group of The McGraw-Hill Companies, Inc.
All rights reserved. Permission granted to reproduce for use with McGraw-Hill MATHEMATICS.

McGraw-Hill School Division
Two Penn Plaza
New York, New York 10121-2298

Printed in the United States of America

ISBN 0-02-100206-1 / 4

3 4 5 6 7 8 9 066 05 04 03 02

GRADE 4
Contents

Chapter 1
Place Value and Money

Chapter 2
Addition and Subtraction

Chapter 3
Data, Statistics, and Graphing

Chapter 4
Multiplication and Division Facts

Chapter 5
Multiply by 1-Digit Numbers

Chapter 6
Multiply by 2-Digit Numbers

Chapter 7
Divide by 1-Digit Numbers

Chapter 8
Divide by 2-Digit Numbers

Chapter 9
Measurement

Chapter 10
Geometry

Chapter 11
Fractions and Probability

Chapter 12
Fraction Operations

Chapter 13
Relate Fractions and Decimals

Chapter 14
Decimal Operations

To the Teacher

Welcome to *McGraw-Hill Mathematics Transition Handbook: Bridge the Gaps!* The goal of these materials is to provide assessment and instruction in the prerequisite skills that some of your students need to be successful in math at this grade level.

For each chapter of the *McGraw-Hill Mathematics* student text, there is a 2-page inventory test called *What Do I Need To Know?* You will find these inventory tests as blackline masters on the A and B pages in this Teacher Guide. The results of the tests will help you diagnose any gaps in student knowledge. You can then provide students with materials needed to reteach or challenge them as appropriate.

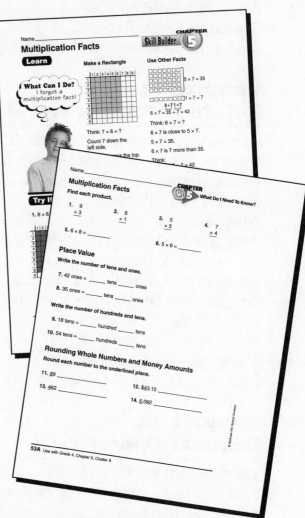

The charts found on the C and D pages following the blackline masters will prescribe a special *Skill Builder* lesson in the handbook for each test item that a student answers incorrectly.

The *Skill Builder* lessons are presented in language that is simple and direct. The lessons are highly visual and have been designed to keep reading to a minimum.

The Learn section begins with a student asking *What Can I Do?* This section provides stepped-out models and one or more strategies to help bridge any gaps in the student's knowledge. Following this is *Try It*, a section of guided practice, and *Power Practice*, a section containing exercises to ensure that your students acquire the math power they need to be successful in each chapter of their mathematics textbook.

Within chapters you will see a feature called *Learn with Partners & Parents*. This activity is intended for students to use at home with parents or siblings or at school with a classmate-partner to practice a math skill in a game-like setting.

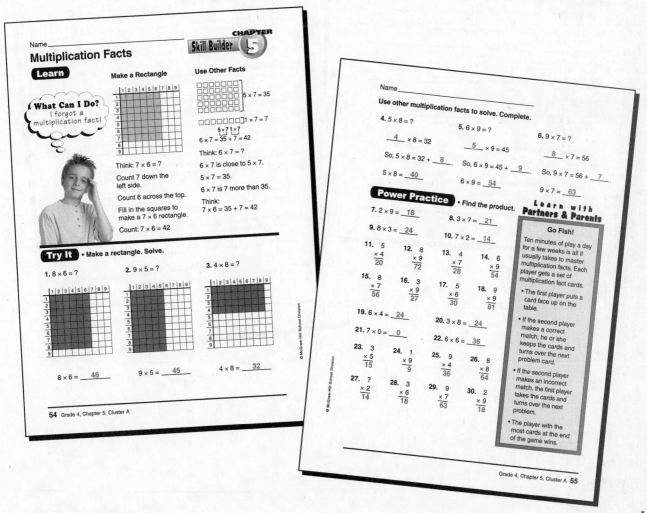

Two *Challenge* activities appear at the end of each chapter in the handbook. These provide a variety of math experiences for students who had no difficulty with the inventory test. Students will enjoy working on the puzzles, riddles, codes, and other more challenging formats. The *Challenge* activities will provide an opportunity for your more advanced students to work independently, allowing you to focus attention on those who need additional instruction before they work on the lessons in their math text.

Name _____

Multiplication with Missing Digits

Some digits are missing from these problems. Use what you know about multiplication to help you replace each letter with the correct digit.

$$\begin{array}{r} 2A \\ \times\ 4 \\ \hline 1B2 \end{array} \qquad \begin{array}{r} D9 \\ \times\ C \\ \hline E14 \end{array}$$

1. Can you replace the letter **A** with a 5? Why or why not? _____
_____

2. What are the only two digits you should try as replacements for **A**? Explain.
_____

3. Tell how you can decide which of the two digits you mentioned in your answer to
question 2 *cannot* replace **A**. _____
_____
_____
_____

4. **A** = _____ **B** = _____ Tell how you know. _____
_____
_____

5. What digit can replace **C**? _____ How do you know? _____ × 9 = 54; 6 is
_____

6. Find all the correct replacement digits for **D** and **E**. _____
_____

© McGraw-Hill School Division

Name _____

$$\begin{array}{r} 33 \\ \times\ F \\ \hline 26G \end{array} \qquad \begin{array}{r} 8H \\ \times\ 7 \\ \hline J0I \end{array} \qquad \begin{array}{r} K3 \\ \times\ 5 \\ \hline L55 \end{array}$$

7. Explain how you can tell that **F** cannot be replaced by 1, 2, or 3.
_____
_____

8. **F** = _____ **G** = _____

9. Find all the possible replacements for **H**, **I**, and **J**. _____

10. How can you tell that there is no solution for the last problem above? _____
_____
_____

11. Make up a problem in which a 2- or 3-digit number is multiplied by a 1-digit
number and 1 or 2 digits are missing. Explain how your problem can be solved.
_____
_____
_____

12. Make up a multiplication problem that has some missing digits and that cannot
be solved. Explain why your problem has no solution.
_____
_____
_____
_____

© McGraw-Hill School Division

x

The Teacher Guide provides a complete lesson plan for each *Skill Builder* and *Challenge*. Each *Skill Builder* lesson plan includes a lesson objective, *Getting Started* activities, teaching suggestions, and questions to check the student's understanding. There is also a section called *What If the Student Can't*, which offers additional activities in case a student needs more support in mastering an essential prerequisite skill or lacks the understanding needed to complete the *Skill Builder* exercises successfully.

The lesson plan for each *Challenge* includes a lesson objective along with suggestions for introducing and using the *Challenge*.

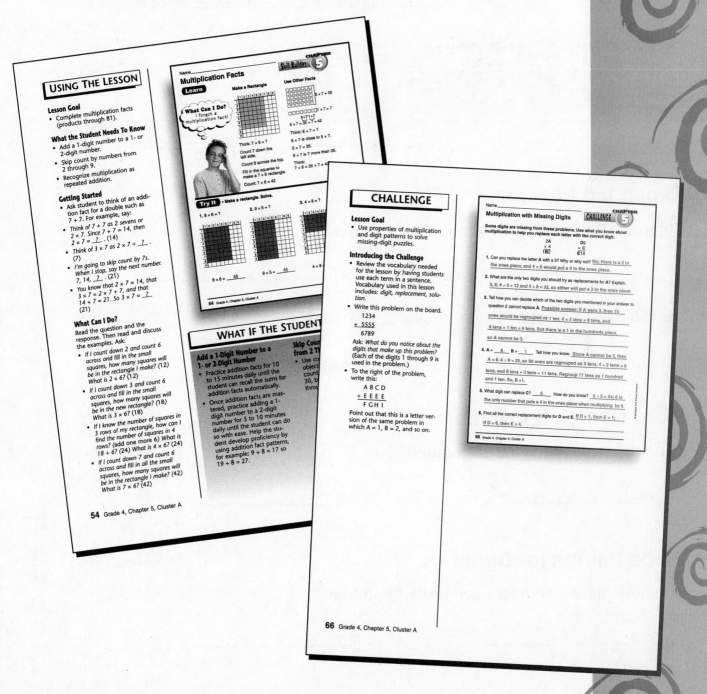

Place-Value Models

Complete the expanded form for each model.

1.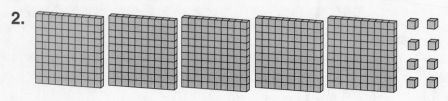

_____ hundreds _____ tens _____ ones

2.

_____ hundreds _____ tens _____ ones

Expanded Form

Complete the expanded form for each number.

3. 58 = _____ tens _____ ones

4. 41 = _____ tens _____ one

5. 458 = _____ hundreds _____ tens _____ ones

6. 103 = _____ hundred _____ tens _____ ones

Word Names for Numbers

Write the word name for each number.

7. 18 _____

8. 39 _____

Place Names for Digits

Write the place name for each underlined digit.

9. 3<u>1</u>2 _____

10. <u>6</u>5 _____

Name_____

Values of Money Amounts

Write the total amount of money.

11.

12.

_____   _____

Number Patterns

**Count by 5s, 10s, or 25s to write the next three numbers
in each addition pattern.**

13. 15, 20, 25, 30, 35, _____, _____, _____

14. 50, 60, 70, 80, 90, _____, _____, _____

15. 75, 100, 125, 150, _____, _____, _____

16. 23, 33, 43, 53, _____, _____, _____

Comparing Whole Numbers

Compare. Use > or <.

17. 12 _____ 21   **18.** 6 _____ 3

19. 40 _____ 14   **20.** 17 _____ 27

CHAPTER 1 PRE-CHAPTER ASSESSMENT

Assessment Goal

This two-page assessment covers skills identified as necessary for success in Chapter 1 Place Value and Money. The first page assesses the major prerequisite skills for Cluster A. The second page assesses the major prerequisite skills for Cluster B. When the Cluster A and Cluster B prerequisite skills overlap, the skill(s) will be covered in only one section.

Getting Started

- Allow students time to look over the two pages of the assessment. Point out the labels that identify the skills covered.

- Have students find math vocabulary terms used in the assessment. List vocabulary terms on the board as students identify them. If necessary, review the meanings of all essential math vocabulary.

Introducing the Assessment

- Explain to students that these pages will help you know if they are ready to start a new chapter in their math textbooks.

- Students who have transferred from another school may not have been introduced to some of these skills. Encourage students to do their best and assure them you will help them learn any needed skills.

Cluster A Challenge

Those students who demonstrate mastery of the skills on this page will not need to use the reteaching worksheets. Instead, these students can do the Cluster A Challenge found on pages 12–13.

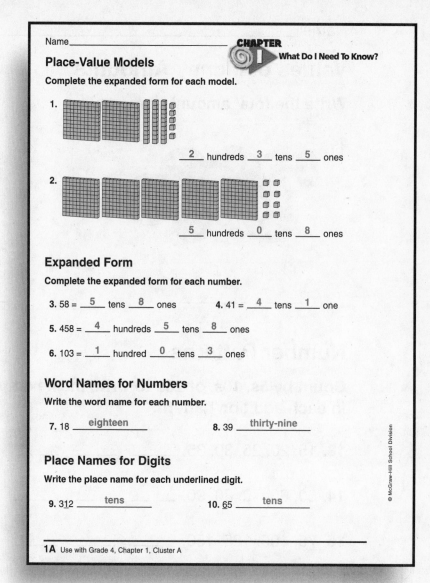

Name_____

CHAPTER 1 What Do I Need To Know?

Place-Value Models

Complete the expanded form for each model.

1.   __2__ hundreds __3__ tens __5__ ones

2.   __5__ hundreds __0__ tens __8__ ones

Expanded Form

Complete the expanded form for each number.

3. 58 = __5__ tens __8__ ones   4. 41 = __4__ tens __1__ one

5. 458 = __4__ hundreds __5__ tens __8__ ones

6. 103 = __1__ hundred __0__ tens __3__ ones

Word Names for Numbers

Write the word name for each number.

7. 18 __eighteen__   8. 39 __thirty-nine__

Place Names for Digits

Write the place name for each underlined digit.

9. 3<u>1</u>2 __tens__   10. <u>6</u>5 __tens__

© McGraw-Hill School Division

1A Use with Grade 4, Chapter 1, Cluster A

CLUSTER A PREREQUISITE SKILLS

The skills listed in this chart are those identified as major prerequisite skills for students' success in the lessons in Cluster A of the chapter. Each skill is covered by one or more assessment items as shown in the middle column. The right column provides the page number for the lessons in this book that reteach the cluster A prerequisite skills.

Skill Name	Assessment Items	Lesson Pages
Place-Value Models	1-2	2-3
Expanded Form	3-6	4
Word Names for Numbers	7-8	5
Place Names for Digit	9-10	6

Name_____

Values of Money Amounts

Write the total amount of money.

11.

_____95 cents_____

12.

_____36 cents_____

Number Patterns

Count by 5s, 10s, or 25s to write the next three numbers in each addition pattern.

13. 15, 20, 25, 30, 35, __40__, __45__, __50__

14. 50, 60, 70, 80, 90, __100__, __110__, __120__

15. 75, 100, 125, 150, __175__, __200__, __225__

16. 23, 33, 43, 53, __63__, __73__, __83__

Comparing Whole Numbers

Compare. Use > or <.

17. 12 __<__ 21

18. 6 __>__ 3

19. 40 __>__ 14

20. 17 __<__ 27

Use with Grade 4, Chapter 1, Cluster B **1B**

CLUSTER B PREREQUISITE SKILLS

The skills listed in this chart are those identified as major prerequisite skills for students' success in the lessons in Cluster B of the chapter. Each skill is covered by one or more assessment items as shown in the middle column. The right column provides the page numbers for the lessons in this book that reteach the Cluster B prerequisite skills

Skill Name	Assessment Items	Lesson Pages
Values of Money Amounts	11-12	7
Number Patterns	13-16	8-9
Comparing Whole Numbers	17-20	10-11

Alternative Assessment Strategies

- Oral administration of the assessment is appropriate for younger students or those whose native language is not English. Read the skills title and directions one section at a time. Check students' understanding by asking them to tell you how they will do the first exercise in the group.

- For some skill types you may wish to use group administration. In this technique, a small group or pair of students complete the assessment together. Through their discussion, you will be able to decide if supplementary reteaching materials are needed.

Intervention Materials

If students are not successful with the prerequisite skills assessed on these pages, reteaching lessons have been created to help them make the transition into the chapter.

Item correlation charts showing the skills lessons suitable for reteaching the prerequisite skills are found beneath the reproductions of each page of the assessment.

Cluster B Challenge

Those students who demonstrate mastery of the skills on this page will not need to use the reteaching worksheets. Instead, these students can do the Cluster B Challenge found on pages 14–15.

USING THE LESSON

Lesson Goal

- Use place-value models to complete expanded forms for two- and three-digit numbers.

What the Student Needs to Know

- Identify the digits in a number.
- Identify the places in two- and three-digit numbers.
- Count by tens using place-value models.
- Count by hundreds using place-value models.

Getting Started

Have students work in small groups. Provide each group with a supply of place-value models for ones, tens, and hundreds. Hold up a 1-cube, a 10-stick, and a 100-square in turn. Ask:

- *What number does this stand for? How are these blocks used to model numbers?* (Numbers may have hundreds, tens, and ones. The blocks show the meanings of the digits in numbers.)
- Have students take turns modeling numbers for others in the group to identify. Start with two-digit numbers and then move on to three-digit numbers.

What Can I Do?

Read the question and the response. Then read and discuss the example. Ask:

- *How many hundreds are pictured?* (3) *How many tens?* (4) *How many ones?* (7) *What number does this stand for?* (347) *How does the place-value chart show what the number means?* (The chart shows the value of each of the three digits in the number. If necessary, review the term *digit*.)

Have students use their place-value blocks to show 347. Then ask questions such as:

- *Take away one hundreds square. What number is left?* (247)
- *Add two more tens sticks. What number do you have now?* (267)

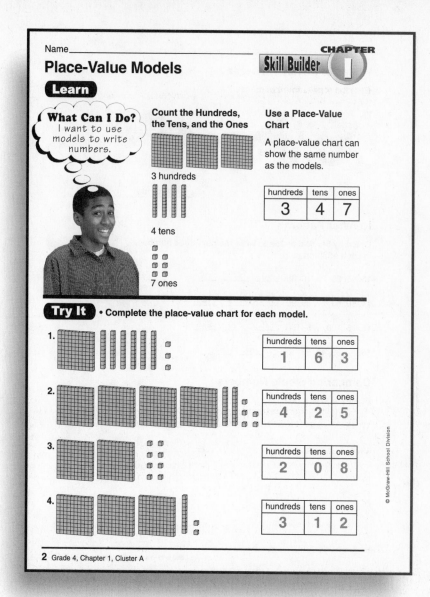

Name_____

Place-Value Models   Skill Builder

Learn

What Can I Do? I want to use models to write numbers.

Count the Hundreds, the Tens, and the Ones

3 hundreds

4 tens

7 ones

Use a Place-Value Chart

A place-value chart can show the same number as the models.

hundreds	tens	ones
3	4	7

Try It • Complete the place-value chart for each model.

1.

hundreds	tens	ones
1	6	3

2.

hundreds	tens	ones
4	2	5

3.

hundreds	tens	ones
2	0	8

4.

hundreds	tens	ones
3	1	2

2 Grade 4, Chapter 1, Cluster A

© McGraw-Hill School Division

WHAT IF THE STUDENT CAN'T

Identify the Digits in a Number

- Write the term *digit* and the symbols 0 through 9 on the board. Ask:
- *How do we use digits to make numbers?* (The digits are combined in different ways.)
- *Does a digit always have the same value in a number?* (No, the value of the digit depends on its place in the number.)
- *Use the digits 1, 2, and 3 to make some different numbers.* (Answers will vary.)

Identify the Places in Two- and Three-Digit Numbers

- Provide students with blank place-value charts for tens and ones. Have them show two-digit numbers with place-value models and record their work in the charts.
- Repeat the activity for three-digit numbers.
- Give students pairs of numbers such as 84 and 48. Ask students to explain how the numbers are the same and how they are different. Repeat with pairs such as 412 and 214. Encourage students to use the names of the places in their discussions.

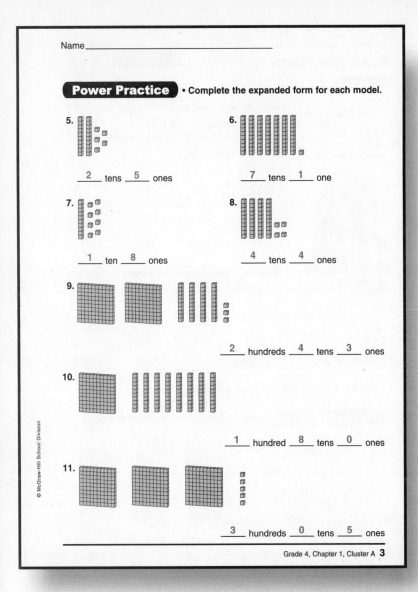

Name_____

Power Practice • Complete the expanded form for each model.

5. ___2___ tens ___5___ ones

6. ___7___ tens ___1___ one

7. ___1___ ten ___8___ ones

8. ___4___ tens ___4___ ones

9. ___2___ hundreds ___4___ tens ___3___ ones

10. ___1___ hundred ___8___ tens ___0___ ones

11. ___3___ hundreds ___0___ tens ___5___ ones

© McGraw-Hill School Division

Grade 4, Chapter 1, Cluster A **3**

WHAT IF THE STUDENT CAN'T

Count by Tens Using Place-Value Models

• Have students work in pairs. Provide each pair with a supply of tens sticks. One student grabs a handful of sticks; the other student counts the sticks by tens.

• One student grabs some tens sticks and counts them. The other student must say the ten that is one more.

Count by Hundreds Using Place-Value Models

• Have students work in pairs using hundreds squares. One student shows a number; the other counts by hundreds to find that number.

Complete the Power Practice

• Have students use place-value models to show each number before they write the answers.

• Provide extra help by working with students using place-value models. Show a number and ask students to name it. Begin with tens and ones; then go on to hundreds.

• Play money may also be used to model three-digit numbers. Use play pennies, dimes, and dollars with students who need more practice.

Try It

Point out that each problem has a picture of place-value blocks and a place-value chart. These are two different ways to show a number. Ask:

• *How many hundreds are in the first problem?* (1) *How does this help you fill in the chart?* (You write a 1 under "hundreds" to show there is 1 hundred in the number.) Repeat for the tens and ones in the first problem. If students are still not sure what to do, go over the second problem in the same way.

• Next, direct students' attention to problem 3. Ask: *What is different about this problem?* (It has no tens.) *What number is used to show nothing?* (zero) *Where does the zero go in this number?* (In the tens place, or in the middle of the chart.)

• Have students complete the Try It section. Have place-value models available for any students who need them.

Power Practice

Have students look over the problems before they begin. Ask:

• *Which problems show tens and ones, but no hundreds?* (The first four problems.) *Do you need to use zeros because there are no hundreds? Why or why not?* (No, it is not necessary to use a zero at the beginning of a number.)

• When all students have finished, have them say and write the standard form number for each problem.

Reinforce the work students have done on the page by asking questions such as:

• *Which number on the page has zero tens?* (305) *Which is the greatest number?* (305) *the least number?* (18)

Lesson Goal

• Write the expanded form for two- and three-digit numbers.

What the Student Needs to Know

• Name the digits in a number.
• Identify two- and three-digit numbers.
• Name the places in a number.

Getting Started

Write the numbers 45 and 54 on the board. Ask:

• *What is the same about these numbers? What is different?* (The numbers use the same digits, but the digits are in different places.)
• *In which number does the digit 5 have a greater value? Why?* (In the 54 the digit 5 has a value of 50.)

What Can I Do?

Read the question and the response. Write the term *expanded form* on the board. Ask:

• *What does expanded form tell you about a number?* (The value of each digit in the number.)
• *What are the three digits in the number three hundred forty-two? What is the value of each digit?* (The 3 is worth 3 hundreds; the 4 is worth 4 tens; the 2 is worth 2 ones.)

Try It

• Ask: *What is the value of the digit 8 in the number eighty-six?* (8 tens or eighty) *How does this help you do the first problem?* (You must write 8 in the blank to show that the digit 8 is worth 8 tens.)
• Have students complete the Try It section.

Power Practice

Have students look over the problems before they begin. Ask:

• *Which problems show tens and ones?* (All except exercise 10.)
• *What is different about the last two problems?* (They also show hundreds.)

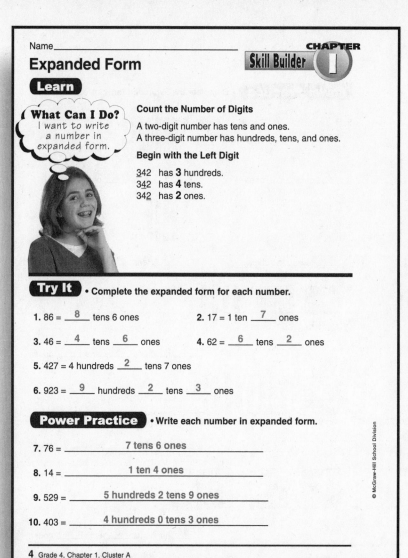

Name_____

Expanded Form

Skill Builder CHAPTER **1**

Learn

What Can I Do? I want to write a number in expanded form.

Count the Number of Digits

A two-digit number has tens and ones.
A three-digit number has hundreds, tens, and ones.

Begin with the Left Digit

342 has **3** hundreds.
342 has **4** tens.
342 has **2** ones.

Try It • Complete the expanded form for each number.

1. 86 = __8__ tens 6 ones
2. 17 = 1 ten __7__ ones
3. 46 = __4__ tens __6__ ones
4. 62 = __6__ tens __2__ ones
5. 427 = 4 hundreds __2__ tens 7 ones
6. 923 = __9__ hundreds __2__ tens __3__ ones

Power Practice • Write each number in expanded form.

7. 76 = _____ 7 tens 6 ones
8. 14 = _____ 1 ten 4 ones
9. 529 = _____ 5 hundreds 2 tens 9 ones
10. 403 = _____ 4 hundreds 0 tens 3 ones

WHAT IF THE STUDENT CAN'T

Name the Digits in a Number

• Write the digits 0 through 9 on the board. Write the term *digit* and pronounce it for students.
• Have each student write three different two-digit numbers. Ask volunteers to tell you what digits are used in each number.

Identify Two- and Three-Digit Numbers

• Write the numbers 777 and 77 on the board. Ask students what is different about the numbers. Listen for the correct use of the term *digit*.

Name the Places in a Number

• Have students show examples of two- and three-digit numbers with place-value models.

Complete the Power Practice

• Discuss incorrect answers with students. Ask them to name the tens and ones digits in the first two problems; the hundreds, tens, and ones digits in the last two problems.
• Point out that the purpose of expanded form is to show that the value of a digit changes with its place in a number.

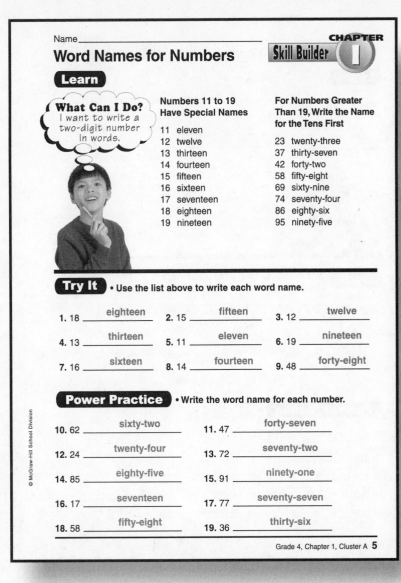

Name_____

Word Names for Numbers

Learn

What Can I Do?
I want to write a two-digit number in words.

Numbers 11 to 19 Have Special Names

11 eleven
12 twelve
13 thirteen
14 fourteen
15 fifteen
16 sixteen
17 seventeen
18 eighteen
19 nineteen

For Numbers Greater Than 19, Write the Name for the Tens First

23 twenty-three
37 thirty-seven
42 forty-two
58 fifty-eight
69 sixty-nine
74 seventy-four
86 eighty-six
95 ninety-five

Try It • Use the list above to write each word name.

1. 18 ___eighteen___
2. 15 ___fifteen___
3. 12 ___twelve___
4. 13 ___thirteen___
5. 11 ___eleven___
6. 19 ___nineteen___
7. 16 ___sixteen___
8. 14 ___fourteen___
9. 48 ___forty-eight___

Power Practice • Write the word name for each number.

10. 62 ___sixty-two___
11. 47 ___forty-seven___
12. 24 ___twenty-four___
13. 72 ___seventy-two___
14. 85 ___eighty-five___
15. 91 ___ninety-one___
16. 17 ___seventeen___
17. 77 ___seventy-seven___
18. 58 ___fifty-eight___
19. 36 ___thirty-six___

© McGraw-Hill School Division

Grade 4, Chapter 1, Cluster A **5**

WHAT IF THE STUDENT CAN'T

Read and Write Word Names for One Through Ten

- Have students work in pairs to write word names on 9 cards and numerals on 9 cards. Students play "Concentration" to practice matching numerals with words.

Read and Write Word Names for Tens

- Repeat the "Concentration" practice game using the words for the tens through ninety.
- Have students use place-value models. One student chooses tens sticks for any number less than 100. The partner identifies the number in three ways; for example, 4 tens, 40, forty.

Complete the Power Practice

- Make sure that students can write the digits of a number correctly if given the name of the number. Then reverse the process: Write a number and ask the student to say its name. Practice until the student can do this easily.

USING THE LESSON

Lesson Goal

- Write the word name for a two-digit number.

What the Student Needs to Know

- Read and write word names for one through ten.
- Read and write word names for tens.

Getting Started

- Have students count aloud to twenty, with individuals taking turns saying the numbers. Note any students who have trouble with the teen numbers.
- Have students count aloud by tens up to ninety. Then have them write the numerals for these numbers.

What Can I Do?

Read the question and the response. Then read and discuss the examples. Ask:

- *Which words are difficult for you to spell?* (Students may mention twelve or other teen numbers.)

Point out the difference between fourteen and forty—the latter word does not use the letter U.

Try It

Have students look at the first eight problems. Ask:

- *How are these numbers alike?* (They are all between 10 and 20.) *Do these number words all end with the suffix -teen?* (No, eleven and twelve are the exceptions.)

Power Practice

- Have the students complete the practice items. Then review each answer.

Lesson Goal
- Write place names for three-digit numbers.

What the Student Needs to Know
- Write two-digit numbers as tens and ones.
- Complete place-value charts for two-digit numbers.

Getting Started
Write the word *digit* on the board. Ask:

- *What does this word mean?* (A digit is one of the symbols used to write numbers.)
- *How many digits are there?* (Ten. They start at 0 and continue through 9.)
- *Does a digit always have the same meaning in a number?* (No, it depends on the place. The digit 3 might mean 3 ones, 3 tens, 3 hundreds, and so on.)

What Can I Do?
Read the question and the response. Then read and discuss the examples. Point out the place-value chart. Ask:

- *What does this chart tell you about the number?* (Each digit is in a different place. Each place has a different name.)
- *Tell me a number that has a 6 in the ones place.* (Answers will vary.) Repeat the question with other digits in other places.

Try It
- *Read the number. What does the digit 4 mean in the number?* (4 hundreds)

Be sure students understand that they are to copy the number into the place-value chart. Then they circle one of three possible answers to the question.

Power Practice
Before students begin, have them look at the first column. Ask:

- *Which numbers have the ones digit underlined? the tens digit? the hundreds digit?*

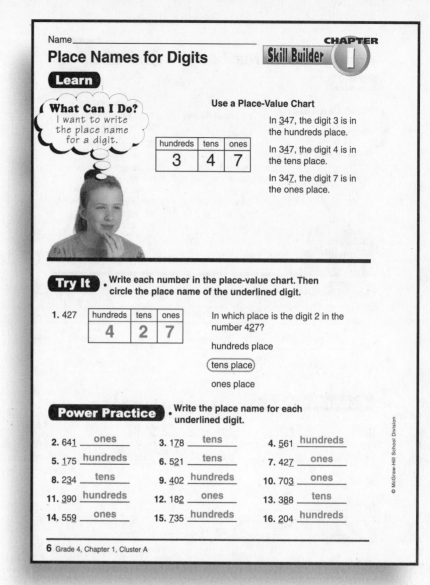

6 Grade 4, Chapter 1, Cluster A

WHAT IF THE STUDENT CAN'T

Write Two-Digit Numbers as Tens and Ones
- On the chalkboard write:

  56 = 50 + 6
  56 = 5 tens + 6 ones

Point out that these are two ways to show the meanings of the digits. Have students create a few examples of their own.

Complete Place-Value Charts for Two-Digit Numbers
- Provide place-value models. Say a two-digit number. Have students show it with models and then tell the number of tens and ones. Repeat several times or have students practice in pairs.

Complete the Power Practice
- Have students practice writing three-digit numbers using place-value models. Have them show three-digit numbers using the models and then record their work on place-value charts like this:

hundreds	tens	ones

Ask them to say each number aloud after they write it.

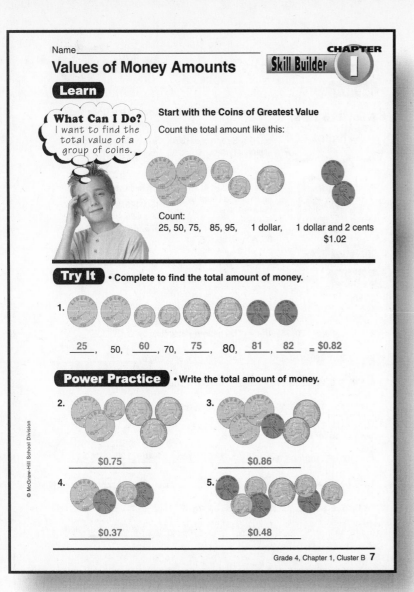

Values of Money Amounts

Skill Builder

Name_____

Learn

What Can I Do?
I want to find the total value of a group of coins.

Start with the Coins of Greatest Value

Count the total amount like this:

Count:
25, 50, 75, 85, 95, 1 dollar, 1 dollar and 2 cents
$1.02

Try It • Complete to find the total amount of money.

1.

__25__, 50, __60__, 70, __75__, 80, __81__, __82__ = $0.82

Power Practice • Write the total amount of money.

2. $0.75

3. $0.86

4. $0.37

5. $0.48

Grade 4, Chapter 1, Cluster B **7**

© McGraw-Hill School Division

WHAT IF THE STUDENT CAN'T

Identify Coins Through Quarters
- Show students one penny. As you show the coin, write on the board, "1 penny, 1 cent, 1¢." Repeat for a nickel, a dime, and a quarter.

Count by Fives
- Have students count aloud by 5s to 100. Repeat, counting aloud by 5 cents to one dollar.
- Have students start at 25¢ and count on by 5s to one dollar. Repeat, starting at 50¢ and 75¢.

Count by Tens
- Have students count aloud by 10s to 100. Repeat, counting aloud by 10 cents to one dollar.
- Have students start at 25¢ and count by 10s to 95¢. Repeat, starting at 50¢ to one dollar and 75¢ to 95¢.

Complete the Power Practice
- Provide pairs of students with play coins. One student models the amount of money in a problem. The partner counts the money aloud. Students change roles for the next problem.

USING THE LESSON

Lesson Goal
- Write the total value of a group of coins.

What the Student Needs to Know
- Identify coins through quarters.
- Count by 5s.
- Count by 10s.

Getting Started
Provide small groups of students with play coins. Ask:
- *What is the value of a penny, a nickel, a dime, and a quarter? Show me one of each.* (Check that all students can identify the coins and tell their values.)
- *How do you count money if the amount is all dimes?* all nickels? (Count by 10s with dimes; count by 5s with nickels.)

What Can I Do?
Read the question and the response. Then read and discuss the example. Ask:
- *How many quarters are there? What is their value?* (3 quarters; 75 cents) Repeat for the other three kinds of coins.
- *Show me how you would count this money.* (If students have trouble, provide play money for them to practice counting.)

Try It
Ask:
- *What kinds of coins are shown in the problem? Tell me the value of each coin.* (quarters: 25 cents; dimes: 10 cents; nickels: 5 cents; pennies: 1 cent)

Point out that the easiest way to count money is to begin with the coins having the greatest value and continue down to the coins with the least value.

Power Practice
- Before students begin, have them name the order in which they will count the coins shown in each problem.

Lesson Goal
- Complete number patterns by counting by 5s, 10s, or 25s.

What the Student Needs to Know
- Count by 5s to 100.
- Count by 10s to 100.
- Count by 25s to 300.

Getting Started
Review counting by 5s and 10s with students. Say:

- *Let's count together by 5s up to 100. Now let's count by 10s.*

- *Can anyone show us how to count by 25s?* If students are not sure, write the first eight numbers on the board for them: 25, 50, 75, 100, 125, 150, 175, 200. Point out that this is like counting money with quarters.

What Can I Do?
Read the question and the response. Then read and discuss the examples. Ask:

- *How can you tell if a number pattern is counting by 5s?* (You add 5 each time to get the next number.)

- Give students several two-digit numbers that do not end in zero. Have them start at the given number and count by 10s.

- A hundred chart can be used to show counting by 10.

1	2	3	4	5	6	7	8	9	10
11	12	13	14	15	16	17	18	19	20
21	22	23	24	25	26	27	28	29	30
31	32	33	34	35	36	37	38	39	40
41	42	43	44	45	46	47	48	49	50
51	52	53	54	55	56	57	58	59	60
61	62	63	64	65	66	67	68	69	70
71	72	73	74	75	76	77	78	79	80
81	82	83	84	85	86	87	88	89	90
91	92	93	94	95	96	97	98	99	100

Each column in the chart is a number pattern based on 10s. For example, the column with 3 at the top gives the pattern 3, 13, 23, and so on. The chart can help students count by 10s when they do not start with 0.

Name _____

Number Patterns

Learn

What Can I Do?
I want to count by 5s, 10s, or 25s.

Look at the Ones Digits

When you start at 0 and count by 5s, the ones digits alternate between 0 and 5.

15, 20, 25, 30, 35, 40

When you start at any number and count by 10s, the ones digits are always the same.

30, 40, 50, 60, 70, 80
14, 24, 34, 44, 54, 64

Look at the Ones and Tens Digits

When you start at 0 and count by 25s, the pattern of the last two digits is 25, 50, 75, 00. The pattern repeats over and over.

150, 175, 200, 225, 250
300, 325, 350, 375, 400
675, 700, 725, 750, 775

Try It • Describe each pattern as counting by 5s, 10s, or 25s.

1. 52, 62, 72, 82, 92, 102 — This pattern is counting by __10s__.

2. 50, 55, 60, 65, 70, 75, 80 — This pattern is counting by __5s__.

3. 240, 250, 260, 270, 280 — This pattern is counting by __10s__.

4. 175, 200, 225, 250, 275 — This pattern is counting by __25s__.

5. 175, 180, 185, 190, 195 — This pattern is counting by __5s__.

Count by 5s for each addition pattern.

6. 85, 90, 95, 100, 105, 110, __115__, __120__, __125__, __130__, __135__, __140__

7. 45, 50, 55, 60, 65, 70, __75__, __80__, __85__, __90__, __95__, __100__, __105__

8. 20, 25, 30, __35__, __40__, __45__   9. 75, 80, 85, __90__, __95__, __100__

10. 140, 145, __150__, __155__, __160__   11. 275, 280, 285, __290__, __295__, __300__

WHAT IF THE STUDENT CAN'T

Count by 5s to 100.
- Use a hundred chart. Duplicate blank charts for students and have them color in the multiples of 5. They should color in two columns, the one with 5 at the top and the one with 10 at the top. Point out that the numbers in the first column they colored all end with the digit 5. The numbers in the second column they colored end with the digit 0.

- Provide pairs of students with play nickels. One student takes a handful of coins and counts the money by 5s. The partner starts at the total and counts on for five more numbers.

Count by 10s to 100.
- Counting by 10s, write the numerals 10 through 100 on the board. Count aloud as a class. Have students take turns writing the number words next to each number. Then each student copies the list to show both numerals and word names.

- Provide pairs of students with play dimes. One student takes a handful of coins and counts the money by 10s. The partner starts at the total and counts on until he or she reaches 100.

Name_____

Count by 10s for each addition pattern.

12. 150, 160, 170, 180, _190_, _200_, _210_, _220_, _230_, _240_

13. 68, 78, 88, 98, 108, _118_, _128_, _138_, _148_, _158_, _168_

14. 15, 25, 35, _45_, _55_, _65_   15. 80, 90, 100, _110_, _120_, _130_

16. 71, 81, 91, _101_, _111_, _121_   17. 46, 56, 66, _76_, _86_, _96_

18. 214, 224, _234_, _244_, _254_   19. 160, 170, _180_, _190_, _200_

Count by 25s for each addition pattern.

20. 50, 75, 100, 125, _150_, _175_, _200_, _225_, _250_, _275_

21. 300, 325, 350, 375, _400_, _425_, _450_, _475_, _500_, _525_

22. 25, 50, _75_, _100_, _125_   23. 175, 200, _225_, _250_, _275_

24. 500, 525, _550_, _575_, _600_   25. 225, 250, _275_, _300_, _325_

Power Practice • Count by 5s, 10s, or 25s to write the next three numbers in each addition pattern.

26. 50, 55, 60, 65, 70, 75, _80_, _85_, _90_

27. 62, 72, 82, 92, 102, _112_, _122_, _132_

28. 150, 175, 200, 225, _250_, _275_, _300_

29. 250, 260, 270, 280, _290_, _300_, _310_

30. 5, 10, 15, 20, 25, 30, _35_, _40_, _45_

31. 625, 650, 675, 700, 725, _750_, _775_, _800_

32. 135, 140, 145, 150, 155, _160_, _165_, _170_

© McGraw-Hill School Division

Grade 4, Chapter 1, Cluster B **9**

WHAT IF THE STUDENT CAN'T

Count by 25s to 300.

- Provide play quarters. Have students first make three dollars with the quarters. They count the money one quarter at a time. Have students use the quarters to count by 25s.

Complete the Power Practice

- Have students use a hundred chart to practice counting by 10s. Point out that each column shows a pattern of counting by 10s. Give students three-digit numbers such as 372. Have them use the hundred chart to count by 10s. For example, for 372 they find 72 on the chart. The numbers beneath it are 82 and 92, so the next two numbers are 382 and 392. Then students go to the top of the column for 402, 412, and so forth.

- Provide play money. Have students show an amount of cents such as 513. Then have them add one dime and tell the new amount. Repeat with a few more dimes.

- *How can you tell if a number pattern is counting by 10s?* (You add 10 each time to get the next number. Or, the ones digit is always the same.)

Try It

- Some students may need help getting started with these problems. Have a volunteer read the first direction. Let students look over the first group of problems. Ask:

- *Which patterns are counting by 10s? How can you be sure?* (Problems 1 and 3. The ones digits are always the same.)

Then have students identify the patterns in which they count by 5s. The remaining problem is one in which they count by 25s.

- The next three sets of problems provide practice in counting by 5s, 10s, and 25s. Have play nickels and quarters available for students who need to use models for the 5s and 25s.

- Direct students' attention to exercise 11. Ask: *What will be different about the answer to this exercise?* (You will need to change the hundreds digit in the answer.)

Power Practice

- Before students begin, have them identify each number pattern as counting by 5s, 10s, or 25s. Remind students to look first at the ones digits. Ask:

- *If the ones digits alternate between 0 and 5, what kind of pattern is it?* (Counting by 5s.) *If the ones digits are all the same, what kind of pattern is it?* (Counting by 10s.) *What pattern do the last two digits make if you are counting by 25s?* (25, 50, 75, 00, 25, 50, 75, 00, and so on)

Lesson Goal
- Compare one- and two-digit whole numbers.

What the Student Needs to Know
- Identify tens and ones digits.
- Use the symbols > and <.
- Count by tens to 100.
- Draw a number line to show numbers in order.

Getting Started
Write the term *compare* on the board. Ask:

- *What does it mean to compare two numbers?* (Decide which number is greater than the other.)

Write on the board:

  18 is greater than 7

  23 is less than 50

- *What symbols are used to show greater than and less than? Use the symbols to write these comparisons in a shorter form.* (18 > 7; 23 < 50)

What Can I Do?
Read the question and the response. Then read and discuss the examples. Have each student draw a number line from 0 through 10. Ask:

- *How does the number line help you compare numbers?* (If one number is to the left of another, it is less.)

Have students count by tens up to 100. Ask:

- *Which comes first, 60 or 50? How does this help you compare 62 and 58?* (50 comes first, so 58 is less than 62)

Try It
Draw a large number line on the board showing the numbers from 0 through 10. Ask:

- *In the first problem, which number is farther to the right on the number line?* (9)

- *In problem 7, should you circle the number that is farther to the right or to the left?* (farther left)

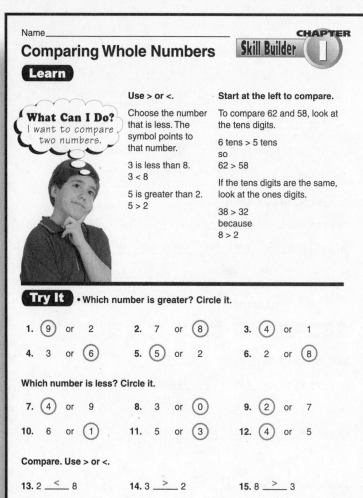

Name_____

Comparing Whole Numbers

Skill Builder

CHAPTER 1

Learn

What Can I Do? I want to compare two numbers.

Use > or <.
Choose the number that is less. The symbol points to that number.

3 is less than 8.
3 < 8

5 is greater than 2.
5 > 2

Start at the left to compare.
To compare 62 and 58, look at the tens digits.

6 tens > 5 tens
so
62 > 58

If the tens digits are the same, look at the ones digits.

38 > 32
because
8 > 2

Try It • Which number is greater? Circle it.

1. (9) or 2   2. 7 or (8)   3. (4) or 1

4. 3 or (6)   5. (5) or 2   6. 2 or (8)

Which number is less? Circle it.

7. (4) or 9   8. 3 or (0)   9. (2) or 7

10. 6 or (1)   11. 5 or (3)   12. (4) or 5

Compare. Use > or <.

13. 2 _<_ 8   14. 3 _>_ 2   15. 8 _>_ 3

16. 1 _<_ 5   17. 4 _<_ 7   18. 6 _>_ 4

10 Grade 4, Chapter 1, Cluster B

© McGraw-Hill School Division

WHAT IF THE STUDENT CAN'T

Identify Tens and Ones Digits
- Use place-value models. Have the student make the number, then you write it. Then you make a number and the student writes it.

- Use place-value charts such as this:

tens	ones

Have students work in pairs using place-value models. One student makes a two-digit number; the other student records the tens and ones in a chart. Students exchange roles and repeat.

Use the Symbols > and <.
- Provide pairs or groups of students with a set of 0–9 digit cards and two cards showing the symbols > and <. Students take turns using the cards to make true number sentences.

Count by Tens to 100
- Use place-value models. Have students model different numbers and count by tens to find each total.

- Use play dimes. Have students work in pairs. One student shows an amount of money; the partner counts by tens to find the total.

Name_____

Use the tens digits to compare.
Circle the number that is greater.

19. (41) or 36   **20.** 77 or (84)

21. (65) or 38   **22.** 23 or (32)

Compare. Look at the tens digits. Use > or <.

23. 28 __<__ 52   **24.** 65 __<__ 90

25. 61 __>__ 44   **26.** 18 __<__ 38

Use the ones digits to compare.
Circle the number that is greater.

27. (67) or 61   **28.** (82) or 81

29. 92 or (95)   **30.** (16) or 13

Compare. Look at the ones digits. Use > or <.

31. 72 __<__ 75   **32.** 25 __<__ 27   **33.** 15 __>__ 12

34. 32 __>__ 31   **35.** 60 __<__ 66   **36.** 95 __<__ 97

Power Practice • Compare. Use > or <.

37. 2 __<__ 7   **38.** 8 __>__ 6   **39.** 3 __>__ 0

40. 5 __>__ 1   **41.** 9 __>__ 7   **42.** 4 __>__ 3

43. 36 __>__ 24   **44.** 82 __>__ 59   **45.** 43 __<__ 73

46. 61 __>__ 16   **47.** 28 __<__ 81   **48.** 77 __>__ 68

49. 34 __>__ 31   **50.** 67 __<__ 69   **51.** 43 __<__ 48

52. 57 __>__ 51   **53.** 19 __>__ 17   **54.** 83 __<__ 88

Grade 4, Chapter 1, Cluster B **11**

Learn with Partners & Parents

Draw and Compare

The players need one set of number cards 0 through 9. Each player needs a card with > and a card with <.

- Turn the cards over and mix them up. Each player draws 5 cards.
- Make two number sentences with your cards, one using > and one using <. Use one-digit and two-digit numbers.
- Check your partner's work to see that it is correct.
- Play five rounds of the game.

WHAT IF THE STUDENT CAN'T

Draw a Number Line to Show Numbers in Order

- Use digit cards for the numbers 0 through 10. Place the number cards on the chalk tray in order from left to right. Then draw a blank number line above the numbers. Have students take turns coming to the board and writing a number on the number line until it is completely labeled.

- Students work in pairs. Each student draws a 0–10 number line and omits two numbers. Students exchange papers and fill in the missing numbers.

Complete the Power Practice

- Look to see which kinds of problems are difficult for the student. If the student can compare one-digit numbers, but not two-digit numbers, provide extra work with place-value models.

- Check to see if the student can compare numbers orally. If so, the student may need help using the symbols > and <.

USING THE LESSON

- Have students do these problems independently, referring as needed to the number line on the board.

- Have students read the directions at the top of page 11. Check that students understand by having them identify the tens digits in the first row of numbers.

- As students work on the remainder of the Try It problems, check for students who are reversing the > and < symbols. Emphasize that the smaller, pointy part of the symbol always points to the lesser of the two numbers.

Power Practice

Before students begin, ask:

- *Find a problem in which the tens digits are different. Explain how you will compare the numbers.* (Use the tens digits.)

- *Find a problem in which the tens digits are the same. Explain how you will compare the numbers.* (Use the ones digits.)

- *How will you decide whether to use the greater than or less than symbol?* (If the first number is greater, use the greater than symbol. If the first number is less, use the less than symbol.)

Learn with Partners & Parents

- Check that students understand they may need to try different arrangements of the cards they draw until they get two true math sentences.

- For a more challenging version of the game, tell students they must each use all five of their cards.

CHALLENGE

Lesson Goal
- Solve puzzles based on properties of the digits in numbers.

Introducing the Challenge
- Review the vocabulary needed for the lesson by having students use each of these terms in a sentence: *digit, even number, odd number, sum, difference.*

- You may need to introduce the concepts of odd and even numbers. Explain that 2, 4, 6, 8, and 10 are called even numbers. Any number with a ones digit of 0, 2, 4, 6, or 8 is even. The odd numbers have ones digits of 1, 3, 5, 7, or 9.

- Write the numbers 27 and 46 on the board. Explain that you are now going to give some clues. Students are to pick the number that matches the clues. Say and ask:

- *My tens digit is less than my ones digit. Does this clue eliminate either number?* (No, in both numbers the tens digit is less than the ones digit.)

- *Both of my digits are even numbers. Does this clue eliminate either number?* (Yes, 7 is an odd number, so this clue eliminates 27. The answer to the puzzle is the other number, 46.)

Name_____

CHAPTER
CHALLENGE 1

Logical Thinking and Number Puzzles

These puzzles will give you a chance to use logical thinking. On this page, match each set of clues to one of the number cards below.

Remember, an even number has a ones digit of 0, 2, 4, 6, or 8. An odd number has a ones digit of 1, 3, 5, 7, or 9.

1. I am a three-digit number. All of my digits are odd numbers. Who am I?

173

2. I am a two-digit number. The difference between my digits is two. Who am I?

86

3. I am less than 50. I am more than 30. Who am I?

49

4. You can subtract two of my digits to get my third digit. Who am I?

909

5. My tens digit is greater than my ones digit. I am less than 50. Who am I?

21

6. Add my first two digits. Subtract my third digit. You will get the number 1. Who am I?

627

86   49   627

173   21   909

© McGraw-Hill School Division

12 Grade 4, Chapter 1, Cluster A

12 Grade 4, Chapter 1, Cluster A

Name_____

These puzzles are a little more difficult because there are no numbers on cards to choose from.

7. I am an odd number
between 30 and 40.
The sum of my digits is 6.
Who am I?

_____33_____

8. I am an even number near 65.
My digits are the same.
Who am I?

_____66_____

9. I am between 52 and 55.
Both of my digits are odd
numbers. Who am I?

_____53_____

10. I am an even number between
65 and 75. My ones digit is
greater than my tens digit.
Who am I?

_____68_____

11. All three of my digits are
the same number. The sum
of my digits is 21. Who am I?

_____777_____

12. I am a three-digit even
number. I am next to 305.
The sum of my digits is 9.
Who am I?

_____306_____

13. I have three digits.
The sum of my digits is 3.
I am greater than 250.
Who am I?

_____300_____

14. Two of my digits are the same.
I read the same both forward
and backwards. I am greater
than 180 and less than 190.
Who am I?

_____181_____

© McGraw-Hill School Division

CHALLENGE

Using the Challenge

- Have a volunteer read the directions for page 12 aloud. Check that students know what to do by asking:

- *Why are there six cards at the bottom of the page?* (There is one card with the answer for each problem.)

- *How will you decide which number goes with each puzzle?* (Use the clues to eliminate numbers that don't work.)

- Have a volunteer read the directions for page 13 aloud. Ask:

- *How are these problems different from the ones on page 12?* (There are no cards at the bottom of the page. To find each answer, students must use the clues and logical reasoning.)

CHALLENGE

Lesson Goal

- Solve puzzles based on making amounts of money using different combinations of coins.

Introducing the Challenge

- Review the vocabulary needed for the lesson by having students use each of these terms in a sentence: *pennies, dimes, nickels, cents, row, column.*

- Provide students with play money for pennies and nickels. Ask:

- *How many different ways can you use pennies and nickels to make 10 cents?* (Students should find these solutions: 2 nickels, 10 pennies, 1 nickel and 5 pennies.)

- *How could you show the different solutions in a chart?* (Accept all suggestions students make. You may wish to have students compare their ideas to the chart shown on page 14.)

Puzzles with Coins

Some puzzles about coins can be solved by making an organized chart or list. Here is an example.

How many ways can you make 20 cents using pennies, dimes, and nickels?

Follow the directions to complete the chart and solve the coin puzzle. The third row of the chart is filled in for you.

dimes	nickels	pennies	sum
2	0	0	20¢
1	2	0	10¢ + 10¢ = 20¢
1	1	5	10¢ + 5¢ + 5¢ = 20¢
1	0	10	10¢ + 10¢ = 20¢
0	4	0	20¢
0	3	5	15¢ + 5¢ = 20¢
0	2	10	10¢ + 10¢ = 20¢
0	1	15	5¢ + 15¢ = 20¢
0	0	20	20¢

1. In the first row, show how to make 20 cents using only dimes.

2. In the second row, show how to make 20 cents using 1 dime and no pennies.

3. The third and fourth rows show the other possibilities using only 1 dime. Complete the fourth row.

4. Now look at the first four rows. Are there any other possibilities using 1 or 2 dimes? Explain your answer.

   No, these are the only four possibilities. When you've used

   2 dimes, you have 20 cents, so there is just one solution with

   2 dimes. When you use 1 dime, there are three different

   solutions, using either 2, 1, or 0 nickels. Pennies are used to

   make up the rest of the 20 cents.

5. The same number goes in the left column in the last five rows. What is this number and what does it mean?

   Zero. It means that all the rest of the solutions have zero

   dimes.

6. Complete the second column by showing a decreasing number of nickels. How does this tell you what to put in the third column?

   Once you've written the number of dimes and nickels, you

   can compute the pennies by subtracting from 20 cents.

7. What is the purpose of the right column in the chart?

   You can check that your entries really add up to 20 cents.

8. What is the answer to the original puzzle?

   The solution is 9 ways.

Here is another coin puzzle for you to try. Show the possibilities in a chart or list. Then write the solution.

9. How many ways can you make 85 cents using quarters, dimes, and nickels?

   22 ways

CHALLENGE

Using the Challenge

- Have a volunteer read the directions for page 14 aloud. Check that students know what to do. Ask:

- *What problem are you going to solve?* (Find all the different combinations of pennies, nickels, and dimes that will have a total of 20 cents.)

- *What is the purpose of the chart on the page?* (It is a way to record the possible answers. It also helps the solver be systematic or organized in listing the solutions.)

- Say: *The questions lead you through the solution process. They provide hints that help you solve the puzzle.*

- Have play money available for those students who wish to use it in solving the puzzle.

- Some students may prefer to solve the puzzle without using the questions to help them. Make sure these students realize that problem 9 presents another and different problem to solve.

1- and 2-Digit Addition

Find each sum.

1. 26 + 5 = _____

2. 57 + 3 = _____

3. 39 + 6 = _____

4. 43
   + 28
   ‾‾‾‾
    71

5. 82
   + 31
   ‾‾‾‾
   113

6. 29
   + 76
   ‾‾‾‾
   105

Word Names and Place Value

Complete the word name for each number.

7. 3,000 = three _____

8. 600 = six _____

Complete the expanded form for each number.

9. 629 = _____ hundreds _____ tens _____ ones

10. 4,247 = _____ thousands _____ hundreds _____ tens _____ ones

Write the place name for the digit 6 in each number.

11. 1,670 _____

12. 35,068 _____

Rounding to the Nearest Ten or Hundred

Round each number to the underlined place.

13. 8̲9 _____

14. 25̲8 _____

15. 4̲09 _____

16. 5,2̲55 _____

Name_____

Rounding to the Nearest Thousand or Dollar

Round each number or amount of money to the underlined place.

17. 8,093 _____

18. 15,626 _____

19. $7.83 _____

20. $25.14 _____

Subtraction Patterns

Use subtraction facts to complete the patterns.

21. 13 − 9 = _____

23 − 9 = _____

22. 17 − 8 = _____

47 − 8 = _____

2-Digit Subtraction

Find each difference.

23.   42
        − 17
        ─────

24.   65
        − 24
        ─────

25.   81
        − 37
        ─────

CHAPTER 2 PRE-CHAPTER ASSESSMENT

Assessment Goal

This two-page assessment covers skills identified as necessary for success in Chapter 2 Addition and Subtraction. The first page assesses the major prerequisite skills for Cluster A. The second page assesses the major prerequisite skills for Cluster B. When the Cluster A and Cluster B prerequisite skills overlap, the skill(s) will be covered in only one section.

Getting Started

- Allow students time to look over the two pages of the assessment. Point out the labels that identify the skills covered.

- Have students find math vocabulary terms used in the assessment. List vocabulary terms on the board as students identify them. If necessary, review the meanings of all essential math vocabulary.

Introducing the Assessment

- Explain to students that these pages will help you know if they are ready to start a new chapter in their math textbooks.

- Students who have transferred from another school may not have been introduced to some of these skills. Encourage students to do their best and assure them you will help them learn any needed skills.

Cluster A Challenge

Those students who demonstrate mastery of the skills on this page will not need to use the reteaching worksheets. Instead, these students can do the Cluster A Challenge found on pages 26–27.

Name_____

1- and 2-Digit Addition

Find each sum.

1. 26 + 5 = ___31___   2. 57 + 3 = ___60___   3. 39 + 6 = ___45___

4. 43
   + 28
   ____
    71

5. 82
   + 31
   ____
   113

6. 29
   + 76
   ____
   105

Word Names and Place Value

Complete the word name for each number.

7. 3,000 = three ___thousand___

8. 600 = six ___hundred___

Complete the expanded form for each number.

9. 629 = ___6___ hundreds ___2___ tens ___9___ ones

10. 4,247 = ___4___ thousands ___2___ hundreds ___4___ tens ___7___ ones

Write the place name for the digit 6 in each number.

11. 1,670 ___hundreds___   12. 35,068 ___tens___

Rounding to the Nearest Ten or Hundred

Round each number to the underlined place.

13. 8̲9 ___90___   14. 2̲58 ___260___

15. 4̲09 ___400___   16. 5,2̲55 ___5,300___

15A Use with Grade 4, Chapter 2, Cluster A

CLUSTER A PREREQUISITE SKILLS

The skills listed in this chart are those identified as major prerequisite skills for students' success in the lessons in Cluster A of the chapter. Each skill is covered by one or more assessment items as shown in the middle column. The right column provides the page number for the lessons in this book that reteach the cluster A prerequisite skills.

Skill Name	Assessment Items	Lesson Pages
1-and 2-Digit Addition	1-6	16-17
Word Names and Place Value	7-12	18-19
Rounding to the Nearest Ten or Hundred	13-16	20

Rounding to the Nearest Thousand or Dollar

Round each number or amount of money to the underlined place.

17. 8,093 _____ 8,000 _____

18. 15,626 _____ 16,000 _____

19. $7.83 _____ $8.00 _____

20. $25.14 _____ $25.00 _____

Subtraction Patterns

Use subtraction facts to complete the patterns.

21. 13 − 9 = __4__   22. 17 − 8 = __9__

23 − 9 = __14__   47 − 8 = __39__

2-Digit Subtraction

Find each difference.

23. 42
    − 17
    ————
     25

24. 65
    − 24
    ————
     41

25. 81
    − 37
    ————
     44

© McGraw-Hill School Division

CLUSTER B PREREQUISITE SKILLS

The skills listed in this chart are those identified as major prerequisite skills for students' success in the lessons in Cluster B of the chapter. Each skill is covered by one or more assessment items as shown in the middle column. The right column provides the page numbers for the lessons in this book that reteach the Cluster B prerequisite skills

Skill Name	Assessment Items	Lesson Pages
Rounding to the Nearest Thousand or Dollar	17-20	21
Subtraction Patterns	21-22	22-23
2-Digit Subtraction	23-25	24-25

CHAPTER 2 PRE-CHAPTER ASSESSMENT

Alternative Assessment Strategies

- Oral administration of the assessment is appropriate for younger students or those whose native language is not English. Read the skills title and directions one section at a time. Check students' understanding by asking them to tell you how they will do the first exercise in the group.

- For some skill types you may wish to use group administration. In this technique, a small group or pair of students complete the assessment together. Through their discussion, you will be able to decide if supplementary reteaching materials are needed.

Intervention Materials

If students are not successful with the prerequisite skills assessed on these pages, reteaching lessons have been created to help them make the transition into the chapter.

Item correlation charts showing the skills lessons suitable for reteaching the prerequisite skills are found beneath the reproductions of each page of the assessment.

Cluster B Challenge

Those students who demonstrate mastery of the skills on this page will not need to use the reteaching worksheets. Instead, these students can do the Cluster B Challenge found on pages 28–29.

Lesson Goal
- Add one- and two-digit numbers.

What the Student Needs to Know
- Add one-digit numbers.
- Name the tens and ones digits in a number.
- Use place-value models to show two-digit numbers.

Getting Started
- Conduct a brief review of the addition facts through 9 + 9. Concentrate on the more difficult problems. Have students write the sums as you call out the facts.
- Write these two problems on the board:

$$\begin{array}{r} 4\,3 \\ +2\,6 \\ \hline \end{array} \qquad \begin{array}{r} 4\,3 \\ +2\,9 \\ \hline \end{array}$$

- *What is different in these problems?* (In the right problem, you need to regroup because 3 plus 9 is greater than 10.)
- *Why is it important to always begin with the ones digits when you add?* Use the example 43 + 29 to explain. (If you start with the tens, you will write 6 under the line. But, the tens digit in the answer is 7 and not 6. You can't add the tens until you know whether or not you need to regroup the ones.)

What Can I Do?
Read the question and the response. Then read and discuss the examples. Ask:

- *How can you use an addition fact to add a one-digit number to a two-digit number?* (Students can use the examples in their answers. Encourage them also to give other problems to demonstrate the strategy.)
- *When you are adding two two-digit numbers, when do you regroup?* (When the sum of the ones digits is ten or greater.)

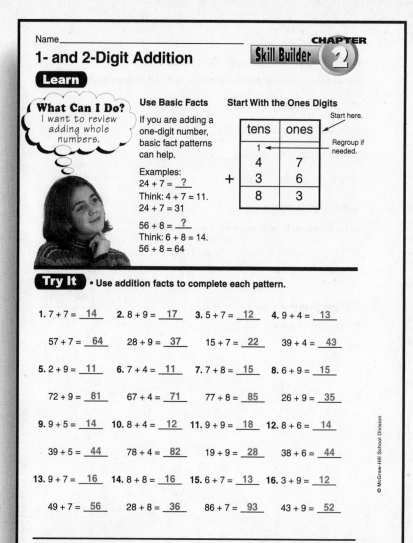

Name_____

1- and 2-Digit Addition

Learn

What Can I Do?
I want to review adding whole numbers.

Use Basic Facts
If you are adding a one-digit number, basic fact patterns can help.

Examples:
24 + 7 = ?
Think: 4 + 7 = 11.
24 + 7 = 31

56 + 8 = ?
Think: 6 + 8 = 14.
56 + 8 = 64

Start With the Ones Digits
Start here.

tens	ones
1	
4	7
3	6
8	3

+
Regroup if needed.

Try It
- Use addition facts to complete each pattern.

1. 7 + 7 = __14__   2. 8 + 9 = __17__   3. 5 + 7 = __12__   4. 9 + 4 = __13__

   57 + 7 = __64__   28 + 9 = __37__   15 + 7 = __22__   39 + 4 = __43__

5. 2 + 9 = __11__   6. 7 + 4 = __11__   7. 7 + 8 = __15__   8. 6 + 9 = __15__

   72 + 9 = __81__   67 + 4 = __71__   77 + 8 = __85__   26 + 9 = __35__

9. 9 + 5 = __14__   10. 8 + 4 = __12__   11. 9 + 9 = __18__   12. 8 + 6 = __14__

   39 + 5 = __44__   78 + 4 = __82__   19 + 9 = __28__   38 + 6 = __44__

13. 9 + 7 = __16__   14. 8 + 8 = __16__   15. 6 + 7 = __13__   16. 3 + 9 = __12__

   49 + 7 = __56__   28 + 8 = __36__   86 + 7 = __93__   43 + 9 = __52__

WHAT IF THE STUDENT CAN'T

Add One-Digit Numbers
- Use addition flash cards. Have students work in pairs to practice their facts.
- Students can use the doubles to help them with some facts; for example, 6 + 6 = 12, so 6 + 7 = 13. Demonstrate this strategy for students.
- Students can use the strategy "make ten." To do this, they break one number into two parts; for example, 6 + 8 = 6 + 4 + 4 = 10 + 4 = 14. By breaking the 8 into 4 + 4, students change the problem into 10 + 4.

Name the Tens and Ones Digits in a Number
- Provide students with place-value models. Students work in pairs. One student models a two-digit number. The other student tells the number of tens and the number of ones.
- Give students pairs of numbers such as 83 and 38 in which the digits are reversed. Have students write each number in expanded form. In this example, students write 83 = 80 + 3 and 38 = 30 + 8.

Name_____

Will you need to regroup? If so, circle the problem.

17. (61 + 19)   18. (28 + 47)   19. 49 + 30   20. (65 + 29)   21. 57 + 12

Power Practice • Find each sum.

22. 76 + 9 = __85__   23. 24 + 7 = __31__

24. 36 + 8 = __44__   25. 59 + 7 = __66__

26. 37 + 6 = __43__   27. 49 + 9 = __58__

28. 17 + 5 = __22__   29. 68 + 8 = __76__

30. 58 + 9 = __67__   31. 86 + 6 = __92__

| 32. | 63 + 16 = 79 | 33. | 38 + 82 = 120 | 34. | 18 + 64 = 82 | 35. | 61 + 30 = 91 | 36. | 48 + 47 = 95 |

37. 59 + 91 = 150   38. 43 + 25 = 68   39. 79 + 85 = 164   40. 25 + 56 = 81   41. 81 + 17 = 98

42. 73 + 28 = 101   43. 32 + 75 = 107   44. 56 + 23 = 79   45. 67 + 34 = 101   46. 49 + 74 = 123

© McGraw-Hill School Division

WHAT IF THE STUDENT CAN'T

Use Place-Value Models to Show Two-Digit Numbers

- Lay out 10 ones and 10 tens for the student. Line up the ones to show that they equal one 10-stick. Have the student count up to 10, touching each cube as he or she counts. Then have the student count by tens up to 100.

- When the student is familiar with the tens and ones models, ask him or her to make some two-digit numbers. Start with numbers less than 20 and then use greater numbers. Ask questions such as:

- *Show me three tens and four ones. What number is*

this? How do you write the two-digit number shown by the models?

Complete the Power Practice

- Use a problem such as 43 + 29 that requires regrouping. Have the student show this problem with place-value models. After laying out the two numbers, he or she will need to trade 10 ones for a ten stick. Relate this action to the regrouping that is done in the problems when the student adds two numbers on paper.

- Have students work in pairs. Provide place-value models so they can show each problem to find the sum.

USING THE LESSON

- *How do you regroup?* (You must add one ten to the tens column.)

Try It

Have a volunteer read the directions. Say:

- *Explain how you will do the first exercise.* (Possible strategy: Add 7 plus 7 to get 14. The ones digit is 4 in both answers. Look at the two-digit number in the second part of the exercise. Add 1 to the tens digit to get 6. The answer is 64.)

- Have a volunteer read the directions at the top of page 17. Ask:

- *How do you know if you need to regroup?* (The sum of the ones digits must be 10 or greater.)

Power Practice

- Have students look over the exercises. Ask:

- *How are exercises 22–31 different from exercises 32–46?* (In exercises 22–31, a one-digit number is added to a two-digit number.)

- *How can you use basic facts for the first rows?* (Use the ones digits and find the sum. Then add one to the tens digit of the two-digit number.)

- *What other method can you use for these exercises?* (Some students may prefer to write the exercises in vertical form.)

- Say: *Look over the two-digit exercises. Find the exercises in which you don't need to regroup.* (exercises 32, 35, 38, 41, 43, 44)

Lesson Goal

- Write numbers through 99,999 in expanded form.

What the Student Needs to Know

- Use a place-value chart.
- Name the digits in a number.
- Use place-value models to show two- and three-digit numbers.

Getting Started

- Write the word *digit* on the board. Ask: *How many digits are there?* (10) *What are they?* (0, 1, 2, 3, 4, 5, 6, 7, 8, and 9) *What are the digits used for?* (Digits are used to make numbers.)
- Write on the board:

  48 = 4 tens 8 ones

  Ask: *How does this sentence show what the number 48 means?* (It shows the value of each digit. The 4 stands for 4 tens; the 8 stands for 8 ones.)
- *How do you find the value of a digit in a number?* (Look at the place that the digit has. Multiply the digit by the value of the place. Encourage students to use two- and three-digit numbers in their explanations.)

What Can I Do?

Read the question. Then read and discuss the example. Ask:

- *What number is shown in the place-value chart?* (forty-six thousand, nineteen)
- *How do you write this number in standard form?* (46,019) *How do you know where to put the comma in the number?* (The comma goes in between the thousands and hundreds digits.)
- Have each student write a different five-digit number. Students take turns reading their numbers and identifying the places for the digits.

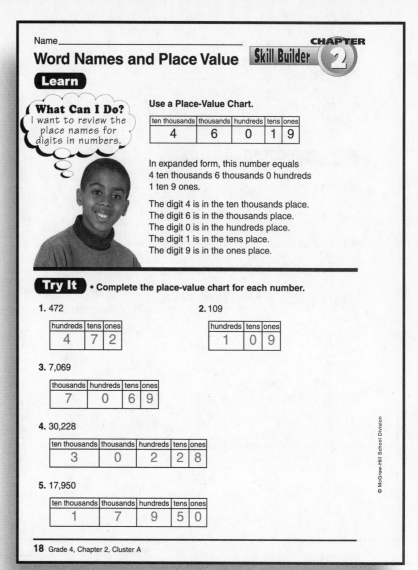

Name_____

Word Names and Place Value   Skill Builder   CHAPTER 2

Learn

What Can I Do?
I want to review the place names for digits in numbers.

Use a Place-Value Chart.

ten thousands	thousands	hundreds	tens	ones
4	6	0	1	9

In expanded form, this number equals 4 ten thousands 6 thousands 0 hundreds 1 ten 9 ones.

The digit 4 is in the ten thousands place.
The digit 6 is in the thousands place.
The digit 0 is in the hundreds place.
The digit 1 is in the tens place.
The digit 9 is in the ones place.

Try It • Complete the place-value chart for each number.

1. 472

hundreds	tens	ones
4	7	2

2. 109

hundreds	tens	ones
1	0	9

3. 7,069

thousands	hundreds	tens	ones
7	0	6	9

4. 30,228

ten thousands	thousands	hundreds	tens	ones
3	0	2	2	8

5. 17,950

ten thousands	thousands	hundreds	tens	ones
1	7	9	5	0

18 Grade 4, Chapter 2, Cluster A

WHAT IF THE STUDENT CAN'T

Use a Place-Value Chart

- Provide place-value models for student. Have him or her show some two-digit numbers, telling you the number of tens and the number of ones.
- After student can represent numbers with place-value models, show him or her how to write a two-digit number as ____ tens ____ ones. Finally, draw a place-value chart. Point out that each digit is identified by the word above it.

Name the Digits in a Number

- Review the meaning of the term *digit*. Write the ten digits 0 through 9 on the board and remind the student the that digits are used to make numbers.
- Use a few examples with three- and four-digit numbers. For example, write 2,147 on the board and say:
- *This number has four digits. What are the digits?* (2, 1, 4, and 7) *What does each digit stand for?* (The 2 stands for 2 thousands; the 1 stands for 1 hundred; the 4 stands for 4 tens; and the 7 stands for 7 ones.)

Name_____

Power Practice • Complete the word name for each number.

© McGraw-Hill School Division

6. 8,000 = eight ___thousand___

7. 500 = five ___hundred___

8. 7,000 = seven ___thousand___

Write the place name for the digit 3 in each number.

9. 2,132 ___tens___

10. 36,504 ___ten thousands___

11. 58,913 ___ones___

12. 3,491 ___thousands___

13. 16,384 ___hundreds___

Complete the expanded form for each number.

14. 674 = __6__ hundreds __7__ tens __4__ ones

15. 590 = __5__ hundreds __9__ tens __0__ ones

16. 7,594 = __7__ thousands __5__ hundreds __9__ tens __4__ ones

17. 23,908 = __2__ ten thousands __3__ thousands __9__ hundreds __0__ tens __8__ ones

18. 47,620 = __4__ ten thousands __7__ thousands __6__ hundreds __2__ tens __0__ ones

Learn with Partners & Parents

Spin and Roll

The players need one 1–6 number cube and a 4-part spinner. Write *ones*, *tens*, *hundreds*, and *thousands* in the four parts.

• Spin the spinner and roll the cube. Create a four-digit number that has the digit you rolled in the place you spun.

• Take turns. The player with the greater number gets one point for that round. The first player to get 10 points wins.

• Try changing the rules so that each number created must have four different digits.

Try It

Have a volunteer read the directions. Ask:

• *What does a place-value chart show?* (The place name for each digit in the number.)

Power Practice

• Allow students time to look over the kinds of exercises. Have three students read the three direction lines. Go over the first exercise in each exercise set to make certain all students know what to do.

• Copy the place-value chart from the beginning of the lesson on the board for student reference.

• Review the spellings of the words used for the places. Students will need to spell these words to complete the first two exercise sets.

Learn with Partners & Parents

• Students can play this game in pairs or in small groups.

• Model one play of the game for students to make sure they understand the directions.

WHAT IF THE STUDENT CAN'T

Use Place-Value Models

• Lay out ten ones, ten 10-sticks, and three hundreds squares. Show the student how 10 ones equals 1 ten; 10 tens equals one hundred. You may want to have the student count up to 10, touching each cube. Then he or she counts by 10s to 100.

• After students are familiar with the models, have them work in pairs to model two- and three-digit numbers. One student shows a number. The partner identifies the number of hundreds, tens, and ones and then tells the name of that number.

Complete the Power Practice

• Look over the student's work to analyze which types of exercises are being answered incorrectly.

• Students may have trouble writing the words for the place names, especially thousands and ten thousands. Ask them to give the answers orally. Provide extra practice in spelling and writing place-value names.

• Students may confuse the digits in numbers. For the last set of exercises, have them first make a place-value chart for each number. Then they transfer each digit on to the proper blank in the answer.

USING THE LESSON

Lesson Goal
- Round to the nearest ten or hundred.

What the Student Needs to Know
- Identify the tens place.
- Identify the hundreds place.
- Identify multiples of 10 and 100.

Getting Started
- Write 40, 50, and 60 on the board. Remind students that these are called *multiples of 10*.
- *What are the two multiples of 10 nearest to 43? to 57?* (40 and 50; 50 and 60)

Repeat with similar questions. Include some three- and four-digit numbers.

- Write 400, 500, and 600 on the board. Remind students that these are called *multiples of 100*.
- *What are the two multiples of 100 nearest to 438? to 572?* (400 and 500; 500 and 600)

Repeat with similar questions. Include some four-digit numbers.

What Can I Do?
Read the question and the response. Then read and discuss the examples. Ask:
- *What are the two multiples of 10 nearest to 3,762?* (3,760 and 3,770) *Which one is the nearest ten?* (3,760) Draw a number line to show how you know.
- *What are the two multiples of 100 nearest to 3,762?* (3,700 and 3,800) *Which one is nearest?* (3,800) Draw a number line to show how you know.

Try It
For Exercises 1–6, have students tell you the tens digits in each number. For Exercises 7–12, have them tell you the hundreds digit.

Power Practice
Have the students look over the practice items. Ask:
- *To which place will you round the first number?* (tens)

Rounding to the Nearest Ten or Hundred

Learn

What Can I Do?
I want to round to the nearest ten or hundred.

Look at the Digit to the Right

thousands	hundreds	tens	ones
3	7	6	2

Underline the place to which you want to round. Then look at the digit to the right.

When rounding to the nearest ten, look at the ones digit. Since 2 is less than 5, 3,762 rounds down to 3,760.

When rounding to the nearest hundred, look at the tens digit. Since 6 is 5 or greater, 3,762 rounds up to 3,800.

Try It • Round each number to the nearest ten.

1. 35 ___40___   2. 83 ___80___   3. 670 ___670___

4. 982 ___980___   5. 1,309 ___1,310___   6. 3,357 ___3,360___

Round each number to the nearest hundred.

7. 293 ___300___   8. 646 ___600___   9. 485 ___500___

10. 8,128 ___8,100___   11. 4,151 ___4,200___   12. 1,207 ___1,200___

Power Practice • Round each number to the underlined place.

13. 4,147 ___4,150___   14. 281 ___300___   15. 867 ___870___

16. 54 ___50___   17. 3,163 ___3,200___   18. 5,247 ___5,250___

© McGraw-Hill School Division

20 Grade 4, Chapter 2, Cluster A

WHAT IF THE STUDENT CAN'T

Identify the Tens Place
- Use place-value charts for two-, three- and four-digit numbers.
- Use place-value models to review the meanings of the digits in two- and three- digit numbers.

Identify the Hundreds Place
- Use place-value charts for some three- and four-digit numbers.

Identify Multiples of 10 and 100
- Count aloud as a class by 10s from 10 to 100. Have students take turns writing these multiples of 10 on the board. Have students name several multiples of 10 that are greater than 100. Point out that a multiple of 10 has a zero in the ones place. Repeat the activity with multiples of 100.

Complete the Power Practice
- Have students work in pairs to draw number lines to show the exercises. When rounding to the nearest ten, the number line is numbered by 1s. When rounding to the nearest hundred, the number line is numbered by 10s.

Rounding to the Nearest Thousand or Dollar

Skill Builder CHAPTER 2

Learn

What Can I Do?
I want to round to the nearest thousand or to the nearest dollar.

Look at the Digit to the Right

Underline the place to which you want to round. Then look at the digit to the right.

When rounding to the nearest thousand, look at the hundreds digit.

6, ④ 2 9

Since 4 is less than 5, 6,429 rounds down to 6,000.

When rounding to the nearest dollar, look at the dimes digit.

$7 .⑤ 7

Since 5 is 5 or greater, $7.57 rounds up to $8.00.

Try It • Round each number to the nearest thousand.

1. 8,303 __8,000__   2. 6,533 __7,000__   3. 75,185 __75,000__

Round each amount of money to the nearest dollar.

4. $5.76 __$6.00__   5. $32.94 __$33.00__   6. $61.32 __$61.00__

Power Practice • Round each number or amount of money to the underlined place.

7. 74,149 __74,000__   8. $91.37 __$91.00__   9. $8.58 __$9.00__

10. $6.45 __$6.00__   11. 6,918 __7,000__   12. 80,206 __80,000__

13. 3,089 __3,000__   14. 40,753 __41,000__   15. $16.64 __$17.00__

© McGraw-Hill School Division

WHAT IF THE STUDENT CAN'T

Identify the Thousands Place

- Have students work in pairs. Provide place-value models and blank place-value charts. One student shows a four-digit number with the models; the partner records the number in a place-value chart. Have students make 10 different four-digit numbers.

Identify Multiples of One Thousand

- Have the student count by 1,000s to 10,000. Write the numbers on the board as they count. Point out the three zeros at the end of each number.

Draw Number Lines to Show the Nearest Thousand or Nearest Dollar

- Provide the student with blank numbers lines that show 11 marks.

⟨←—+—+—+—+—+—+—+—+—+—+—→⟩

Demonstrate how to number by 100s or dimes. Then have him or her model any of the exercises on the page.

Complete the Power Practice

- Use number lines together with place-value models to round the thousands problems. Use number lines with play money to round the money problems.

USING THE LESSON

Lesson Goal

- Round to the nearest thousand or dollar.

What the Student Needs to Know

- Identify the thousands place.
- Identify multiples of 1,000.
- Draw number lines to show the nearest thousand or nearest dollar.

Getting Started

- Write 5,489 on the board. Show students how to draw a number line from 5,000 to 6,000. Number by 100s. Say:
- *Why does 5,489 go on this number line?* (because it is a number between 5,000 and 6,000) *Which thousand is nearer?* (5,000)
- Write $2.58 on the board. Show a number line from $2.00 to $3.00. Number by dimes: $2.00, $2.10, $2.20, and so on. Have students point to the location of $2.58 and tell which dollar it rounds to.

What Can I Do?

Read the question and the response. Then read and discuss the examples. Ask:

- *What are the two multiples of 1,000 nearest to 6,429?* (6,000 and 7,000) *Which digit do you look at when you round to the nearest thousand?* (The hundreds digit)
- *What are the two dollars nearest to $7.57?* ($7.00 and $8.00) *How do you choose which dollar to round to?* (Look at the digit for the dimes. If it is less than 5, round down. If it is 5 or greater, round up.)

Try It

For Exercises 1–3, have students tell the two thousands nearest each number. For Exercises 4–6, have them tell the two dollars nearest each amount.

Power Practice

- Have the students complete the practice items. Then review each answer.

Lesson Goal
- Subtract a one-digit number from a two-digit number.

What the Student Needs to Know
- Complete subtraction facts.
- Identify tens and ones digits.
- Use addition to check subtraction.

Getting Started
- Conduct a brief review of the subtraction facts, concentrating on the more difficult problems. Have students write the entire fact rather than only the answer. Remind students that they can check subtraction with addition. If necessary, demonstrate this procedure.
- Write these two problems on the board:

56   56
− 5   − 8

Ask: *How are these problems the same? How are they different?* (The problems have the same top number, but a different number is being subtracted. The first problem does not require regrouping, but the second problem does.)

- *What strategy would you use for a problem like 56 − 8?* (Accept all student answers. If any student suggests using the related subtraction fact, explain that this is the strategy they will see presented in the lesson.)

What Can I Do?
Read the question and the response. Point out that there are two different problems, one in vertical form and one in horizontal form. The same strategy—use the related fact—is modeled with each problem. Ask:

- *How are 53 − 8 and 13 − 8 related?* (They have the same ones digits.)
- *How can you use the answer to 13 − 8 to do the problem 53 − 8?* (Since 13 − 8 equals 5, the ones digit in the answer to 53 − 8 will also be 5. The tens digit must be one less than 5, or 4. Model this chain of reasoning for students.)

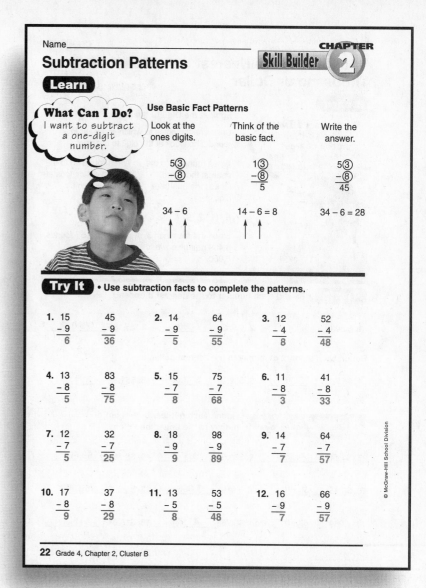

WHAT IF THE STUDENT CAN'T

Complete Subtraction Facts
- Provide subtraction flash cards. Have students work in pairs to find out which facts each student knows and doesn't know. Each student makes a list of the facts he or she needs to work on.
- Demonstrate how to use the related addition fact. For example, to find 15 − 8, the student can think, "What number plus 8 equals 15?"
- Show the student how to use the strategy "Make Ten." For example, to find 15 − 8, the student breaks the subtracted number into two parts: 15 − 5 − 3. This equals 10 − 3, or 7.

Identify Tens and Ones Digits
- Provide place-value models and have students show several two-digit numbers. He or she uses models to identify the tens, the ones, and write the number.
- Using a two-digit number such as 48, ask: *How many tens are there in this number?* (4 tens) *Which digit, 4 or 8, is the tens digit?* (the digit 4) *How many ones are there?* (8 ones) *Which digit is the ones digit?* (the digit 8)

Name_____

13. 14 − 8 = _6_   **14.** 17 − 9 = _8_

84 − 8 = _76_   47 − 9 = _38_

15. 12 − 7 = _5_   **16.** 13 − 9 = _4_

32 − 7 = _25_   93 − 9 = _84_

17. 15 − 8 = _7_   **18.** 16 − 8 = _8_

65 − 8 = _57_   76 − 8 = _68_

Learn with Partners & Parents

Count Down from 40

You and a partner need a set of 0–9 digit cards.

- Turn the cards over and mix them up. Each player draws 5 cards.
- The first player chooses a card and subtracts that number from 40. The second player chooses a card and subtracts that number from the first difference. Continue. The last player who can subtract is the winner.

Power Practice • Find each difference.

19. 52
−9
‾‾‾
43

20. 71
−2
‾‾‾
69

21. 52
−7
‾‾‾
45

22. 43
−8
‾‾‾
35

23. 91
−3
‾‾‾
88

24. 85
−6
‾‾‾
79

25. 72
−6
‾‾‾
66

26. 75
−8
‾‾‾
67

27. 32
−7
‾‾‾
25

28. 44
−6
‾‾‾
38

29. 62 − 5 = _57_   **30.** 25 − 9 = _16_

31. 61 − 4 = _57_   **32.** 70 − 3 = _67_

33. 83 − 6 = _77_   **34.** 74 − 7 = _67_

35. 42 − 4 = _38_   **36.** 32 − 5 = _27_

© McGraw-Hill School Division

Grade 4, Chapter 2, Cluster B **23**

WHAT IF THE STUDENT CAN'T

Use Addition to Check Subtraction

- Use simple problems such as 4 + 3 = 7 to demonstrate the addition-subtraction relationship. The two parts, 3 and 4, are added together to make the whole, 7. Subtracting either part from the whole gives a related subtraction fact:

  3 + 4 = 7

  7 − 3 = 4

  7 − 4 = 3

- Some people think of subtraction as "un-doing" addition. Suggest that students try thinking of the relationship in these terms.

Complete the Power Practice

- Have the student use a separate sheet of paper. For each exercise, he or she writes the related subtraction fact and then the exercise with its answer. Have the student use the horizontal form so matching ones digits are lined up.

USING THE LESSON

Try It

Point out that the two problems in each exercise have the same ones digits.

- Some students may find this relationship easier to see when the problems are in horizontal form. If so, have them do Exercises 13–18 first.

- Have students work the first row. Ask: *What do you notice about the ones digits in the answers?* (In each pair of exercises, the ones digits are the same.)

- *What do you notice about the tens digits in the answers?* (The first exercise is a subtraction fact, so there is no tens digit. In the second exercise, the tens digit is one less than the top number.)

- *How can you use addition to check your answers?* (Add the answer to the number subtracted.)

Power Practice

- Before students begin, have them say the related subtraction fact for each problem in the first row.

- Remind students not to make the mistake of subtracting a greater number from a lesser number.

Learn with Partners & Parents

- As students play the game, encourage them to do the subtraction mentally by using related subtraction facts.

- A longer game can be created by using two sets of digit cards and having students start with 99 rather than 40.

Lesson Goal
- Subtract two-digit numbers.

What the Student Needs to Know
- Complete subtraction facts.
- Identify tens and ones digits.
- Use place-value models to show two-digit numbers.

Getting Started
- Have students work in small groups on a brief review of subtraction facts. Each student writes the five facts he or she thinks are the most difficult. Students quiz each other using their "hard facts."
- Write these two problems on the board:

    76   76
  – 35   – 38

  Ask: *How are these problems the same? How are they different?* (The problems have the same top number, but a different number is being subtracted. The first problem does not require regrouping, but the second problem does.)

What Can I Do?
Read the question and the response. Then read and discuss the examples. Ask:
- *Why are the problems in boxes?* (The boxes show the tens and ones digits. They remind students to line up digits in the correct columns.)
- *Explain the steps in the first problem.* (Start with the ones digits: 7 minus 6 is 1. Then subtract the tens: 8 minus 3 is 5.)

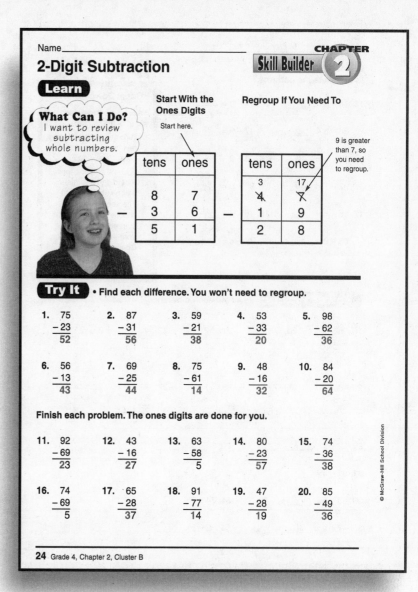

Name_____

Skill Builder

2-Digit Subtraction

Learn

What Can I Do? I want to review subtracting whole numbers.

Start With the Ones Digits — Start here.

Regroup If You Need To

9 is greater than 7, so you need to regroup.

tens	ones
8	7
3	6
5	1

tens	ones
3 ~~4~~	17 ~~7~~
1	9
2	8

Try It • Find each difference. You won't need to regroup.

1. 75 −23 = 52	2. 87 −31 = 56	3. 59 −21 = 38	4. 53 −33 = 20	5. 98 −62 = 36
6. 56 −13 = 43	7. 69 −25 = 44	8. 75 −61 = 14	9. 48 −16 = 32	10. 84 −20 = 64

Finish each problem. The ones digits are done for you.

11. 92 −69 = 23	12. 43 −16 = 27	13. 63 −58 = 5	14. 80 −23 = 57	15. 74 −36 = 38
16. 74 −69 = 5	17. 65 −28 = 37	18. 91 −77 = 14	19. 47 −28 = 19	20. 85 −49 = 36

© McGraw-Hill School Division

24 Grade 4, Chapter 2, Cluster B

WHAT IF THE STUDENT CAN'T

Complete Subtraction Facts
- Provide subtraction flash cards. Have students work in pairs to find out which facts each student knows and doesn't know.
- Have students work in small groups to review and share fact strategies such as using a related addition fact, using doubles, making ten, and so on.

Identify Tens and Ones Digits
- Review the meaning of the term *digit*. Ask: *What are digits used for?* (The ten digits 0 through 9 are used to write numbers.) Have each student write three different two-digit numbers using the digits 2, 5, and 8.
- Provide place-value models and have the student show several two-digit numbers. He or she uses models to identify the tens, the ones, and write the number.

Will you need to regroup? If so, circle the problem.

21. 78 − 24	22. (53 − 16)	23. 84 − 31	24. (42 − 29)	25. (84 − 77)	
26. 95 − 65	27. 76 − 30	28. (53 − 18)	29. 57 − 12	30. (36 − 19)	
31. (61 − 19)	32. 98 − 47	33. 49 − 30	34. (65 − 29)	35. 68 − 22	

Power Practice • Find each difference.

36. 84 − 28 56	37. 87 − 28 59	38. 79 − 12 67	39. 96 − 57 39	40. 63 − 41 22
41. 42 − 36 6	42. 86 − 56 30	43. 65 − 46 19	44. 78 − 23 55	45. 94 − 32 62
46. 76 − 19 57	47. 98 − 87 11	48. 75 − 30 45	49. 84 − 19 65	50. 77 − 46 31
51. 65 − 21 44	52. 81 − 37 44	53. 67 − 23 44	54. 95 − 28 67	55. 57 − 19 38

© McGraw-Hill School Division

USING THE LESSON

- *Explain the steps in the second problem.* (Start with the ones. Since 9 is more than 7, you must regroup. Change the 4 tens to 3 tens and add a ten to the ones to get 17 ones. Subtract the ones: 17 minus 9 is 8; subtract the tens: 3 minus 1 is 2.)

- If students have difficulty explaining the steps, provide place-value models and have them show the two problems.

Try It

- Have a volunteer read the directions. Ask: *Why won't you need to regroup in the first ten problems?* (In the ones column, the bottom number is less than the top number.)

- Have a different student read the next direction line. Ask: *Can you just subtract the tens without looking at the ones?* (No, you must show the regrouping process from the ones column.)

- Have another student read the directions at the top of page 25. Ask: *How will you decide if you need to regroup?* (Look at the ones column. You need to regroup if the number being subtracted is greater than the top number.)

Power Practice

- Before students begin, have them tell you whether or not they will need to regroup for each problem in the first row. If students seem uncertain, continue with the discussion using the remaining problems.

- As students work, watch to see if any are having extra difficulties. If so, provide these students with place-value models and help them show the problems.

WHAT IF THE STUDENT CAN'T

Use Place-Value Models To Show Two-Digit Numbers

- Provide the student with a supply of tens and ones models. Show how ten ones have the same value as one of the 10-sticks. Have the student use 10-sticks to count to 50. Then model a number such as 58 and have the student find the total.

- Provide pairs of students with place-value models and blank tens and ones charts like this:

tens	ones

Have students work in pairs. One student writes a two-digit number in a chart; the partner shows the number using place-value models.

Complete the Power Practice

- Analyze students' work to find out what kinds of errors they are making. Some common errors are: subtracting the top number from the bottom number; forgetting to regroup in the tens; frequent errors in the basic subtraction facts.

- It may help some students to write problems in place-value charts like those shown at the beginning of the lesson. Provide blank charts for students to use.

CHALLENGE

Lesson Goal
- Use number patterns to complete lists of triangular and square numbers.

Introducing the Challenge
- Review the vocabulary needed for the lesson by having students use each term in a sentence. Vocabulary used in this lesson includes: number pattern, odd number.
- Have students work in small groups. Provide each group with a supply of circular or square counters. Have students look at the pictures on page 26 and then make the first five triangular numbers with counters. Ask:
- *How many counters will you need to add to make the next triangular number?* (6) *What is happening to the number of counters?* (The number added increases by one each time.)

Name _____

Numbers with Shape!

CHALLENGE CHAPTER 2

Look at the number pattern 1, 3, 6, 10, 15,.... Each time you add one more. The pattern is plus 2, plus 3, plus 4, plus 5, and so on.

$1 + ②= 3$
$3 + ③= 6$
$6 + ④= 10$

The numbers in this pattern are called triangular numbers. They can be arranged in triangular shapes like this:

1. The figure should show 21 dots.

```
                                      O
                          O          OO
               O         OO         OOO
      O       OO        OOO        OOOO
O    OO      OOO       OOOO       OOOOO
1st  2nd     3rd       4th        5th
```

1. In the space at the right, draw the 6th triangular number.

2. Create the next ten triangular numbers.

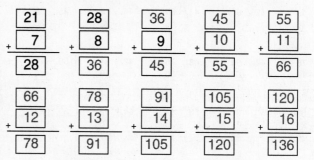

21	28	36	45	55
+ 7	+ 8	+ 9	+ 10	+ 11
28	36	45	55	66

66	78	91	105	120
+ 12	+ 13	+ 14	+ 15	+ 16
78	91	105	120	136

3. The 17th triangular number is 153. How can you use this to check your work in Problem 2?

Possible answer: Subtract 17 from 153 and see if you get the 16th number.

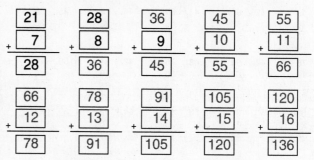

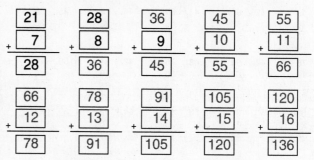

26 Grade 4, Chapter 2, Cluster A

© McGraw-Hill School Division

Name_____

Here is another number pattern: 1, 4, 9, 16, 25,.... This time, you add the odd numbers. The pattern is plus 3, plus 5, plus 7, plus 9, and so on. The numbers in this pattern are called square numbers.

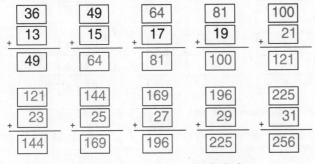

The third square number is 9.

4. Draw the first six square numbers below.

   The figures should show 1, 4, 9, 16, 25, and 36.

5. Create the next ten square numbers.

36	49	64	81	100
+ 13	+ 15	+ 17	+ 19	+ 21
49	64	81	100	121

121	144	169	196	225
+ 23	+ 25	+ 27	+ 29	+ 31
144	169	196	225	256

6. The drawing shows a way to relate the triangular and square numbers. Explain this relationship.

3rd + 4th

The 1st and 2nd triangular numbers equal the 2nd square

number, the 2nd and 3rd triangular numbers equal the 3rd

square, the 3rd and 4th triangular numbers equal the 4th

square, and so on.

Grade 4, Chapter 2, Cluster A **27**

CHALLENGE

Using the Challenge

- Have students read the top part of page 26 and work together to complete the problems on the page. Encourage them to use their counters to model the triangular numbers.

- You may wish to show students another way to arrange the counters to make triangular numbers:

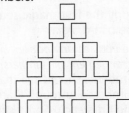

   In this kind of arrangement, the next number is created by adding a row at the bottom. Some students may prefer to show their numbers in this way.

- Tell students that numbers can make patterns other than triangles. Ask for suggested shapes. If no one mentions a square, show students one example of such a number. Then have them read the page and do all but the last problem.

- Some students may need help with the last problem. Show them with counters of two colors how two triangular numbers can be joined together to make a square. Or, alternately, any square number can be divided into two triangular numbers.

CHALLENGE

Lesson Goal

- Use logical thinking to find missing numbers in magic squares.

Introducing the Challenge

- Review the vocabulary needed for the lesson by having students use each term in a sentence. Vocabulary used in this lesson includes: row, column, diagonal, flip, turn, double a number.
- Copy the first magic square on the board. Ask:
- *Do you see any patterns in this arrangement of numbers?* (Students should see that the numbers 1 through 9 are used one time each. Some students may realize that the sums of columns or rows is always 15.)
- Write the term *magic square* on the board. Ask if any students know what this means. If no one does, have them read the top of page 28 to find out what a magic square is.

Name _____

Magic Squares

This is a magic square. In a magic square the sum of every row, column, and diagonal must be the same number. For this magic square, the magic sum is 15. If you flip or turn a magic square, you'll get another magic square.

8	1	6
3	5	7
4	9	2

Complete each magic square. Each row, column, and diagonal must have a sum of 15. Each square uses the numbers 1 through 9.

1.

6	1	8
7	5	3
2	9	4

2.

2	7	6
9	5	1
4	3	8

3.

4	3	8
9	5	1
2	7	6

4.

2	9	4
7	5	3
6	1	8

5.

4	9	2
3	5	7
8	1	6

6.

6	7	2
1	5	9
8	3	4

Use the magic square at the right.

7. Double each number to create a new magic square.

8	3	4
1	5	9
6	7	2

16	6	8
2	10	18
12	14	4

Show that your new square is magic by writing these sums.

8. 1st row: 16 + 6 + 8 = 30

9. 2nd row: 2 + 10 + 18 = 30

10. 3rd row: 12 + 14 + 4 = 30

11. 1st column: 16 + 2 + 12 = 30

12. 2nd column: 6 + 10 + 14 = 30

13. 3rd column: 8 + 18 + 4 = 30

14. 1st diagonal: 12 + 10 + 8 = 30

15. 2nd diagonal: 16 + 10 + 4 = 30

Name_____

Magic squares can use larger numbers. Use logical reasoning to complete each magic square. Start by finding the magic sum.

16.

11	18	13
16	14	12
15	10	17

sum: __42__

17.

21	26	25
28	24	20
23	22	27

sum: __72__

18.

51	52	47
46	50	54
53	48	49

sum: __150__

19.

32	18	28
22	26	30
24	34	20

sum: __78__

20.

45	35	85
95	55	15
25	75	65

sum: __165__

21.

56	21	28
7	35	63
42	49	14

sum: __105__

Magic squares can have more than 9 numbers. This one uses the numbers 1 through 25.

22. Add the numbers in the right diagonal to find the magic sum. __65__

23. Make a list of the numbers from 1 through 25. Check off the ones that have been used.

24. Complete the left diagonal next. Then do the top row.

25. Continue until you have finished the entire square.

17	24	1	8	15
23	5	7	14	16
4	6	13	20	22
10	12	19	21	3
11	18	25	2	9

CHALLENGE

Using the Challenge

- Have a volunteer read the first set of directions aloud. Check that students know what to do by asking:
- *For the first problem, what numbers have already been used?* (6, 1, 8, and 5) *What numbers are left to use?* (2, 3, 4, 7, and 9)
- Make sure all students understand that each of the numbers 1 through 9 can be used only once.
- When students have finished page 28, ask them to state a conclusion from problems 7 through 15. (Possible statement: If you double each number in a magic square, you will get another magic square.)
- Some students may want to write the numbers 1 through 9 on slips of paper. Then they can move the papers around until they have an arrangement that works.

Name_____

Time to the Half Hour

Write the time for each clock.

1.

_____

2.

_____

Ordinal Numbers

Start at the left of the row of letters. Which letter is in each place?

B E G A D T Q W

3. third _____

4. sixth _____

5. 4th _____

6. 2nd _____

Order Whole Numbers

Put each list in order from least to greatest.

7. 86, 82, 68, 93, 108, 96 _____

8. 123, 118, 126, 98, 114 _____

9. 426, 642, 624, 402, 604 _____

Subtracting Whole Numbers

Find each difference.

10. 48 – 12 = _____

11. 117 – 76 = _____

Points on a Number Line

Write the number that shows the location of each point.

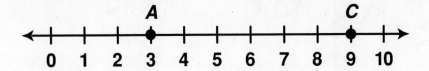

12. point C _____   **13.** point A _____

Mark a point at each location.

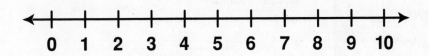

14. point D on the number 6   **15.** point E on the number 1

Number Patterns

Complete each addition pattern.

16. 5, 10, 15, 20, 25, _____, _____, _____

17. 14, 16, 18, 20, 22, _____, _____, _____

18. 4, 8, 12, 16, 20, _____, _____, _____

19. 50, 60, 70, 80, _____, _____, _____

20. 800, 1,000, 1,200, 1,400, _____, _____, _____

Assessment Goal

This two-page assessment covers skills identified as necessary for success in Chapter 3 Data, Statistics, and Graphing. The first page assesses the major prerequisite skills for Cluster A. The second page assesses the major prerequisite skills for Cluster B. When the Cluster A and Cluster B prerequisite skills overlap, the skill(s) will be covered in only one section.

Getting Started

- Allow students time to look over the two pages of the assessment. Point out the labels that identify the skills covered.

- Have students find math vocabulary terms used in the assessment. List vocabulary terms on the board as students identify them. If necessary, review the meanings of all essential math vocabulary.

Introducing the Assessment

- Explain to students that these pages will help you know if they are ready to start a new chapter in their math textbooks.

- Students who have transferred from another school may not have been introduced to some of these skills. Encourage students to do their best and assure them you will help them learn any needed skills.

Cluster A Challenge

Those students who demonstrate mastery of the skills on this page will not need to use the reteaching worksheets. Instead, these students can do the Cluster A Challenge found on pages 40–41.

Name_____

Time to the Half Hour

Write the time for each clock.

1. _3:30_

2. _6:00_

Ordinal Numbers

Start at the left of the row of letters. Which letter is in each place?

B E G A D T Q W

3. third ___G___

4. sixth ___T___

5. 4th ___A___

6. 2nd ___E___

Order Whole Numbers

Put each list in order from least to greatest.

7. 86, 82, 68, 93, 108, 96 _____68, 82, 86, 93, 96, 108_____

8. 123, 118, 126, 98, 114 _____98, 114, 118, 123, 126_____

9. 426, 642, 624, 402, 604 _____402, 426, 604, 624, 642_____

Subtracting Whole Numbers

Find each difference.

10. 48 − 12 = ___36___

11. 117 − 76 = ___41___

29A Use with Grade 4, Chapter 3, Cluster A

© McGraw-Hill School Division

CLUSTER A PREREQUISITE SKILLS

The skills listed in this chart are those identified as major prerequisite skills for students' success in the lessons in Cluster A of the chapter. Each skill is covered by one or more assessment items as shown in the middle column. The right column provides the page number for the lessons in this book that reteach the cluster A prerequisite skills.

Skill Name	Assessment Items	Lesson Pages
Time to the Half Hour	1-2	30
Ordinal Numbers	3-6	31
Order Whole Numbers	7-9	32-33
Subtracting Whole Numbers	10-11	34-35

Name_____

Points on a Number Line

Write the number that shows the location of each point.

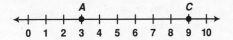

12. point C ___9___   13. point A ___3___

Mark a point at each location.

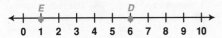

14. point D on the number 6   15. point E on the number 1

Number Patterns

Complete each addition pattern.

16. 5, 10, 15, 20, 25, ___30___, ___35___, ___40___

17. 14, 16, 18, 20, 22, ___24___, ___26___, ___28___

18. 4, 8, 12, 16, 20, ___24___, ___28___, ___32___

19. 50, 60, 70, 80, ___90___, ___100___, ___110___

20. 800, 1,000, 1,200, 1,400, ___1,600___, ___1,800___, ___2,000___

© McGraw-Hill School Division

Use with Grade 4, Chapter 3, Cluster B **29B**

CLUSTER B PREREQUISITE SKILLS

The skills listed in this chart are those identified as major prerequisite skills for students' success in the lessons in Cluster B of the chapter. Each skill is covered by one or more assessment items as shown in the middle column. The right column provides the page numbers for the lessons in this book that reteach the Cluster B prerequisite skills

Skill Name	Assessment Items	Lesson Pages
Points on a Number Line	12-15	36-37
Number Pattern	16-20	38-39

CHAPTER 3 PRE-CHAPTER ASSESSMENT

Alternative Assessment Strategies

- Oral administration of the assessment is appropriate for younger students or those whose native language is not English. Read the skills title and directions one section at a time. Check students' understanding by asking them to tell you how they will do the first exercise in the group.

- For some skill types you may wish to use group administration. In this technique, a small group or pair of students complete the assessment together. Through their discussion, you will be able to decide if supplementary reteaching materials are needed.

Intervention Materials

If students are not successful with the prerequisite skills assessed on these pages, reteaching lessons have been created to help them make the transition into the chapter.

Item correlation charts showing the skills lessons suitable for reteaching the prerequisite skills are found beneath the reproductions of each page of the assessment.

Cluster B Challenge
Those students who demonstrate mastery of the skills on this page will not need to use the reteaching worksheets. Instead, these students can do the Cluster B Challenge found on pages 42–43.

Lesson Goal

- Read hour and half hour times on an analog clock.

What the Student Needs to Know

- Identify the hour hand and minute hand.
- Tell time to the hour.
- Tell the number of minutes in an hour and half hour.

Getting Started

- Use a large model clock or draw a clock on the board. Set the hands to show 10 o'clock. Ask:
- *What time is shown?* (10 o'clock) *Which hand is the hour hand?* (the short hand) *Where is it?* (on the 10) *Which hand is the minute hand?* (the long hand) *Where is it?* (on the 12)
- Write *10 o'clock* on the board and remind students that this is one way to record a time.

What Can I Do?

Read the question and the response. Then read and discuss the example. Ask:

- *What time is shown on the clock?* (four thirty, or half past four) *How many minutes are in an hour?* (60) *How do you know that 30 minutes have passed since 4 o'clock?* (The minute hand has moved from the 12 to the 6.)
- Write 4:30 on the board. Ask students to tell which number is the hour and which is the minutes.

Try It

- *How will you decide the hour?* (Look at the number the hour hand is on or the number it has passed.)
- *How will you decide the minutes?* (Look at the number the minute hand is on.)

Power Practice

- Have the students complete the practice items. Then review each answer.

WHAT IF THE STUDENT CAN'T

Identify the Hour Hand and Minute Hand

- Show students a model clock or use a large wall clock. Point to the two hands and ask how they are different. Then remind students that the hour hand is shorter than the minute hand.

Tell Time to the Hour

- Use a model clock set to 9 o'clock. Move the hands until the clock reads 10 o'clock. Point out that it is an exact hour when the long hand (the minute hand) is on the 12.

Tell the Number of Minutes in an Hour and Half Hour

- Have students study a large wall clock in which every minute is marked. Point to the small marks and have students count them to see there are 60 marks. As the minute hand goes all the way around the clock, it passes 60 of these marks.

Complete the Power Practice

- Have students work in pairs. Provide them with model clocks or sheets with blank clocks. One student shows or draws a time to the hour or half hour; the partner identifies the time.

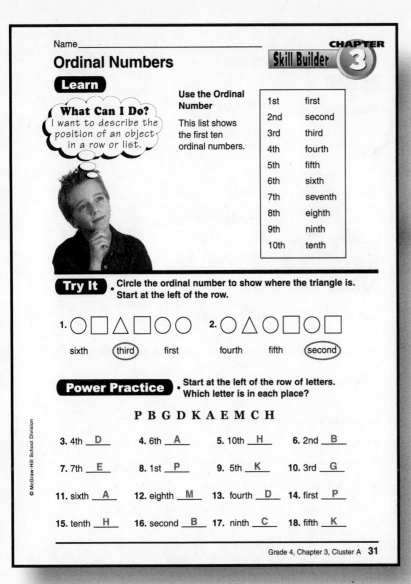

Learn

What Can I Do?
I want to describe the position of an object in a row or list.

Use the Ordinal Number

This list shows the first ten ordinal numbers.

1st	first
2nd	second
3rd	third
4th	fourth
5th	fifth
6th	sixth
7th	seventh
8th	eighth
9th	ninth
10th	tenth

Try It • Circle the ordinal number to show where the triangle is. Start at the left of the row.

1. ○ □ △ □ ○ ○
sixth (third) first

2. ○ △ ○ □ □ ○
fourth fifth (second)

Power Practice • Start at the left of the row of letters. Which letter is in each place?

P B G D K A E M C H

3. 4th _D_   4. 6th _A_   5. 10th _H_   6. 2nd _B_

7. 7th _E_   8. 1st _P_   9. 5th _K_   10. 3rd _G_

11. sixth _A_   12. eighth _M_   13. fourth _D_   14. first _P_

15. tenth _H_   16. second _B_   17. ninth _C_   18. fifth _K_

Grade 4, Chapter 3, Cluster A **31**

WHAT IF THE STUDENT CAN'T

Use *First*, *Next*, and *Last* to Describe Position

• Make three large signs reading *first*, *next*, *last*. Hand the signs to three students and have them line up in the appropriate order. Other students can call out corrections if the order is not correct.

Use and Spell Word Names Through Ten

• Write the numbers 1 through 10 on the board. Have students take turns coming up and writing the number word next to each. Have students use each number word in a sentence.

Recognize a Suffix

• Write on the board: four, six, seven, eight, ten. Have students copy the words and add the suffix -th to change them into ordinal numbers.

• Review the spellings of the other ordinals: *first, second, third, fifth,* and *ninth.*

Complete the Power Practice

• Line up ten toys or small objects. Point to the one on the student's left and say that one is first. Ask students to identify what is second, and so forth.

USING THE LESSON

Lesson Goal

• Use ordinal numbers through tenth.

What the Student Needs to Know

• Use *first, next,* and *last* to describe position.

• Use and spell word names through ten.

• Recognize a suffix.

Getting Started

• Ask five students to come to the front of the room. Have them line up, facing left. Ask:

• *Who is first? Who is last? What kind of number can you use to show someone's place in line?* (Students should suggest using the ordinal numbers 1st, 2nd, 3rd, 4th, and 5th. Repeat with another group of students, having each one write his or her ordinal number on the board.)

What Can I Do?

• Read the question and the response. Then read and discuss the numbers and words in the chart. Ask:

• *What suffix do you add to a number so it shows a location?* (Most of the time you use -th. The numbers 1, 2, and 3 need different suffixes.)

Try It

Have students identify the three kinds of geometric shapes used in the exercises. Emphasize they always start at the left by asking:

• *In Exercise 1, which shape is first?* (circle) *Which shape is second?* (square)

Repeat the questions for the next exercise.

Power Practice

• Before students begin, have them count the letters. Then ask them to tell you which letter is first, which is second, and which is tenth.

USING THE LESSON

Lesson Goal
- Put a list of numbers in order from least to greatest.

What the Student Needs to Know
- Compare two numbers.
- Identify place values in two- and three-digit numbers.
- Identify numbers in the same decade.

Getting Started
- Review comparing two- and three-digit numbers. Use these pairs as examples: 82 and 87, 46 and 64, 314 and 34, 314 and 341, 314 and 431. Ask questions such as:
- *If two numbers don't have the same number of digits, which number is less?* (The number with fewer digits.)
- *If two numbers have the same number of digits, how do you compare them?* (Look at the left-hand digits first. If these are the same, look at the next digits. You may need to demonstrate this procedure for students.)
- Have students count aloud to 10 and then by 10s to 100. Say:
- *When you count up, the numbers are in order from least to greatest. Tell me how you would rearrange a list of numbers to put them in this order.* (Have students use 4 or 5 numbers to explain their strategies.)

What Can I Do?
Read the question and the response. Then read and discuss the examples. Ask:
- *These numbers all have two digits. How do you find the least number in a list like this?* (Look at the tens digits. Choose the least of these.)
- *What is the least number in the first example?* (28) *There are two numbers left. Which is less? How do you know?* (68 is less because its tens digit 6 is less than the tens digit in the other number.)

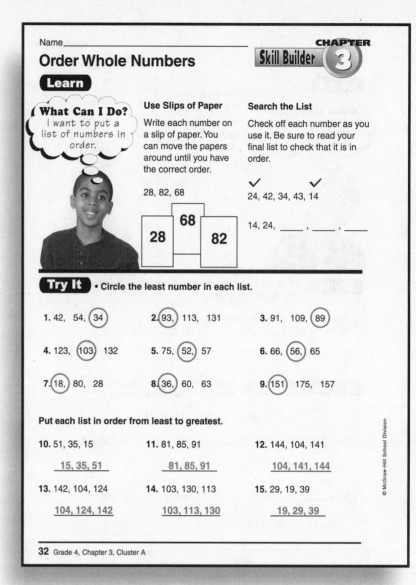

WHAT IF THE STUDENT CAN'T

Compare Two Numbers
- Give students pairs of two-digit numbers such as 64 and 61. The tens digits should be the same. Have students make number lines to show the numbers and then circle the number that is less.
- Provide pairs of students with place-value models. Give them pairs of numbers such as 45 and 71. The tens digits should be different. Each student shows one number with the models. Then they decide which number is less.

Identify Place Values in Two- and Three-Digit Numbers
- Use place-value charts such as this:

hundreds	tens	ones

Have each student use the digits of his or her telephone number to make some different three-digit numbers.
- Provide pairs of students with place-value models. One student shows a three-digit number; the other student names the number and then tells a number that is 10 more.

Name_____

Circle the least number in each list.

16. 32, 36, 43, (23), 63, 24, 64, 30, 33

17. 162, 160, 116, (106), 112, 126, 161

18. 77, 87, (67), 76, 86, 68, 88, 77

19. 108, 118, (98), 109, 181, 99, 101

20. 43, (27), 72, 70, 40, 34, 74, 40

21. 145, 141, (140), 150, 154, 144, 155

Learn with Partners & Parents

Number News

You and your partner will need a newspaper.

- Each person finds 10 numbers in the newspaper.
- Record the numbers you find. Write a sentence about each number, for example: "The team won by 13 points."
- Work with your partner to put *all* 20 numbers in order from least to greatest.

Power Practice • Put each list in order from least to greatest.

22. 62, 66, 26, 60, 16, 12, 22, 20
12, 16, 20, 22, 26, 60, 62, 66

23. 103, 101, 107, 117, 113, 104
101, 103, 104, 107, 113, 117

24. 150, 115, 155, 105, 101, 125
101, 105, 115, 125, 150, 155

25. 43, 44, 44, 43, 45, 54, 50, 40
40, 43, 43, 44, 44, 45, 50, 54

26. 29, 24, 23, 28, 32, 35, 31, 26
23, 24, 26, 28, 29, 31, 32, 35

27. 342, 345, 434, 355, 454, 432
342, 345, 355, 432, 434, 454

28. 240, 241, 204, 202, 224, 214
202, 204, 214, 224, 240, 241

29. 71, 74, 47, 41, 14, 17, 44, 11
11, 14, 17, 41, 44, 47, 71, 74

30. 92, 95, 97, 87, 89, 85, 93, 88
85, 87, 88, 89, 92, 93, 95, 97

31. 199, 189, 191, 187, 192, 185
185, 187, 189, 191, 192, 199

© McGraw-Hill School Division

Grade 4, Chapter 3, Cluster A **33**

WHAT IF THE STUDENT CAN'T

Identify Numbers in the Same Decade

- Have students count aloud by 10s up to 200. Then give them various two-digit numbers. For each number, students must say two other numbers with the same tens digit. Repeat the activity with three-digit numbers.
- Use the lists on page 33 for practice. For a particular list, ask students to find all the numbers with a tens digit of a given number.

Complete the Power Practice

- Have students work on ordering with shorter lists of num-

bers. You can have them use just the first three numbers in each list.

- Students may enjoy learning to use a stem-and-leaf plot to order numbers. Have them start by making a large T. The first tens digit goes to the left side and its ones digit goes to the right. Each number is recorded. For the list 62, 66, 26, 60, 16, 12, 22, 20, the diagram looks like this:

tens	ones
1	2, 6
2	0, 2, 6
6	0, 2, 6

USING THE LESSON

- Have students study the second example. Ask: *The first two numbers are done. What is the next number in order? Why?* (34; it has the least tens digit of the three numbers that are left)
- Have students finish the second example and explain their strategies for ordering the numbers.

Try It

Have a volunteer read the first directions. Ask:

- *Why does this help you get warmed up for putting numbers in order?* (This is the first step—to find the least number in the list.)
- As students move on to the exercises at the bottom of page 32, watch to see if any are having difficulty. If so, have them copy the numbers on separate slips of paper so they can move the numbers around.

Power Practice

- Before students begin, have them identify the least number in each exercise.
- Have the students complete the practice items. Then review each answer.

Learn with Partners & Parents

- As an alternative to newspapers, students can use magazines, science textbooks, or history textbooks.
- You may wish to have students record only numbers less than 1,000.
- The numbers students find can be used for a bulletin board display with a title such as "Numbers In Our World."

Grade 4, Chapter 3, Cluster A **33**

Lesson Goal
- Subtract a two-digit number from a two- or three-digit number.

What the Student Needs to Know
- Complete subtraction facts.
- Identify the greater of two numbers.
- Use place-value models to show regrouping in subtraction.

Getting Started
- Write on the board: 149 and 56. Ask: *How would you subtract these numbers?* (Have a volunteer come to the board and set up the problem. Emphasize the importance of lining up the ones and tens digits vertically.)
- Write these problems on the board:

  185 – 32 = ____   185
                          – 32

Ask: *How are these problems different?* (In the first, the numbers are written side-by-side. In the second, one number is written underneath the other.)

Explain that the second way of writing a problem is called *vertical form.*

- Write these problems on the board:

  185   185
  – 32   – 37

Ask: *How are these problems different?* (The number being subtracted isn't the same. In the second problem, 7 is greater than 5 so regrouping will be needed.)

What Can I Do?
Read the question and the response. Then read and discuss the examples. Ask:

- *Why is it important to line up the digits correctly?* (If you don't, you may subtract the wrong numbers.) *Which example shows digits that are not lined up correctly?* (Possible answer: the second version of 126 minus 49; In this problem, the 49 is too far to the left.)

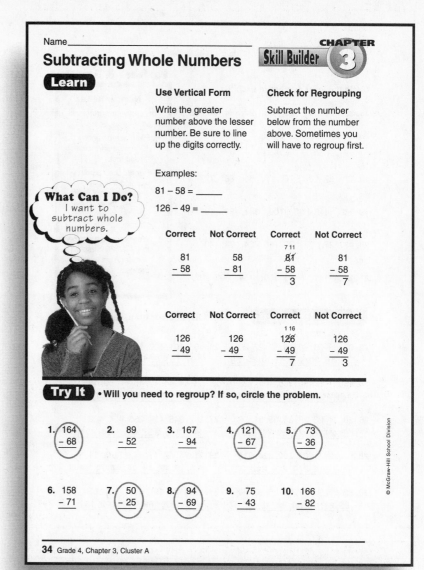

Name_____

Subtracting Whole Numbers

Skill Builder — CHAPTER 3

Learn

Use Vertical Form
Write the greater number above the lesser number. Be sure to line up the digits correctly.

Check for Regrouping
Subtract the number below from the number above. Sometimes you will have to regroup first.

What Can I Do? I want to subtract whole numbers.

Examples:

81 – 58 = _____

126 – 49 = _____

Correct	Not Correct	Correct	Not Correct
81 – 58	58 – 81	7 11 8̶1̶ – 58 3	81 – 58 7

Correct	Not Correct	Correct	Not Correct
126 – 49	126 – 49	1 16 12̶6̶ – 49 7	126 – 49 3

Try It • Will you need to regroup? If so, circle the problem.

1. (164 – 68) 2. 89 – 52 3. 167 – 94 4. (121 – 67) 5. (73 – 36)

6. 158 – 71 7. (50 – 25) 8. (94 – 69) 9. 75 – 43 10. 166 – 82

34 Grade 4, Chapter 3, Cluster A

WHAT IF THE STUDENT CAN'T

Complete Subtraction Facts
- Post a large addition facts table.

+	0	1	2	3	4	5	6	7	8	9	10
0	0	1	2	3	4	5	6	7	8	9	10
1	1	2	3	4	5	6	7	8	9	10	11
2	2	3	4	5	6	7	8	9	10	11	12
3	3	4	5	6	7	8	9	10	11	12	13
4	4	5	6	7	8	9	10	11	12	13	14
5	5	6	7	8	9	10	11	12	13	14	15
6	6	7	8	9	10	11	12	13	14	15	16
7	7	8	9	10	11	12	13	14	15	16	17
8	8	9	10	11	12	13	14	15	16	17	18
9	9	10	11	12	13	14	15	16	17	18	19
10	10	11	12	13	14	15	16	17	18	19	20

Demonstrate for students how to use the table to find a subtraction fact they do not know.

- Have pairs of students use subtraction flash cards to practice the facts. One student draws a card; the partner says the complete subtraction fact.

Identify the Greater of Two Numbers
- Have students work in pairs. Give each pair two 1–6 number cubes. One student rolls the cubes; the partner makes two two-digit numbers and tells which is greater.
- Provide place-value models for ones, tens, and hundreds. Have students work in small groups. Each student uses models to show a two-digit

Name_____

11. 145 – 61 = ___84___   12. 72 – 36 = ___36___

13. 117 – 43 = ___74___   14. 139 – 82 = ___57___

15. 47 – 16 = ___31___   16. 81 – 59 = ___22___

17. 58 – 24 = ___34___   18. 104 – 75 = ___29___

19. 151 – 82 = ___69___   20. 128 – 65 = ___63___

21. 76 – 29 = ___47___   22. 61 – 38 = ___23___

23. How much more is 85 than 47? ___38___

24. Find the difference between 53 and 128. ___75___

25. Subtract 28 from 91. ___63___

26. How much less is 72 than 151? ___79___

27. Find the difference between 117 and 39. ___78___

28. How much more is 93 than 68? ___25___

WHAT IF THE STUDENT CAN'T

or a three-digit number. Then each student finds a number that is less than his or hers and a number that is greater.

Use Place-Value Models to Show Regrouping in Subtraction

• Have the student show 56 with the blocks. The student should put out 5 tens and 6 ones. Ask: *How would you subtract 13 from 56?* (Take away 3 ones and 1 ten. Count to find the answer.) *Could you subtract 9?* (No, there are not enough ones. You need to trade one ten for ten ones. Then you have 16 ones and can take away 9.)

Continue with several examples before you move on to the written form of these problems.

Complete the Power Practice

• Have students work in pairs. Provide place-value models. One student shows an exercise; the other records the answer. Students exchange roles for the next exercise.

• If students have trouble lining up the digits in problems, have them use lined paper turned sideways. The lines on the paper make columns students can use to keep their digits correctly aligned.

USING THE LESSON

• Have students work in small groups. Provide place-value models and have students take turns showing the example problems.

• *What does it mean to regroup in a subtraction problem?* (Take one ten from the tens column and add it to the ones column.) *When do you need to regroup?* (When the ones digit being subtracted is greater than the digit it is subtracted from.)

Try It

Have a volunteer read the directions. Ask:

• *Which digits do you look at to decide if you need to regroup?* (the ones digits) Find a problem in which regrouping is needed.

Power Practice

• Have a student read the directions. Ask:

• *What does it mean to write a problem in vertical form?* (Write the greater number on top and the other number directly underneath it.)

• *How will you decide which number to write on top?* (The top number must be the one that is greater.)

• When students have finished the page, point out that the last six problems show a variety of ways to state a subtraction problem. Have students use the number 43 and 34 and state a subtraction problem in as many ways as they can. (*Possible answers: How much more is 43 than 34? How much less is 34 than 43? What is the difference between 34 and 43? Subtract 34 from 43.*)

Lesson Goal
- Identify or mark points on a number line.

What the Student Needs to Know
- Recognize equal intervals.
- Relate number lines to familiar scales.
- Count to 10.

Getting Started
- Draw a large blank number line on the board, using a ruler to make the marks 3 inches apart. Write a zero under the left-hand mark. Ask:
- *What is this diagram? What can you use it for?* (a number line; possible uses are rounding numbers, skip counting, making a line plot)
- Write the number 1 under the second mark. Point out that you have now established the meaning of each section or interval. Each interval stands for 1 unit. If you had written 2, each interval would stand for 2 units.
- Have volunteers come up to the board and complete the number line by writing the numbers 2 through 10 under the appropriate marks.
- Draw students' attention to the arrowheads on the left and right sides of the number line. Ask:
- *What does the arrow on the right side mean?* (The counting numbers continue on from 10. The next number is 11.) *What does the arrow on the left side mean?* (Some students may know that the negative numbers ⁻1, ⁻2, and so on are to the left of zero. If you wish to discuss this, a thermometer is a good model for numbers less than zero.)

What Can I Do?
Read the question and the response. Then read and discuss the example. Ask:
- *What is meant by a point? How do you show the location of a point on a number line?* (A point

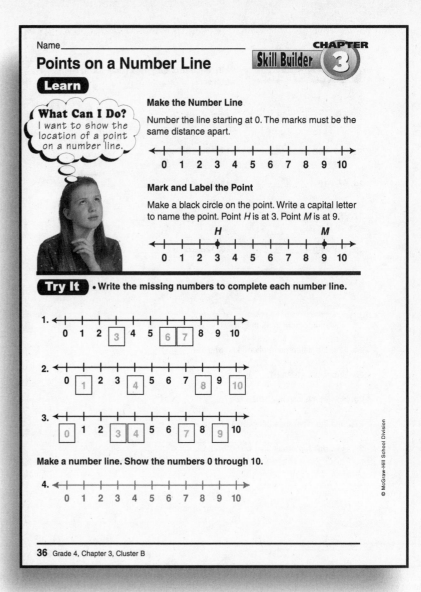

WHAT IF THE STUDENT CAN'T

Recognize Equal Intervals
- Draw two number lines on the board, one in which the intervals are equally spaced and one in which the intervals are obviously not equally spaced. Number the marks from 0 onward, counting by 1s. Have students discuss the two lines, identifying how they are alike and how they are different.
- Show students a ruler and ask students what would happen if the marks were *not* the same distance apart. (Possible response: The ruler would not be very useful because it wouldn't give the same measure every time.)

Relate Number Lines to Familiar Scales
- Show students a thermometer and ask them how this measuring tool is like a number line. (The marks are an equal distance apart; the numbers are in order.)
- Have students describe other tools that use number-line type scales. Students may mention rulers, measuring cups, bathroom scales, odometers on cars, protractors for angles. List students' ideas on the board. Emphasize that the marks must always be an equal distance apart.

Name_____

Power Practice • Write the number that shows the location of each point.

```
      B              D   A           C
  <---+--+--+--+--+--+--+--+--+--+--+--->
      0  1  2  3  4  5  6  7  8  9  10
```

5. point A ___7___   6. point B ___0___

7. point C ___10___   8. point D ___6___

```
          G   E        H              F
  <---+--+--+--+--+--+--+--+--+--+--+--->
      0  1  2  3  4  5  6  7  8  9  10
```

9. point E ___2___   10. point F ___9___

11. point G ___1___   12. point H ___5___

Mark a point at each location.

13. point S at the number 0   14. point T at the number 4

15. point U at the number 8   16. point V at the number 5

```
      S           T  V           U
  <---+--+--+--+--+--+--+--+--+--+--+--->
      0  1  2  3  4  5  6  7  8  9  10
```

17. point W at the number 2   18. point X at the number 10

19. point Y at the number 6   20. point Z at the number 3

```
          W  Z        Y              X
  <---+--+--+--+--+--+--+--+--+--+--+--->
      0  1  2  3  4  5  6  7  8  9  10
```

© McGraw-Hill School Division

Grade 4, Chapter 3, Cluster B **37**

WHAT IF THE STUDENT CAN'T

Count to 10

- Count aloud as a class from 0 through 10. Ask students to suggest ways to show in writing what you have just done. Students might make a list of the numbers separated by commas, or they might make a number line.

- Students may be able to count in a language other than English. Write the numerals 0 through 10 on the board in a vertical list. Have the student say the numbers in his or her own language. Then say each number in English and write the word next to the symbol.

Complete the Power Practice

- Check to see if students understand the directions by asking: *What were you supposed to do in this problem?* Once you have clarified the directions, students can try again to do the exercises.

- Make sure that students understand what is meant by a point and can relate the concept of point to the black dots on the number lines. Ask questions such as: *In the first number line, how many points are marked with letters?* (four) *What points are marked?* (B, D, A, and C) *Where are these points located?* (0, 6, 7, and 10)

is a specific location or spot; a black dot and capital letter are used to mark the location of a point.)

- *Mark the beginning letter of your first name at the 8; mark the first letter of your last name at the 0.* (Check that students understand how to mark points on the number line.)

Try It

These first problems give students practice in completing number lines. Ask:

- *How do you know what numbers to write in the blank spaces on the lines?* (When completed, the numbers must go in order from 0 through 10.)

- *For Exercise 4, how will you get the marks to be an equal distance apart?* (Line them up with the marks on the line in Exercise 3. Have rulers available for those students who wish to use them.)

Power Practice

- Point out that there are two direction lines on this page. Have students read both directions to themselves and look over the problems. Ask:

- *What are the two kinds of skills on this page?* (Write a number for the location of a point; mark a point at a specific location.)

- When students have finished the page, the completed number lines can be used for practice in finding the distance between two points on a number line. Ask questions such as:

- *Look at the number line at the top of page 37. What is the distance between points A and C?* (3 units) *What are two ways to find this distance?* (Count the units on the number line; subtract the two numbers.)

Lesson Goal

- Complete number patterns based on counting by various numbers.

What the Student Needs to Know

- Identify the ones digit in a number.
- Subtract adjacent numbers in a list.
- Add 2, 5, 10, 50, 100, or 200.

Getting Started

Lead students in counting by 2s starting at zero. Ask:

- *What other numbers can you count by?* (Students may suggest 1s, 5s, 10s, or other numbers. As each student suggests a number, have him or her count for at least five numbers starting with that number.)

- *When you count by a number such as 2, do you have to start with 0?* (No, you can start with any number at all.)

- *Describe how to find the next number when counting by 2.* (You add 2 to the number you just named.)

What Can I Do?

Read the question and the response. Then read and discuss the suggested strategies. Ask:

- *What numbers are shown in the hundred chart?* (The counting numbers from 1 through 100.) *How are the numbers arranged in the chart?* (There are 10 numbers in each row.)

- Have the students count by 10s to 100. Then ask: *Where are these numbers in the hundred chart?* (in the far right column) *What other number patterns can you find in the chart?* (Help students locate the multiples of 5 and 2.)

- Have students count aloud by 100s up to 1,000. Ask: *Is counting by 100s more like counting by 1s or counting by 10s?* (Answers may vary. Possible answer: It is more like counting by 1s. You use the numbers words for 1–10 as you count by 100s.)

Name_____

Number Patterns

Learn

What Can I Do?
I want to write more numbers in an addition pattern.

Use a Hundreds Chart

When counting by 2s, 10s, and 5s, a hundreds chart can help. The 2s are every other number. The 10s are in the right column. The 5s are in the middle and right columns.

1	2	3	4	5	6	7	8	9	10
11	12	13	14	15	16	17	18	19	20
21	22	23	24	25	26	27	28	29	30
31	32	33	34	35	36	37	38	39	40
41	42	43	44	45	46	47	48	49	50
51	52	53	54	55	56	57	58	59	60
61	62	63	64	65	66	67	68	69	70
71	72	73	74	75	76	77	78	79	80
81	82	83	84	85	86	87	88	89	90
91	92	93	94	95	96	97	98	99	100

Use a Pattern You Already Know

When counting by 50s, think of counting by 5s. Add a zero to each number.

When counting by 100s, think of counting by 10s. Add a zero to each answer.

Try It • Write the next six numbers in each pattern.

1. Count by 2s: 0, 2, 4, __6__, __8__, __10__, __12__, __14__, __16__

2. Count by 5s: 0, 5, 10, __15__, __20__, __25__, __30__, __35__, __40__

3. Count by 10s: 0, 10, 20, __30__, __40__, __50__, __60__, __70__, __80__

4. Count by 10s: 90, 100, 110, __120__, __130__, __140__, __150__, __160__, __170__

5. Count by 50s: 0, 50, 100, __150__, __200__, __250__, __300__, __350__, __400__

6. Count by 50s: 450, 500, 550, __600__, __650__, __700__, __750__, __800__, __850__

7. Count by 100s: 0, 100, 200, __300__, __400__, __500__, __600__, __700__, __800__

8. Count by 200s: 600; 800; 1,000; __1,200__; __1,400__; __1,600__; __1,800__; __2,000__; __2,200__

WHAT IF THE STUDENT CAN'T

Identify the Ones Digit in a Number

- Provide pairs of students with place-value models for hundreds, tens, and ones. One student shows a two- or three-digit number; the partner writes the number and identifies the ones digit. Students change roles for the next number.

- Have students write three different two-digit numbers in expanded form; for example, 48 = 4 tens 8 ones. Ask students to tell you the ones digit in each number. Repeat the activity with three different three-digit numbers.

Subtract Adjacent Numbers in a List

- Use any of the lists in the Power Practice. Ask: *Who can show me how to subtract the first two numbers in this list?* (Accept all suggestions. Point out that the second number is written first when using horizontal form; the second number is written on top when using vertical form.)

- If students are making mistakes when trying to subtract mentally, tell them to write out the subtraction problems in vertical form to make sure they have accurate answers.

Name_____

Describe each pattern.

9. 30, 35, 40, 45, 50, 55, 60, 65, 70

This pattern is counting by ___5s___.

10. 60, 70, 80, 90, 100, 110, 120

This pattern is counting by ___10s___.

11. 50, 100, 150, 200, 250, 300

This pattern is counting by ___50s___.

12. 40, 42, 44, 46, 48, 50

This pattern is counting by ___2s___.

13. 300, 400, 500, 600, 700, 800

This pattern is counting by ___100s___.

Learn with Partners & Parents

Spin, Roll, Count

You and your partner will need a three-part spinner and two 0–6 number cubes.

• Label the spinner: by 2s, by 5s, by 10s.

• When it is your turn, spin the spinner to find out what number to count by.

• Roll the cubes. Count from 0 until you just pass this number.

• Listen carefully as your partner counts. If needed, give a hint such as, "The next number ends in 4."

Power Practice • Write what the next three numbers in each pattern would be.

14. 1,400; 1,500; 1,600; _1,700_, _1,800_, _1,900_

15. 200, 250, 300, 350, _400_, _450_, _500_

16. 12, 14, 16, 18, _20_, _22_, _24_

17. 60, 65, 70, 75, 80, _85_, _90_, _95_

18. 400, 500, 600, 700, _800_, _900_, _1,000_

19. 150, 155, 160, 165, 170, _175_, _180_, _185_

© McGraw-Hill School Division

Grade 4, Chapter 3, Cluster B **39**

WHAT IF THE STUDENT CAN'T

Add 2, 5, 10, 50, 100, or 200

• Encourage students to learn to add these numbers mentally. For 2 and 5, point out the patterns in the ones digits when counting by these numbers.

• Once students have mastered adding 2 and 5, have them apply these skills to adding 50 and 200.

Complete the Power Practice

• Check to see if students have correctly identified the pattern. To do so, they should have subtracted the first two numbers in the list. This is the number they add to get

the next number. They add it to the *last* number in the list.

• Emphasize that the *same* number must be added each time.

• Students who are having a great deal of difficulty may need more work with patterns that begin at zero.

• Use a long number line on the board to show students the patterns for counting by 2s and 5s. Have students draw little "jumps" from one number to the next.

USING THE LESSON

Try It

Have students read the direction to themselves. Ask:

• *If you are counting by 2s, what number do you add to get the next number in the pattern?* (2) *How is this different from counting by 5s or 10s?* (When counting by 5s, add 5. When counting by 10s, add 10.)

• As students work on the Try It exercises, encourage them to use strategies. For example, in Exercise 7 students might write the numbers 3 through 8 in the blanks, and then go back and write two zeros after each number.

• When all students have finished, have them share the strategies they used to do the exercises.

• Have a volunteer read the directions at the top of page 39. Ask: *How is this different from the exercises you did on page 38?* (Instead of continuing number patterns, students are asked to identify them.)

• *How will you decide what each pattern is?* (Subtract the first two numbers to find out what number is being used to make the pattern. Students should note that this may not work for other patterns.)

Power Practice

• Before students begin, have them describe each pattern. To do so, students should subtract the first two numbers in the pattern.

Learn with Partners & Parents

• This game can be played with two or more students.

• Allow students time to read and discuss the directions. Make sure they understand that they are to start counting at 0 with every turn.

CHALLENGE

Lesson Goal
- Relate the numbers on a clock to different geometry shapes.

Introducing the Challenge
- Vocabulary used in this lesson includes: square, rectangle, hexagon, triangle, right triangle. For each shape, have students describe the key properties using ideas such as number of sides, number of equal sides, number of right angles.
- If circular geoboards are available, students can make different shapes with the rubber bands. Have students experiment with the geoboards, making shapes with three and then four sides.
- Here is a way to make manipulative models for the problems. Draw circular clocks on a ditto. From construction paper, cut out a square, a rectangle, a hexagon, and the three types of triangles. Students can rotate the construction-paper shapes to find the answers to the problems.

Name_____

Clock Geometry

You can make different geometric shapes by connecting the numbers on a circular clock.

In the drawing, the numbers 1, 4, 7, and 10 are connected to make a square. The square is named by the numbers you use. Its name is 1-4-7-10.

square: 1-4-7-10

1. Show all the different squares you can make on a circular clock. Write the name of each square using the numbers you connect.

    1-4-7-10   2-5-8-11   3-6-9-12

2. One rectangle is 10-2-4-8. Find the other five rectangles with this shape.

  1-3-7-9   3-5-9-11   4-6-10-12   5-7-11-1   6-8-12-2

3. A hexagon is a shape with six sides. Draw two hexagons in which all the sides are the same length. Write the names.

  1-3-5-7-9-11   2-4-6-8-10-12

---

40 Grade 4, Chapter 3, Cluster A

Name_____

4. The triangle on the first clock has three equal sides. Show all the different triangles with this same shape.

    1-5-9   2-6-10   3-7-11   4-8-12

5. Look at the triangle on the first clock. Two of its sides are equal. Show four more triangles with this shape.

There are 12 possibilities in all. They are: 1-6-8, 2-7-9, 3-8-10, 4-9-11, 5-10-12, 6-11-1, 7-12-2, 8-1-3, 9-2-4, 10-3-5, 11-4-6, 12-5-7

6. The shape 3-6-12 is a right triangle. The right angle is on the number 3. Show five more right triangles.

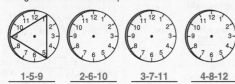

There are 12 possibilities in all. They are: 1-4-10, 2-5-11, 3-6-12, 4-7-1, 5-8-2, 6-9-3, 7-10-4, 8-11-5, 9-12-6, 10-1-7, 11-2-8, 12-3-9

7. How many different right triangles can you draw on a circular clock using 3 numbers? Explain how to draw them all.

12; one with the right angle on each of the 12 numbers. Possible

method: Start with your pencil on 1. Add 3 for the next number. Add 6

for the third number. You will get the triangle 1-4-10. Repeat this

procedure starting on each of the 12 clock numbers.

CHALLENGE

Using the Challenge

- Have a volunteer read the top of page 40 aloud as the other students follow along.

- Explain that students will be connecting the numbers on clock faces to make several different kinds of geometric shapes. The puzzle in each case will be to find all the possible ways a shape can be made.

- Have students try the first problem on their own. If they get stuck, say: *One answer is shown at the top of the page. Find two other answers.*

- When students have finished Problem 1, ask: *How many ways are there to make a square?* (three) *Why are there not 12 different ways, one for each number on the clock?* (As you rotate the square, the same numbers are used in a different order.)

- As students continue to work the problems, check to see they are looking for all the possibilities.

CHALLENGE

Lesson Goal

- Identify number patterns on a calendar.

Introducing the Challenge

- Review the vocabulary needed for the lesson by having students use each term in a sentence. Vocabulary used in this lesson includes: row, column, sum, date.

- Use the calendar for the current month. Ask students to find a number pattern in the calendar. (The numbers in the columns show counting by 7s.)

- As another warm-up question, ask: *A month starts on Monday and has 30 days. On what day of the week does the month end? How do you know?* (On Tuesday; the numbers in the column under Monday will be 1, 8, 15, 22, and 29. The 30th is on a Tuesday.)

Name_____

Calendar Surprises

Use the calendar at the right.

1. Three numbers in a row are circled. What is their sum? __42__

2. Circle a different row of three numbers and find their sum.

   Answers will vary. _____

3. Repeat Step 2 four more times.

   Answers will vary. _____ _____ _____

Sun	Mon	Tue	Wed	Thu	Fri	Sat
				1	2	3
4	5	6	7	8	9	10
11	12	13	14	15	16	17
18	19	20	21	22	23	24
25	26	27	28	29	30	

Use the calendar at the right.

4. Three numbers in a column are circled. What is their sum? __36__

5. Circle a different column of three numbers and find their sum.

   Answers will vary. _____

6. Repeat Step 2 four more times.

   Answers will vary. _____

Sun	Mon	Tue	Wed	Thu	Fri	Sat
				1	2	3
4	5	6	7	8	9	10
11	12	13	14	15	16	17
18	19	20	21	22	23	24
25	26	27	28	29	30	

Use the calendar for the current month.

7. Choose four different sets of three dates in a row. Find their sums.

   Answers will vary. _____ _____ _____

8. Choose four different sets of three dates in a column. Find their sums.

   Answers will vary. _____ _____ _____

42 Grade 4, Chapter 3, Cluster B

Name_____

**Use what you learned in Problems 1–8
to make some conclusions about calendars.**

9. The sum of three dates in a row
   or column is equal to three times _____ the middle number _____.

10. If you are told the sum of three numbers in a row, how can
    you find the middle number?

    _____ Divide the sum by 3. _____

11. If you are told the sum of three numbers in a row, how can
    you find all three numbers?

    _____ Divide the sum by 3. Subtract 1 to find the first number. _____

    _____ Add 1 to find the third number. _____

12. If you are told the sum of three numbers in a column, how can
    you find the middle number?

    _____ Divide the sum by 3. _____

13. If you are told the sum of three numbers in a column, how can
    you find all three numbers?

    _____ Divide the sum by 3. Subtract 7 to find the first number. _____

    _____ Add 7 to find the third number. _____

Now try these problems.

14. The sum of three numbers in a row
    is 30. What are the three numbers?

    _____ 9, 10, 11 _____

15. The sum of three numbers in a row
    is 15. What are the three numbers?

    _____ 4, 5, 6 _____

16. The sum of three numbers in a
    column is 24. What are the three
    numbers?

    _____ 1, 8, 15 _____

17. The sum of three numbers in a
    column is 60. What are the three
    numbers?

    _____ 13, 20, 27 _____

Grade 4, Chapter 3, Cluster B **43**

CHALLENGE

Using the Challenge

- It is quite important that all students are clear about the difference between a row and a column. If there is any doubt, draw a calendar on the board. Shade one row and label it "row." Shade a column and label it "column."

- Before students begin, tell them they should be looking for patterns or general rules. Have students read all the problems on both pages so that they can see the kinds of conclusions they will be asked to make.

- Students can work in small groups on the challenge problems. If so, have them find more than four examples for Problems 3, 6, 7, and 8.

Name_____

Number Patterns

Complete each addition pattern.

1. 3, 6, 9, _____, _____

2. 8, 16, 24, _____, _____

3. 4, 8, 12, _____, _____

4. 6, 12, 18, _____, _____

Use Addition Properties

Use the properties of addition to complete each statement.

5. $11 + 6 =$ _____ $+ 11$

6. $14 +$ _____ $= 14$

7. _____ $+ 12 = 12 + 9$

8. $6 =$ _____ $+ 0$

Doubling Numbers

Double each number. You can add the number to itself, or you can multiply by 2.

9. 16 _____ **10.** 9 _____ **11.** 5 _____ **12.** 12 _____ **13.** 7 _____

Reading a Table

Use the table at the right.

14. How many rows are in the table? _____

15. How many columns are in the table? _____

16. What letter is in the 2nd row

and the 4th column? _____

X	K	R	W
C	P	A	Z
E	F	N	Q

Name_____

Meaning of Division

Use the objects at the right for each problem.

17. Separate the triangles into groups of 3.

18. How many groups of 3 are there? _____

19. How many triangles were left? _____

20. Separate the squares into groups of 5.

21. How many groups of 5 are there? _____

22. How many squares were left? _____

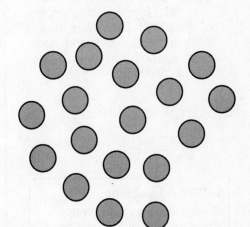

23. Separate the circles into groups of 4.

24. How many groups of 4 are there? _____

25. How many circles were left? _____

CHAPTER 4 PRE-CHAPTER ASSESSMENT

Assessment Goal

This two-page assessment covers skills identified as necessary for success in Chapter 4 Multiplication and Division Facts. The first page assesses the major prerequisite skills for Cluster A. The second page assesses the major prerequisite skills for Cluster B. When the Cluster A and Cluster B prerequisite skills overlap, the skill(s) will be covered in only one section.

Getting Started

- Allow students time to look over the two pages of the assessment. Point out the labels that identify the skills covered.

- Have students find math vocabulary terms used in the assessment. List vocabulary terms on the board as students identify them. If necessary, review the meanings of all essential math vocabulary.

Introducing the Assessment

- Explain to students that these pages will help you know if they are ready to start a new chapter in their math textbooks.

- Students who have transferred from another school may not have been introduced to some of these skills. Encourage students to do their best and assure them you will help them learn any needed skills.

Cluster A Challenge

Those students who demonstrate mastery of the skills on this page will not need to use the reteaching worksheets. Instead, these students can do the Cluster A Challenge found on pages 50-51.

Name_____

Number Patterns

Complete each addition pattern.

1. 3, 6, 9, __12__, __15__   2. 8, 16, 24, __32__, __40__

3. 4, 8, 12, __16__, __20__   4. 6, 12, 18, __24__, __30__

Use Addition Properties

Use the properties of addition to complete each statement.

5. $11 + 6 = \underline{6} + 11$ 6. $14 + \underline{0} = 14$

7. $\underline{9} + 12 = 12 + 9$ 8. $6 = \underline{6} + 0$

Doubling Numbers

Double each number. You can add the number to itself, or you can multiply by 2.

9. 16 __32__   10. 9 __18__   11. 5 __10__   12. 12 __24__   13. 7 __14__

Reading a Table

Use the table at the right.

14. How many rows are in the table? __3__

15. How many columns are in the table? __4__

16. What letter is in the 2nd row and the 4th column? __Z__

X	K	R	W
C	P	A	Z
E	F	N	Q

© McGraw-Hill School Division

43A Use with Grade 4, Chapter 4, Cluster A

CLUSTER A PREREQUISITE SKILLS

The skills listed in this chart are those identified as major prerequisite skills for students' success in the lessons in Cluster A of the chapter. Each skill is covered by one or more assessment items as shown in the middle column. The right column provides the page number for the lessons in this book that reteach the cluster A prerequisite skills.

Skill Name	Assessment Items	Lesson Pages
Number Patterns	1-4	44
Use Addition Properties	5-8	45
Doubling Numbers	9-13	46
Reading a Table	14-16	47

Name_____

Meaning of Division

Use the objects at the right for each problem.

17. Separate the triangles into groups of 3.

18. How many groups of 3 are there? ___5___

19. How many triangles were left? ___2___

20. Separate the squares into groups of 5.

21. How many groups of 5 are there? ___5___

22. How many squares were left? ___2___

23. Separate the circles into groups of 4.

24. How many groups of 4 are there? ___4___

25. How many circles were left? ___3___

© McGraw-Hill School Division

CLUSTER B PREREQUISITE SKILLS

The skills listed in this chart are those identified as major prerequisite skills for students' success in the lessons in Cluster B of the chapter. Each skill is covered by one or more assessment items as shown in the middle column. The right column provides the page numbers for the lessons in this book that reteach the Cluster B prerequisite skills

Skill Name	Assessment Items	Lesson Pages
Meaning of Division	17-25	48-49

CHAPTER 4 PRE-CHAPTER ASSESSMENT

Alternative Assessment Strategies

• Oral administration of the assessment is appropriate for younger students or those whose native language is not English. Read the skills title and directions one section at a time. Check students' understanding by asking them to tell you how they will do the first exercise in the group.

• For some skill types you may wish to use group administration. In this technique, a small group or pair of students complete the assessment together. Through their discussion, you will be able to decide if supplementary reteaching materials are needed.

Intervention Materials

If students are not successful with the prerequisite skills assessed on these pages, reteaching lessons have been created to help them make the transition into the chapter.

Item correlation charts showing the skills lessons suitable for reteaching the prerequisite skills are found beneath the reproductions of each page of the assessment.

Cluster B Challenge

Those students who demonstrate mastery of the skills on this page will not need to use the reteaching worksheets. Instead, these students can do the Cluster B Challenge found on pages 52–53.

USING THE LESSON

Lesson Goal
- Complete number patterns based on addition.

What the Student Needs to Know
- Describe number patterns based on addition.
- Add 1-digit numbers to 2-digit numbers.
- Subtract 1- and 2-digit numbers.

Getting Started
- Have students count aloud by 2s to 20. Ask: *What kind of number pattern is this? How do you find the next number in the pattern?* (Two is added each time; add 2 to the last number.)

What Can I Do?
Read the question and the response. Then read and discuss the example. Ask:
- *Why do you subtract the first two numbers?* (To find the number being added in the pattern)
- *What are the next two numbers? Explain how you know.* (21 and 24; 18 plus 3 is 21; 21 plus 3 is 24)

Try It
Have a student read the direction line. Check that students understand they are not to complete each pattern. Ask:
- *How will you find the number to add for the pattern in exercise 1?* (Subtract 12 from 14.)
- *How will you find what to add that number to in exercise 1?* (This is always the last given number. In this exercise it is 16.)

Power Practice
- Before students begin have them identify the number being added in each pattern. They should be able to do this subtraction using mental math.
- Have the students complete the practice items. Then review each answer.

Number Patterns

Learn

What Can I Do?
I want to write more numbers in an addition pattern.

Subtract to Find the Number Added

Subtract to find the number that is added.

Example:

12, 15, 18, ___, ___ ⟶ 15 − 12 = 3

The number 3 is added each time to get the next number in the pattern. To find the next number, add 3 to 18.

Try It • Explain how to find the next number in each addition pattern.

1. 12, 14, 16, _?_, _?_   Add _2_ to _16_.

2. 4, 8, 12, _?_, _?_   Add _4_ to _12_.

3. 15, 18, 21, _?_, _?_   Add _3_ to _21_.

4. 6, 9, 12, _?_, _?_   Add _3_ to _12_.

5. 15, 20, 25, _?_, _?_   Add _5_ to _25_.

6. 16, 24, 32, _?_, _?_   Add _8_ to _32_.

Power Practice • Complete each addition pattern.

7. 6, 8, 10, _12_, _14_

8. 8, 12, 16, _20_, _24_

9. 10, 12, 14, _16_, _18_

10. 25, 30, 35, _40_, _45_

11. 18, 21, 24, _27_, _30_

12. 16, 20, 24, _28_, _32_

13. 14, 16, 18, _20_, _22_

14. 24, 28, 32, _36_, _40_

15. 24, 32, 40, _48_, _56_

16. 12, 16, 20, _24_, _28_

17. 18, 24, 30, _36_, _42_

18. 20, 25, 30, _35_, _40_

19. 9, 12, 15, _18_, _21_

20. 8, 10, 12, _14_, _16_

21. 21, 24, 27, _30_, _33_

WHAT IF THE STUDENT CAN'T

Describe Number Patterns Based on Addition
- Write this pattern on the board: 10, 20, 30, 40, 50. Remind students that a list of numbers like this is a *number pattern*. Ask students for the rule used to make this pattern.

Add 1-Digit Numbers to 2-Digit Numbers
- Have students work in pairs and use flash cards to review their addition facts. Each student makes a list of any facts he or she needs to practice.
- Remind students how to use related facts to do problems such as 56 + 3.

Subtract 1- and 2-Digit Numbers
- Have students use flash cards to review subtraction facts.
- Give pairs of students two 1–6 number cubes. A student rolls twice to make two 2-digit numbers. The numbers are subtracted and then the partner takes a turn.

Complete the Power Practice
- Have students work in pairs. Each student creates an addition pattern based on counting by 2s or by other numbers. Students analyze each other's patterns and write the next two numbers.

Name_____

Use Addition Properties

Learn

What Can I Do?
I want to use addition properties.

Look for the Commutative Property

You can add numbers in any order. Look to see if the numbers in the sentence are switched.

Example: 4 + 18 = ___ + 4
Think: 4 + 18 = 18 + 4

Look for Zero Properties

Zero added to any number is the same number. Look to see if this property will make the sentence true.

Example: 5 + ___ = 5
Think: 5 + 0 = 5

Example: ___ + 0 = 8
Think: 8 + 0 = 8

Try It • Use the Commutative Property.

1. 23 + _16_ = 16 + 23
2. 14 + 8 = _8_ + 14
3. _28_ + 13 = 13 + 28
4. _11_ + 9 = 9 + 11
5. 17 + _0_ = 0 + 17
6. 6 + 35 = 35 + _6_

Use the Zero Property.

7. 25 + _0_ = 25
8. 6 = _6_ + 0
9. 8 = _0_ + 8
10. _0_ + 11 = 11
11. 13 = 13 + _0_
12. _15_ + 0 = 15

Power Practice • Use the properties of addition to complete each sentence.

13. _12_ + 4 = 4 + 12
14. 0 + _10_ = 10
15. 15 + 36 = 36 + _15_
16. 12 = 12 + _0_
17. _18_ + 29 = 29 + 18
18. _0_ + 9 = 9
19. 18 + 35 = 35 + _18_
20. 3 + 19 = _19_ + 3
21. 0 + _21_ = 21
22. 17 = 0 + _17_
23. _0_ + 8 = 8
24. 14 + _16_ = 16 + 14
25. 6 + _16_ = 16 + 6
26. 23 = 0 + _23_
27. 7 + _0_ = 7

Grade 4, Chapter 4, Cluster A **45**

WHAT IF THE STUDENT CAN'T

Explain the Meaning of Addition

• Give students counters. Have them make two small groups of counters and count the number in each group. Then have students push the groups together.

• Have a volunteer use the + sign to write what they have modeled.

Describe a Number Sentence

• Write on the board: 10 + 3 = 13 and label it "number sentence." Have a student read the sentence aloud. Write the word form of the sentence under the equation.

Complete a Number Sentence to Make It True

• Ask students to explain what is meant by the = sign. (The expressions on the two sides of the equals sign have the same value.) Explain that whatever number is written in the blank must make the two sides of the equation equal.

Complete the Power Practice

• Have students first find the exercises that use the Commutative Property. These have two addends on each side of the equals sign. The exercises remaining are those that use the zero property.

USING THE LESSON

Lesson Goal

• Use the commutative and zero properties of addition to complete number sentences.

What the Student Needs to Know

• Explain the meaning of addition.

• Describe a number sentence.

• Complete a number sentence to make it true.

Getting Started

Write on the board: 3 + 5 = 5 + 3. Ask:

• *What does this number sentence show?* (You can add the numbers in either order.)

• Explain that this is one property of the operation addition. Ask: *Is this property true of subtraction?* (No, you cannot subtract numbers in either order.)

What Can I Do?

Read the question and the response. Then read and discuss the examples. Ask:

• *What is an addition property?* (It is a rule that is true for any numbers you add.)

Try It

Have students look over the first two groups of exercises. Ask:

• *Do you need to do any addition for these exercises? Explain.* (No, students use the properties to fill in the blanks.)

Power Practice

• Before students begin, ask: *How can you check that you have each answer correct?* (The expressions on either side of the equal sign must be equal. Students can add to confirm this.)

• Have the students complete the practice items. Then review each answer.

Lesson Goal
- Double numbers.

What the Student Needs to Know
- Add 1- and 2-digit numbers.
- Multiply numbers by 2.
- Recognize even numbers.

Getting Started
- Have a student write the numbers from 1 through 10 in a row on the board.
- Have the class count aloud by 2s from 2 to 20. Then have a student write these numbers in a row directly under the first list. Ask:
- *How are the two lists of numbers related?* (Each number is twice that of the one above it.)
- Write on the board: twice, double, two times. Have students use these terms in sentences to illustrate that they all have the same meaning.

What Can I Do?
Read the question and the response. Then read and discuss the examples. Ask:
- *What are two ways to double a number?* (Add it to itself; multiply it by 2.) *Which way is easier for you?* (Have students give their opinions.)

Try It
Have students look over the first six exercises Ask:
- *In which exercises will you add?* (1, 4, 5) *In which will you multiply?* (2, 3, 6)

Power Practice
- Have the students complete the practice items. Then review each answer.

Learn with Partners & Parents
- Remind students that the even numbers have a ones digit of 0, 2, 4, 6, or 8.

Name_____

Doubling Numbers

Learn

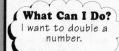

What Can I Do? I want to double a number.

Add the Number to Itself

5 + 5 = 10,
so 5 doubled is 10.

13 + 13 = 26,
so 13 doubled is 26.

Multiply the Number by 2

2 × 3 = 6, so
3 doubled is 6.

2 × 8 = 16, so
8 doubled is 16.

Learn with Partners & Parents

Double Digit and Out

Each player needs to make a game board. To make your game board, write the even numbers from 0 through 18 on a card or piece of paper. Write each number twice.

- Take turns. Use the digits of your house number and your telephone number. Double each digit and cross out the answer on your game board.

- The player to cross out more numbers on the game board is the winner.

Try It
Find each sum or product. Then complete each sentence.

1. 12 + 12 = __24__
   12 doubled is __24__.

2. 2 × 9 = __18__
   9 doubled is __18__.

3. 2 × 4 = __8__
   4 doubled is __8__.

4. 16 + 16 = __32__
   16 doubled is __32__.

5. 7 + 7 = __14__
   7 doubled is __14__.

6. 2 × 3 = __6__
   3 doubled is __6__.

Power Practice • Double each number.

7. 11 __22__

8. 4 __8__

9. 14 __28__

10. 18 __36__

11. 2 __4__

12. 30 __60__

13. 7 __14__

14. 25 __50__

15. 10 __20__

16. 20 __40__

17. 15 __30__

18. 6 __12__

WHAT IF THE STUDENT CAN'T

Add 1- and 2-Digit Numbers
- Post an addition facts table for students who still need help with some of the facts.
- Remind students that they always add the ones first. Demonstrate with problems such as 16 + 16 and 18 + 18 in which regrouping is needed.

Multiply Numbers by 2
- Have students make number lines showing the multiples of 2 from 0 through 20. Students can make "jumps" on the number lines to find products such as three 2s or eight 2s.

Recognize Even Numbers
- Provide each student with a hundred chart. Have students color 2, 4, 6, 8, and 10. Then have them color the columns under these numbers. Point out that these are called "even numbers." The ones digit of any even number must be 0, 2, 4, 6, or 8.

Complete the Power Practice
- For each exercise, one student uses addition to double the number, and the other uses multiplication. Then students compare their answers.

Reading a Table

Skill Builder **CHAPTER 4**

Learn

What Can I Do?
I want to read information in a table.

Use the Rows and Columns

A table has rows and columns. In this table, the columns are numbered 1, 2, 3. The rows have letters.

	1	2	3
A	red	green	yellow
B	blue	brown	purple
C	pink	orange	white
D	gray	black	tan

Try It • Use the table at the top of the page.

1. Write the colors in row C. _____pink, orange, white_____

2. Write the colors in column 3. _____yellow, purple, white, tan_____

3. Write the color in row B column 3. _____purple_____

Power Practice • Use the table at the right.

4. How many rows are there? __3__

5. How many columns are there? __6__

6. What letter is in the 2nd row and the 3rd column? __I__

7. What letter is in the 3rd row and the 6th column? __R__

A	B	C	D	E	F
G	H	I	J	K	L
M	N	O	P	Q	R

© McGraw-Hill School Division

WHAT IF THE STUDENT CAN'T

Use *Top, Bottom, Left,* and *Right* to Describe Location

• Write the words on the board. Have students practice using them in sentences to refer to objects in the classroom.

Use Ordinal Numbers Through 6th

• Have six students line up at the front of the room facing left. Hand each one a sign with one of the ordinals 1st through 6th. Mix up the students and have them get back in the correct order.

Complete the Power Practice

• Have students write the numbers 1 through 6 across the top of the table to label the columns. They write the numbers 1, 2, and 3 down the side to label the rows.

• To complete exercise 6, have students color the 2nd row red and the 3rd column yellow. There will be an orange box where the row and column meet. The letter in that box is in the 2nd row and the 3rd column. If necessary, repeat with another table for exercise 7.

USING THE LESSON

Lesson Goal
• Read a table.

What the Student Needs to Know
• Use *top, bottom, left,* and *right* to describe location.
• Use ordinal numbers through 6th.

Getting Started
• On the board draw a blank table like this:

Have students come up to the board and write their names in the boxes. Write the numbers 1, 2, 3, 4 on the top; the letters A, B, C to the left. Ask students to tell who is in locations such as A1 and C4.

• Write the words *row* and *column* on the board. Say: *Use the words to describe the table.* (The table has 3 rows and 4 columns.)

What Can I Do?
Read the question and the response. Then discuss the examples. Ask:
• *What kinds of information does the table show?* (names of colors)

Have students pick their favorite color. The students take turns telling you where their choice is; for example, "My favorite color is in row B and column 3."

Try It
Students use the colors table for the first three exercises. Say:
• *Name the rows.* (A, B, C, D) *Name the columns.* (1, 2, 3)

Power Practice
• Have the students complete the practice items. Then review each answer.

USING THE LESSON

Lesson Goal

- Make division models to find quotients and remainders.

What the Student Needs to Know

- Identify equal groups.
- Divide objects into equal groups.

Getting Started

- Give each student 12 counters. Have them make 2 equal groups. Watch to see how students are doing this and have them discuss their strategies.

- If necessary, demonstrate this method of sharing—one for you, one for me, one for you, one for me, and so forth.

- Repeat the activity by having students use all 12 counters to make 3 equal groups and then 4 equal groups.

- Explain to students that sometimes there are counters left over when equal groups are created. Have students use 7 counters to make 3 equal groups. Ask: *How many in each group? How many are left over?* (2 in each group; 1 left over)

What Can I Do?

Read the question and the response. Then read and discuss the examples. Give each student one more counter to make a total of 13 counters. Have students use their counters to model the problems shown. Ask:

- *How are the groups shown in the pictures?* (Each group has a ring or circle around it.)

- *What does it mean for there to be 1 object left?* (All the objects possible have been put into groups. There is 1 object left over.)

- You may wish to introduce the term *remainder* for the number of objects left over after equal groups have been made. The term *remainder* is the one students will use when they do paper-and-pencil division problems.

Name_____

Meaning of Division

Learn

What Can I Do? I want to review the meaning of division.

Make Equal Groups
Use counters to show 13 divided into 3 equal groups.

There are 4 in each group. There is one left.
13 ÷ 3 is 4 with 1 left.

Make Groups of the Same Number
Use counters to show 11 divided into groups of 4.

There are 2 groups.
There are 3 left.
11 ÷ 4 is 2 with 3 left.

Try It • Use counters, coins, or small objects to do each problem.

Count out 7 counters. Use as many of the counters as you can to make 2 equal groups.

1. How many counters are there in each group? ___3___

2. How many counters are left? ___1___

Count out 10 counters. Use as many of the counters as you can to make 3 equal groups.

3. How many counters are there in each group? ___3___

4. How many counters are left? ___1___

Count out 20 counters. Make groups of 6.

5. How many groups are there? ___3___

6. How many counters are left? ___2___

Count out 14 counters. Make groups of 5.

7. How many groups are there? ___2___

8. How many counters are left? ___4___

WHAT IF THE STUDENT CAN'T

Identify Equal Groups

- Provide the student with counters of two colors or two different shapes. Make two piles, one with each type of counter. Ask how to tell if the groups have the same number.

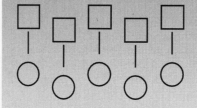

- Demonstrate for students how to line up the counters to show there are the same number.

Tell students this is called a one-to-one correspondence. It is one way to show that the two groups have the same number of objects.

Divide Objects Into Equal Groups

- Provide counters and large sheets of paper. Have students fold the paper in half. Then put one counter on the left side, then one on the right side, and so on, until they have divided the counters into 2 equal groups. Have students fold the paper again and use it to make 4 equal groups.

Power Practice • Use the drawings of objects for each problem.

9. Separate the circles into groups of 5.

Check students' work.

10. How many groups of 5 are there? ___3___
11. How many circles are left? ___2___

12. Separate the triangles into groups of 2.

Check students' work.

13. How many groups of 2 are there? ___4___
14. How many triangles are left? ___1___

15. Separate the squares into groups of 4.

Check students' work.

16. How many groups of 4 are there? ___4___
17. How many squares are left? ___1___

18. Separate the stars into groups of 3.

Check students' work.

19. How many groups of 3 are there? ___4___
20. How many stars are left? ___2___

Learn with Partners & Parents

Remainder Roll

You and your partner will need a 1–6 number cube and a jar or bag filled with counters or any small objects.

- Each partner grabs two handfuls of counters.
- Roll the number cube. This is the number in each group.
- Make groups with the number you rolled until you have used all your counters.
- The player with fewer counters left gets one point for this round.
- Play 15 rounds.

Grade 4, Chapter 4, Cluster B **49**

WHAT IF THE STUDENT CAN'T

- Provide counters and yarn or string. Students make circles with the yarn to use in making their equal groups. Start with 2 circles for 2 equal groups. Then increase the number to 3 and then 4 circles.

- Check that students understand the meaning of "left" in these exercises. The word describes the objects that don't fit into the groups. It does not mean a location.

Complete the Power Practice

- Have students work in pairs. Provide counters so that students can model each of the problems. Watch to make sure students are checking that the groups have the same number of objects.

USING THE LESSON

Try It

Each student will need 20 counters for these problems. Have a volunteer read the directions and the first exercise. Ask:

- *How many counters are you going to use for this exercise?* (7) *What are you supposed to do with the counters?* (Make 2 equal groups.) *How will you make sure you have equal groups?* (Students may suggest lining up the counters to show one-to-one correspondence.)

- After all students have finished, ask: *How are Exercises 5–8 different from Exercises 1–4?* (In the last four exercises, students are told the number in each group. In the first four exercises, they are told the number of equal groups.)

Power Practice

- Have students study exercise 9. Ask: *How will you "separate" the circle into groups?* (Draw a circle or ring around each group.)

- Have the students complete the practice items. Then review each answer.

Learn with Partners & Parents

- Check that students understand that *both* players make equal groups with the number rolled.

- Have students return the counters to the jar or bag after every round.

CHALLENGE

Lesson Goal

- Discover patterns in addition and multiplication of odd and even numbers.

Introducing the Challenge

- Review the vocabulary needed for the lesson by having students use each term in a sentence. Vocabulary used in this lesson includes: even number, odd number, product, sum

- Have students look at page 50. Ask: *What is the table on this page?* (Students should recognize the times table. It shows all the products up through 10 times 10.) Have students show you where a few products are located; for example, 6 x 7 or 3 x 5. Repeat the questions with the addition table on page 51.

Name_____

Patterns with Odd and Even Numbers

Even numbers end in the digits 0, 2, 4, 6, and 8. Odd numbers end in the digits 1, 3, 5, 7, and 9. Look for odd and even patterns in this multiplication facts table. You will need crayons or pencils in three different colors.

1. Color the products of two even numbers Color 1. Color the products of two odd numbers Color 2. Color the products of even and odd numbers Color 3.

×	0	1	2	3	4	5	6	7	8	9	10
0	0	0	0	0	0	0	0	0	0	0	0
1	0	1	2	3	4	5	6	7	8	9	10
2	0	2	4	6	8	10	12	14	16	18	20
3	0	3	6	9	12	15	18	21	24	27	30
4	0	4	8	12	16	20	24	28	32	36	40
5	0	5	10	15	20	25	30	35	40	45	50
6	0	6	12	18	24	30	36	42	48	54	60
7	0	7	14	21	28	35	42	49	56	63	70
8	0	8	16	24	32	40	48	56	64	72	80
9	0	9	18	27	36	45	54	63	72	81	90
10	0	10	20	30	40	50	60	70	80	90	100

Summarize your findings by writing *odd* or *even* in each blank.

2. If you multiply an even number times an even number,

   you get an __even__ number.

3. If you multiply an odd number times an odd number,

   you get an __odd__ number.

4. If you multiply an odd number times an even number,

   you get an __even__ number.

Name_____

Now look for patterns in the addition facts table.

5. Color the sums of two even numbers Color 1. Color the sums of two odd numbers Color 2. Color the sums of even and odd numbers Color 3.

+	0	1	2	3	4	5	6	7	8	9	10
0	0	1	2	3	4	5	6	7	8	9	10
1	1	2	3	4	5	6	7	8	9	10	11
2	2	3	4	5	6	7	8	9	10	11	12
3	3	4	5	6	7	8	9	10	11	12	13
4	4	5	6	7	8	9	10	11	12	13	14
5	5	6	7	8	9	10	11	12	13	14	15
6	6	7	8	9	10	11	12	13	14	15	16
7	7	8	9	10	11	12	13	14	15	16	17
8	8	9	10	11	12	13	14	15	16	17	18
9	9	10	11	12	13	14	15	16	17	18	19
10	10	11	12	13	14	15	16	17	18	19	20

Summarize your findings by writing *odd* or *even* in each blank.

6. If you add an even number to an even number,

   you get an ___even___ number.

7. If you add an odd number to an odd number,

   you get an ___even___ number.

8. If you add an odd number to an even number,

   you get an ___odd___ number.

CHALLENGE

Using the Challenge

- Students will need crayons or markers in three different colors. Have a volunteer read the directions and Problem 1 aloud.

- Check that students can identify odd and even numbers by giving several examples.

- Explain that students will use the colors to divide the table into three different regions. Have students read the three statements under the table. The purpose of coloring the table is to complete these rules about multiplying odd and even numbers.

- It may be easier for students to begin with the bottom row of the table. One factor in this row is 10, an even number. If 10 is multiplied by another even number, students color the product Color 1. If 10 is multiplied by an odd number, students color the product Color 3.

- After students have finished page 50, assign page 51 for independent work.

CHALLENGE

Lesson Goal

- Find all the possible rectangles or right triangles with a given area.

Introducing the Challenge

- Review the vocabulary needed for the lesson by having students use each term in a sentence. Vocabulary used in this lesson includes: area, length, width, square unit, rectangle, opposite corners, right triangle

- Provide students with about 30 square counters. Have them use 6 counters to make a 2-by-3 rectangle. Ask: *How many counters did you use?* (6) *What is the area of your rectangle?* (6 square units) *What is its length and width?* (2 and 3 units)

- Have students make a different rectangle using the 6 counters. They should put the 6 counters in a row or column to get a rectangle that is 6 units long and 1 unit wide.

Experiments with Area

The **area** of a rectangle equals the length times the width. This rectangle has an area of 12 square units.

To find other rectangles with the same area, divide 12 by different numbers. You can divide it by 1 and 2 to get two more rectangles. Possible answers are given.

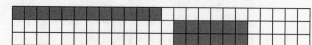

1. Draw two different rectangles with an area of 12 square units.

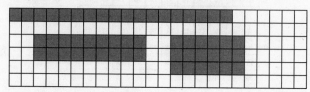

2. Draw all the different possible rectangles that have an area of 18 square units.

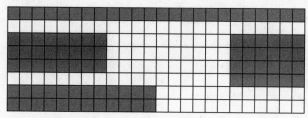

3. Draw all the different possible rectangles that have an area of 24 square units.

© McGraw-Hill School Division

Name_____

The rectangle has an area of 24 square units. If you connect the opposite corners, you get two right triangles. Each triangle has one-half the area of the rectangle. Each triangle has an area of 12 square units.

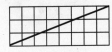

4. Draw three other right triangles that have an area of 12 square units.

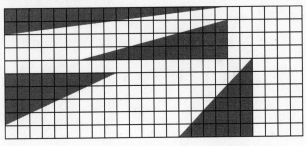

5. If you connect the opposite corners of a rectangle 1 unit wide and 36 units long, you'll get two right triangles. Each has an area of 18 square units. Find and draw all the other right triangles that have an area of 18 square units.

CHALLENGE

Using the Challenge

- Most students will need counters for these problems. Provide each student with about 40 counters.

- Have a volunteer read the directions for page 52 aloud. Check that students know what to do by asking:

- *What is the length and width of the small rectangle?* (3 units wide, 4 units long) *Use 12 counters to show me a rectangle with a width of 2 units.* (Students should make a 2-by-6 rectangle.)

- On page 53, help students recognize that they can first make rectangles with double the area of the given right triangles. After they have found all the possible different rectangles, they draw the diagonal of each to form the different right triangles.

Multiplication Facts

Find each product.

1.   9
   $\times\,3$
_____

2.   8
   $\times\,1$
_____

3.   5
   $\times\,5$
_____

4.   7
   $\times\,4$
_____

5. $6 \times 8 =$ _____

6. $5 \times 6 =$ _____

Place Value

Write the number of tens and ones.

7. 42 ones = _____ tens _____ ones

8. 35 ones = _____ tens _____ ones

Write the number of hundreds and tens.

9. 18 tens = _____ hundred _____ tens

10. 54 tens = _____ hundreds _____ tens

Rounding Whole Numbers and Money Amounts

Round each number to the underlined place.

11. <u>8</u>9 _____

12. $4<u>3</u>.15 _____

13. <u>4</u>62 _____

14. <u>5</u>,092 _____

Name_____

Adding Whole Numbers

Find each sum.

15. 24
       + 3
       ____

16. 48
       + 7
       ____

17. 36
       + 5
       ____

18. 56 + 3 = _____

19. 18 + 5 = _____

Estimating Products

Round the factor to the underlined digit to estimate the product.

20. 4 × 3̲78 = 4 × _____

21. 5 × 2̲,069 = 5 × _____

Estimate: _____

Estimate: _____

Tables of Ordered Pairs

Complete each table.

22. Rule: Multiply by 8.

Input	2	5	7	9	10
Output	16	40			

23. Rule: Multiply by _____.

Input	3	5	7	9	
Output	21	35			70

Graphing Ordered Pairs

Plot the point for each ordered pair.

24. (1, 4)

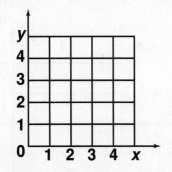

25. (4, 3)

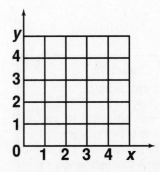

CHAPTER 5 PRE-CHAPTER ASSESSMENT

Assessment Goal

This two-page assessment covers skills identified as necessary for success in Chapter 5 Multiply by 1-Digit Numbers. The first page assesses the major prerequisite skills for Cluster A. The second page assesses the major prerequisite skills for Cluster B. When the Cluster A and Cluster B prerequisite skills overlap, the skill(s) will be covered in only one section.

Getting Started

- Allow students time to look over the two pages of the assessment. Point out the labels that identify the skills covered.
- Have students find math vocabulary terms used in the assessment. List vocabulary terms on the board as students identify them. If necessary, review the meanings of all essential math vocabulary.

Introducing the Assessment

- Explain to students that these pages will help you know if they are ready to start a new chapter in their math textbooks.
- Students who have transferred from another school may not have been introduced to some of these skills. Encourage students to do their best and assure them you will help them learn any needed skills.

Cluster A Challenge

Those students who demonstrate mastery of the skills on this page will not need to use the reteaching worksheets. Instead, these students can do the Cluster A Challenge found on pages 66–67.

Name_____

Multiplication Facts

Find each product.

1. $\begin{array}{r} 9 \\ \times 3 \\ \hline 27 \end{array}$ 2. $\begin{array}{r} 8 \\ \times 1 \\ \hline 8 \end{array}$ 3. $\begin{array}{r} 5 \\ \times 5 \\ \hline 25 \end{array}$ 4. $\begin{array}{r} 7 \\ \times 4 \\ \hline 28 \end{array}$

5. $6 \times 8 = $ __48__   6. $5 \times 6 = $ __30__

Place Value

Write the number of tens and ones.

7. 42 ones = __4__ tens __2__ ones

8. 35 ones = __3__ tens __5__ ones

Write the number of hundreds and tens.

9. 18 tens = __1__ hundred __8__ tens

10. 54 tens = __5__ hundreds __4__ tens

Rounding Whole Numbers and Money Amounts

Round each number to the underlined place.

11. 89 _____90_____   12. $43.15 _____$40.00_____

13. 462 _____500_____   14. 5,092 _____5,000_____

53A Use with Grade 4, Chapter 5, Cluster A

CLUSTER A PREREQUISITE SKILLS

The skills listed in this chart are those identified as major prerequisite skills for students' success in the lessons in Cluster A of the chapter. Each skill is covered by one or more assessment items as shown in the middle column. The right column provides the page number for the lessons in this book that reteach the cluster A prerequisite skills.

Skill Name	Assessment Items	Lesson Pages
Multiplication Facts	1-6	54-55
Place Value	7-10	56-57
Rounding Whole Numbers and Money Amounts	11-14	58-59

Name_____

Adding Whole Numbers

Find each sum.

15.	24	16.	48	17.	36
	+ 3		+ 7		+ 5
	27		55		41

18. 56 + 3 = ___59___

19. 18 + 5 = ___23___

Estimating Products

Round the factor to the underlined digit to estimate the product.

20. 4 × 3̲78 = 4 × ___400___

21. 5 × 2̲,069 = 5 × ___2,000___

Estimate: ___1,600___

Estimate: ___10,000___

Tables of Ordered Pairs

Complete each table.

22. Rule: Multiply by 8.

Input	2	5	7	9	10
Output	16	40	56	72	80

23. Rule: Multiply by ___7___.

Input	3	5	7	9	10
Output	21	35	49	63	70

Graphing Ordered Pairs

Plot the point for each ordered pair.

24. (1, 4)

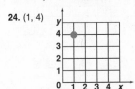

25. (4, 3)

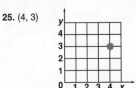

© McGraw-Hill School Division

Use with Grade 4, Chapter 5, Cluster B **53B**

Alternative Assessment Strategies

- Oral administration of the assessment is appropriate for younger students or those whose native language is not English. Read the skills title and directions one section at a time. Check students' understanding by asking them to tell you how they will do the first exercise in the group.

- For some skill types you may wish to use group administration. In this technique, a small group or pair of students complete the assessment together. Through their discussion, you will be able to decide if supplementary reteaching materials are needed.

Intervention Materials

If students are not successful with the prerequisite skills assessed on these pages, reteaching lessons have been created to help them make the transition into the chapter.

Item correlation charts showing the skills lessons suitable for reteaching the prerequisite skills are found beneath the reproductions of each page of the assessment.

Cluster B Challenge

Those students who demonstrate mastery of the skills on this page will not need to use the reteaching worksheets. Instead, these students can do the Cluster B Challenge found on pages 68–69.

CLUSTER B PREREQUISITE SKILLS

The skills listed in this chart are those identified as major prerequisite skills for students' success in the lessons in Cluster B of the chapter. Each skill is covered by one or more assessment items as shown in the middle column. The right column provides the page numbers for the lessons in this book that reteach the Cluster B prerequisite skills

Skill Name	Assessment Items	Lesson Pages
Adding Whole Numbers	15-19	60
Estimating Products	20-21	61
Tables of Orderd Pairs	22-23	62-63
Graphing Ordered Pairs	24-25	64-65

Lesson Goal

• Complete multiplication facts (products through 81).

What the Student Needs To Know

• Add a 1-digit number to a 1- or 2-digit number.

• Skip count by numbers from 2 through 9.

• Recognize multiplication as repeated addition.

Getting Started

• Ask student to think of an addition fact for a double such as 7 + 7. For example, say:

• *Think of 7 + 7 as 2 sevens or 2 × 7. Since 7 + 7 = 14, then 2 × 7 =* ? *.* (14)

• *Think of 3 × 7 as 2 × 7 +* ? *.* (7)

• *I'm going to skip count by 7s. When I stop, say the next number. 7, 14,* ? *.* (21)

• *You know that 2 × 7 = 14, that 3 × 7 = 2 × 7 + 7, and that 14 + 7 = 21. So 3 × 7 =* ? (21)

What Can I Do?

Read the question and the response. Then read and discuss the examples. Ask:

• *If I count down 2 and count 6 across and fill in the small squares, how many squares will be in the rectangle I make?* (12) *What is 2 × 6?* (12)

• *If I count down 3 and count 6 across and fill in the small squares, how many squares will be in the new rectangle?* (18) *What is 3 × 6?* (18)

• *If I know the number of squares in 3 rows of my rectangle, how can I find the number of squares in 4 rows?* (add one more 6) *What is 18 + 6?* (24) *What is 4 × 6?* (24)

• *If I count down 7 and count 6 across and fill in all the small squares, how many squares will be in the rectangle I make?* (42) *What is 7 × 6?* (42)

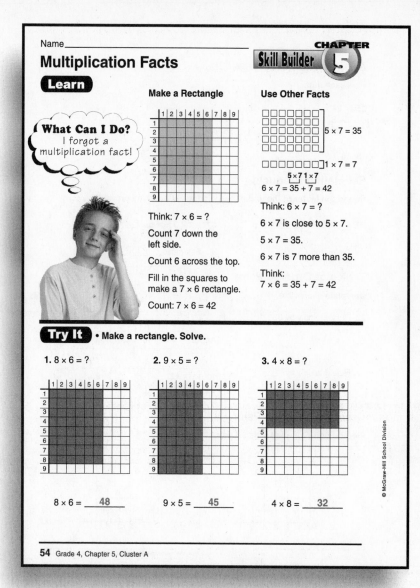

WHAT IF THE STUDENT CAN'T

Add a 1-Digit Number to a 1- or 2-Digit Number

• Practice addition facts for 10 to 15 minutes daily until the student can recall the sums for addition facts automatically.

• Once addition facts are mastered, practice adding a 1-digit number to a 2-digit number for 5 to 10 minutes daily until the student can do so with ease. Help the student develop proficiency by using addition fact patterns, for example: 9 + 8 = 17 so 19 + 8 = 27.

Skip Count by Numbers from 2 Through 9

• Use counters, pictured sets of objects, or a number line to count by 2s to 20, by 3s to 30, by 4s to 40, and so on through counting by 9s to 90.

Name_____

Use other multiplication facts to solve. Complete.

4. $5 \times 8 = ?$

___4___ $\times 8 = 32$

So, $5 \times 8 = 32 +$ ___8___.

$5 \times 8 =$ ___40___

5. $6 \times 9 = ?$

___5___ $\times 9 = 45$

So, $6 \times 9 = 45 +$ ___9___.

$6 \times 9 =$ ___54___

6. $9 \times 7 = ?$

___8___ $\times 7 = 56$

So, $9 \times 7 = 56 +$ ___7___.

$9 \times 7 =$ ___63___

Power Practice • Find the product.

7. $2 \times 9 =$ ___18___

8. $3 \times 7 =$ ___21___

9. $8 \times 3 =$ ___24___

10. $7 \times 2 =$ ___14___

11. $\begin{array}{r} 5 \\ \times 4 \\ \hline 20 \end{array}$

12. $\begin{array}{r} 8 \\ \times 9 \\ \hline 72 \end{array}$

13. $\begin{array}{r} 4 \\ \times 7 \\ \hline 28 \end{array}$

14. $\begin{array}{r} 6 \\ \times 9 \\ \hline 54 \end{array}$

15. $\begin{array}{r} 8 \\ \times 7 \\ \hline 56 \end{array}$

16. $\begin{array}{r} 3 \\ \times 9 \\ \hline 27 \end{array}$

17. $\begin{array}{r} 5 \\ \times 6 \\ \hline 30 \end{array}$

18. $\begin{array}{r} 9 \\ \times 9 \\ \hline 81 \end{array}$

19. $6 \times 4 =$ ___24___

20. $3 \times 8 =$ ___24___

21. $7 \times 0 =$ ___0___

22. $6 \times 6 =$ ___36___

23. $\begin{array}{r} 3 \\ \times 5 \\ \hline 15 \end{array}$

24. $\begin{array}{r} 1 \\ \times 9 \\ \hline 9 \end{array}$

25. $\begin{array}{r} 9 \\ \times 4 \\ \hline 36 \end{array}$

26. $\begin{array}{r} 8 \\ \times 8 \\ \hline 64 \end{array}$

27. $\begin{array}{r} 7 \\ \times 2 \\ \hline 14 \end{array}$

28. $\begin{array}{r} 3 \\ \times 6 \\ \hline 18 \end{array}$

29. $\begin{array}{r} 9 \\ \times 7 \\ \hline 63 \end{array}$

30. $\begin{array}{r} 2 \\ \times 9 \\ \hline 18 \end{array}$

Learn with Partners & Parents

Go Fish!

Ten minutes of play a day for a few weeks is all it usually takes to master multiplication facts. Each player gets a set of multiplication fact cards.

• The first player puts a card face up on the table.

• If the second player makes a correct match, he or she keeps the cards and turns over the next problem card.

• If the second player makes an incorrect match, the first player takes the cards and turns over the next problem.

• The player with the most cards at the end of the game wins.

WHAT IF THE STUDENT CAN'T

Recognize Multiplication as Repeated Addition

• Have students use counters or draw pictures to make arrays like the ones shown at the top of page 54. Their arrays should have from 2 to 9 objects in each row. Have them skip count to find the total number of objects in the array. Then have them count by 1s to check their total. Finally, ask them to write an addition sentence and a multiplication sentence for each array.

Complete the Power Practice

• Discuss each incorrect answer. Have the student model any fact he or she missed using counters or pictured sets and then write the correct product.

USING THE LESSON

• *How many squares are there in 5 rows of 7 squares?* (35) *How many squares will there be if 1 more row of 7 is added?* (42) *What multiplication sentence can you write for 6 rows of 7 squares?* ($6 \times 7 = 42$)

Try It

• Check students' understanding of how to use a multiplication fact they already know to find another multiplication fact.

• For exercises 1–3, students might think of the multiplication sentence in terms of rows of a rectangle. For example, for 8×6 they might think of 8 rows of 6 squares each. If they know the number of squares in 5 rows of 6, they can add 6 more to find 6×6; then they can add another 6 to find 7×6, and so on. For items 4–6, students use the strategy of adding 1 more 8 to 4×8, 1 more 9 to 5×9, and 1 more 7 to 8×7.

Power Practice

• Select several of the exercises and have volunteers describe some different methods they can use to show that the product they have written is correct.

• Review some ways that students can remind themselves of how to find facts that they have forgotten: draw a rectangle, use facts they know and add to or subtract from the known products, skip count, use the Commutative Property, or use the Distributive Property to break the fact into two simpler, known facts.

Learn with Partners & Parents

• Have students record the multiplication facts they don't know so they can do some further work with these facts.

• Each partner might use connecting cubes or draw diagrams to model one or more of the facts they missed.

USING THE LESSON

Lesson Goal

- Rename ones or tens as tens or hundreds.

What the Student Needs to Know

- Use place-value models to show ones and tens.
- Use place-value charts to show 2- and 3-digit numbers.
- Count by tens to 100.

Getting Started

- Have students work in small groups. Provide each group with a supply of place-value models for ones, tens, and hundreds.
- Check that all students know the meanings of the models by asking: *There are three different kinds of models. What are they?* (ones, tens, hundreds) *How are the different kinds of models related?* (10 ones = 1 ten; 10 tens = 1 hundred)
- Have students use 10 tens sticks to count by 10s to 100. Reinforce the fact that 10 tens equals 1 hundred.

What Can I Do?

Read the question and the response. Then read and discuss the examples. Ask:

- *What does it mean to rename a number?* (Find a different symbol, expression, or word that has the same value.)
- Have students put out 28 ones models. Ask: *What number did you show? How can you show this number with fewer models?* (Students may suggest using 1 ten stick and 18 ones, or 2 tens and 8 ones.) Say:
- *In this lesson you'll be looking for the least number of models. What is the least number for 28?* (2 tens 8 ones)

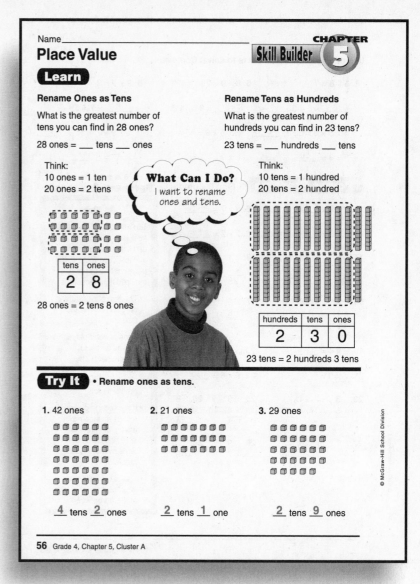

WHAT IF THE STUDENT CAN'T

Use Place-Value Models To Show Ones and Tens

- Introduce students to place-value models by showing them one cube and one ten stick. Have the student count out ten ones. Explain that this is equal to one ten stick.
- Have students work in pairs to model numbers less than 30. One student shows a number with all ones; the partner shows the number with tens and ones.

Use Place-Value Charts To Show 2- and 3-Digit Numbers

- Write 64 on the board. Ask: *What does the digit 6 stand for in this number?* (6 tens or 60) *What does the digit 4 stand for?* (4 ones or 4)
- Show students this place-value chart.

tens	ones
6	4

- Repeat the questions and explanation for a 3-digit number such as 238.

hundreds	tens	ones
2	3	8

Name_____

Rename tens as hundreds.

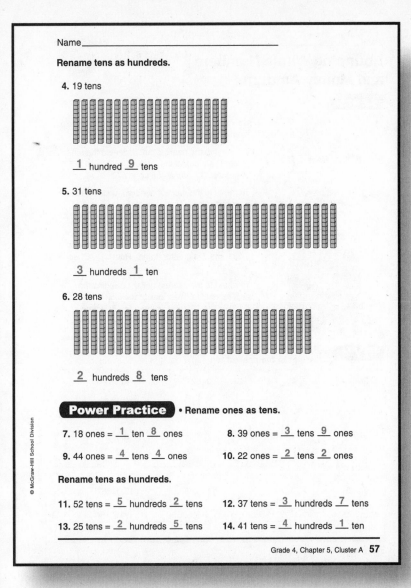

4. 19 tens

<u>1</u> hundred <u>9</u> tens

5. 31 tens

<u>3</u> hundreds <u>1</u> ten

6. 28 tens

<u>2</u> hundreds <u>8</u> tens

Power Practice • Rename ones as tens.

7. 18 ones = <u>1</u> ten <u>8</u> ones   **8.** 39 ones = <u>3</u> tens <u>9</u> ones

9. 44 ones = <u>4</u> tens <u>4</u> ones   **10.** 22 ones = <u>2</u> tens <u>2</u> ones

Rename tens as hundreds.

11. 52 tens = <u>5</u> hundreds <u>2</u> tens   **12.** 37 tens = <u>3</u> hundreds <u>7</u> tens

13. 25 tens = <u>2</u> hundreds <u>5</u> tens   **14.** 41 tens = <u>4</u> hundreds <u>1</u> ten

Grade 4, Chapter 5, Cluster A **57**

WHAT IF THE STUDENT CAN'T

Count by Tens to 100

- Have the class count aloud by tens to 100. Repeat, having a student write the numbers 10 through 100 on the board. Then have volunteers come to the board and write the word name for each ten.

- Provide students with tens sticks. Have them use the sticks to count by 10s.

- Use a hundred chart. The tens are all in the right column. Have students say each ten and then write the number word.

Complete the Power Practice

- Provide place-value models. Have students work in pairs or small groups. Have them show each exercise with the models before completing the number sentence.

- Emphasize that the expressions on both sides of an equal sign must have the same value. Students can use this fact to check answers; for example, 37 tens and 3 hundreds 7 tens are both equal to 370.

USING THE LESSON

- Have students put out 23 tens. If the supply of models is limited, have one student per group do this. Ask: *How many tens are there?* (23 tens) *What number is this?* (230)

- *How can you show this number using fewer models?* (1 hundred and 13 tens; 2 hundreds 3 tens) *Which way uses the least number of models?* (2 hundreds 3 tens)

Try It

- Have place-value models available for students who want to model the exercises.

- Have a volunteer read the directions.

- Tell students to circle a group of ten ones in the first exercise. They continue circling tens until there are not enough ones to make a ten. Students' papers may look like this:

- Point out that, when you rename ones as tens, there are often some ones left over.

- Have a student read the direction on the top of page 57. Ask: *How will you group these tens to show hundreds?* (Draw a circle around each group of 10 tens.)

Power Practice

- Do exercises 7 and 11 as a whole-class activity to make sure students know what they are to do.

Lesson Goal

• Round whole numbers and money to a given place.

What the Student Needs to Know

• Identify the tens or hundreds digit.
• Identify the dollars digit.
• Make a number line to show counting by ones, tens, or hundreds.

Getting Started

• Review rounding to the nearest ten. Write the number 47 on the board. Ask: *What are the two nearest tens?* (40 and 50) Draw a number line showing the numbers from 40 to 50. Have a student mark the location of 47. Ask: *Which ten is closer to 47, 40 or 50?* (50)

• Remind students of the rules for rounding by using the examples 43, 48, and 45. Ask: *Which numbers round down to 40?* (43) *Which numbers round up to 50?* (45, 48) *How do you use the ones digit when rounding to the nearest ten?* (If the ones digit is 5 or greater than 5, round up. If the ones digit is less than 5, round down.)

• Draw a number line showing the numbers from 730 to 740. Ask: *If you are rounding to the nearest ten, which numbers round down to 730?* (731, 732, 733, 734) *Which numbers round up to 740?* (735, 736, 737, 738, 739)

What Can I Do?

Read the question and the response. Then read and discuss the examples. Ask:

• *Which digit do you underline?* (The digit in the place to which you are rounding.) *How do you use the digit to the right of this place?* (If it is 5 or greater than 5, round up. If it is less than 5, round down.)

Name_____

Rounding Whole Numbers and Money Amounts

Learn

What Can I Do?
I want to review rounding numbers and money.

Use the digit to the right of the place you are rounding to.

To round to the nearest ten, underline the tens place. Then look at the ones. In 4$\underline{6}$5, the 5 is 5 or greater. So, round 4$\underline{6}$5 up to 470.

To round to the nearest hundred, underline the hundreds place. Then look at the tens. In $\underline{3}$09, the 0 is less than 5. Round $\underline{3}$09 down to 300.

To round to the nearest thousand, underline the thousands place. Then look at the hundreds. In $\underline{6}$,721, the 7 is greater than 5. Round $\underline{6}$,721 up to 7,000.

To round to the nearest dollar, underline the digit for dollars. Then look at the digit to the right. In 2\underline{4}$.19, the 1 is less than 5. Round 2\underline{4}$.19 down to $24.00.

Try It • In each number, underline the tens digit. Then round the number to the nearest ten.

1. 9$\underline{4}$	2. 1$\underline{8}$	3. 6$\underline{2}$	4. 4$\underline{6}$
90	20	60	50

5. 5$\underline{7}$9	6. 3$\underline{1}$0	7. 7$\underline{2}$5	8. 2$\underline{0}$3
580	310	730	200

9. 9,1$\underline{5}$5	10. 7,3$\underline{3}$1	11. 3,4$\underline{8}$0	12. 6,1$\underline{5}$7
9,160	7,330	3,480	6,160

58 Grade 4, Chapter 5, Cluster A

© McGraw-Hill School Division

WHAT IF THE STUDENT CAN'T

Identify the Tens or Hundreds Digit

• Provide place-value models. Have students work in pairs to model 2- and 3-digit numbers. One student shows a number; the partner writes the number and identifies the hundreds, tens, and ones digits.

• Have students practice writing 2- and 3-digit numbers in expanded form. Give them worksheets with blank exercises such as these:

__ __ __ = __hundreds __tens __ones

__ __ = __ tens __ ones

Identify the Dollars Digit

• Provide students with play money to model amounts up through $9.99. Students work in pairs. One student shows an amount of money; the partner writes the total and identifies the digits that show the dollars, the dimes, and the pennies.

• Have students work in groups of three. Give them three 1–6 number cubes. One student rolls the dollars digit, the next student rolls the dimes digit, the last student rolls the pennies digit. Students record their numbers in charts like this:

Name_____

Underline the hundreds digit. Then round the number to the nearest hundred.

13. 7̲26	14. 5̲70	15. 1̲33	16. 2̲38
700	600	100	200

17. 6,2̲09	18. 3,6̲54	19. 8,0̲42	20. 2,4̲17
6,200	3,700	8,000	2,400

Underline the dollars digit. Then round to the nearest dollar.

21. $8̲.75	22. $1̲.27	23. $2̲.49	24. $6̲.53
$9	$1	$2	$7

25. $40̲.97	26. $36̲.52	27. $91̲.74	28. $52̲.16
$41	$37	$92	$52

Power Practice • Round each to the underlined place.

29. 8̲53 900	30. 4̲3 40	31. 2,5̲81 3,000	32. 6̲09 600
33. $6̲.39 $6	34. 7,3̲95 7,400	35. 2̲74 270	36. $4̲.85 $5
37. 6̲9 70	38. $47̲.49 $47	39. 6,2̲77 6,000	40. 1̲37 140
41. 5,0̲13 5,000	42. 1̲39 100	43. 5̲3 50	44. $86̲.18 $86
45. 8̲35 840	46. $9̲.73 $10	47. 3,8̲41 3,800	48. 7̲33 700

WHAT IF THE STUDENT CAN'T

dollars	dimes	pennies

Make a Number Line To Show Counting by Ones, Tens, or Hundreds

- Have students work in groups.
  Give each group a 1–6 number cube and worksheets with blank number lines. The students roll the cube four times to get a 4-digit number. Then they make the number lines to show how to round it to the nearest ten, hundred, and thousand.

Complete the Power Practice

- Some students may be using the wrong digit to make the rounding decision. For example, they may use the ones digit when rounding to the nearest hundred. Ask the students to write an enlarged version of an exercise. Have them first point to the place to which they are rounding (the underlined digit). Then have them point to the digit to the right of that place.
- Have students work in pairs or small groups. Then create number-line models to help them do the more difficult exercises.

USING THE LESSON

- *If you are rounding 465 to the nearest ten, what are the two possible choices for the answer?* (460 and 470) *If you are rounding 465 to the nearest hundred, what are the two possible choices?* (400 and 500)
- If students seem to need more review, have them work in small groups to draw a number-line model for each example exercise.

Try It

Have the students read the directions silently. Ask: *After underlining the tens digit, how will you complete each of these exercises?* (Look at the ones digit to decide whether to round up or down.)

- Have students tell the two nearest tens for each exercise. You may wish to have students write these on the page. Then they can go back and circle the rounded number for each exercise.
- Have a volunteer read the directions at the top of page 59. Ask students to tell you the hundreds digit for each exercise. Then have them state the two nearest hundreds.
- In the next exercise group, have students identify the dollars digit and the two nearest dollars.

Power Practice

- Have students find one or two exercises in which the tens digit is underlined. Have them explain how they will round; for example, in 835, the ones digit is 5. So, 835 will be rounded up to 840.
- Repeat the questions with one exercise each that involves rounding to the nearest hundred, thousand, and dollar.

Lesson Goal

• Add a 1-digit number to a 2-digit number.

What the Student Needs to Know

• Identify ones digits.
• Complete addition facts.
• Recognize multiples of 10.

Getting Started

• Conduct a brief review of the addition facts, emphasizing the more difficult facts. If necessary, post an addition facts table for student reference.

What Can I Do?

Read the question and the response. Then read and discuss the examples. Ask:

• *What addition fact is "hidden" in 54 + 3? (4 + 3 = 7) Give another problem that uses this fact.* (Possible answers: 14 + 3, 24 + 3)

• *Why is 56 + 4 + 3 easier to do than 56 + 7?* (The first two numbers have a sum of 60.)

• Have each student write and solve a problem using the strategy of making a multiple of 10.

Try It

• Have students tell you the addition fact that corresponds to each exercise.

Power Practice

• Have students state the addition fact for each exercise.

• Ask for volunteers to explain the strategy of making multiples of 10 for one or two exercises.

• Point out that students have a choice of two strategies: using basic facts or making multiples of 10.

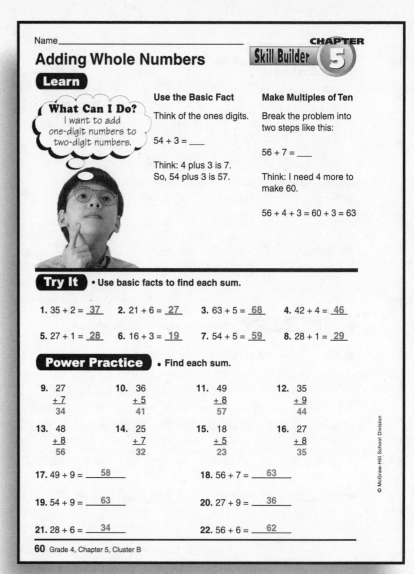

Name_____

CHAPTER 5

Adding Whole Numbers   *Skill Builder*

Learn

What Can I Do?
I want to add one-digit numbers to two-digit numbers.

Use the Basic Fact

Think of the ones digits.

54 + 3 = ___

Think: 4 plus 3 is 7.
So, 54 plus 3 is 57.

Make Multiples of Ten

Break the problem into two steps like this:

56 + 7 = ___

Think: I need 4 more to make 60.

56 + 4 + 3 = 60 + 3 = 63

Try It • Use basic facts to find each sum.

1. 35 + 2 = _37_   2. 21 + 6 = _27_   3. 63 + 5 = _68_   4. 42 + 4 = _46_

5. 27 + 1 = _28_   6. 16 + 3 = _19_   7. 54 + 5 = _59_   8. 28 + 1 = _29_

Power Practice • Find each sum.

9. 27
   + 7
   34

10. 36
    + 5
    41

11. 49
    + 8
    57

12. 35
    + 9
    44

13. 48
    + 8
    56

14. 25
    + 7
    32

15. 18
    + 5
    23

16. 27
    + 8
    35

17. 49 + 9 = _58_   18. 56 + 7 = _63_

19. 54 + 9 = _63_   20. 27 + 9 = _36_

21. 28 + 6 = _34_   22. 56 + 6 = _62_

WHAT IF THE STUDENT CAN'T

Identify Ones Digits

• Write a two-digit number such as 83 on the board. Ask: *How many tens are in this number? How many ones?* (8 tens, 3 ones) Remind students that the 8 is called the tens digit. It tells the number of tens. The 3 is the ones digit because it tells the number of ones.

Complete Addition Facts

• Have students work in pairs using flash cards to identify any unknown facts. Students draw a picture to illustrate each fact, for example, 8 birds on a wire with 7 more birds flying in to join them.

Recognize Multiples of 10

• Remind students that any number ending in zero is a multiple of 10.

• For each 2-digit number in the lesson, have students state the nearest multiple of 10 that is greater. To do this, they add 1 to the tens digit and use a zero for the ones digit.

Complete the Power Practice

• Students work in pairs. One student copies a problem on another sheet of paper. The partner writes the related addition fact, then the first student finds the original sum.

Estimating Products

Learn

What Can I Do?
I want to estimate the answer to a multiplication problem.

Round the Greater Factor	Multiply to Estimate
Round the greater number so that it has only one digit that is not zero.	
$62 \times 3 \rightarrow 60 \times 3$	$60 \times 3 = 180$ So, 62×3 is about 180.
$8 \times 2,549 \rightarrow 8 \times 3,000$	$8 \times 3,000 = 24,000$ So, $8 \times 2,549$ is about 24,000.
$785 \times 6 \rightarrow 800 \times 6$	$800 \times 6 = 4,800$ So, 785×6 is about 4,800.

Try It • Round the factor to the underlined digit.

1. $7 \times \underline{5}7 \rightarrow 7 \times \underline{60}$

2. $2 \times \underline{3}2 \rightarrow 2 \times \underline{30}$

3. $9 \times \underline{9}41 \rightarrow 9 \times \underline{900}$

4. $8 \times \underline{2}56 \rightarrow 8 \times \underline{300}$

5. $5 \times \underline{4},098 \rightarrow 5 \times \underline{4,000}$

6. $3 \times \underline{7},413 \rightarrow 3 \times \underline{7,000}$

Power Practice • Round the factor to the underlined digit to estimate the product.

7. $3 \times \underline{6}7 \rightarrow 3 \times \underline{70}$

estimate: __210__

8. $9 \times \underline{1}8 \rightarrow 9 \times \underline{20}$

estimate: __180__

9. $4 \times \underline{2}15 \rightarrow 4 \times \underline{200}$

estimate: __800__

10. $7 \times \underline{8}91 \rightarrow 7 \times \underline{900}$

estimate: __6,300__

11. $6 \times \underline{7},828 \rightarrow 6 \times \underline{8,000}$

estimate: __48,000__

12. $5 \times \underline{3},587 \rightarrow 5 \times \underline{4,000}$

estimate: __20,000__

WHAT IF THE STUDENT CAN'T

Round to the Nearest Ten, Hundred, or Thousand

- Draw number line models using 2-digit numbers. Remind students of the rules for rounding: If the ones digit is greater than 5 or greater, round up. If the ones digit is less than 5, round down.

Complete Multiplication Facts

- Have students work in pairs using flash cards to identify those facts they do not know. Then have students form small groups to create and share fact strategies for the unknown facts.

Multiply Multiples of 10, 100, and 1000

- Students use place-value models to show patterns such as 3×4, 3×40, 3×400.

- Using problems such as 8×600, have students identify the greater factor. Explain that they attach this number of zeros to the product of the two nonzero digits.

Complete the Power Practice

- If students are not rounding correctly, have them identify the two nearest multiples first. For example, the two hundreds nearest to 215 are 200 and 300.

USING THE LESSON

Lesson Goal

- Use rounding to estimate the product of a 1-digit number times a 1-, 2-, 3-, or 4-digit number.

What the Student Needs to Know

- Round to the nearest ten, hundred, or thousand.
- Complete multiplication facts.
- Multiply multiples of 10, 100, and 1,000.

Getting Started

- Write this pattern on the board: 3 x 7, 3 x 70, 3 x 700, 3 x 7,000. Ask: *What is 3 times 7?* (21) *How can you use this fact to find the other products?* (For 3 x 70, attach one zero to 21; for 3 x 700, attach two zeros; for 3 x 7,000, attach three zeros.)

What Can I Do?

Read the question and the response. Then have students study the three examples in the middle column. Ask:

- *How have the three problems been changed?* (The greater number has been rounded.) *Why is this a good way to estimate a product*? (You can use a related multiplication fact.)

- Have students read the third column to learn how the estimating is completed.

Try It

- Have students identify the underlined digit in the first exercise. Ask: *How will you round this number?* (Look at the digit to the right. It is greater than 5, so 57 rounds up to 60.)

Power Practice

- For one of the exercises, have students tell how they will do the rounding. Then have them name the basic multiplication fact to use. Check that they know how many zeros to attach. Then have them complete the exercises.

Lesson Goal

- Complete a table of ordered pairs.

What the Student Needs to Know

- Identify the rows and columns in a table.
- Complete number sentences with missing factors.
- Complete multiplication facts.

Getting Started

- Draw this input-output table on the board:

Rule: Add 4.				
Input				
Output				

Have students suggest five numbers for the top row. Then explain that the table tells them to add 4 to each number. Have volunteers do the addition to complete the second row.

- Explain that these kinds of tables work like machines—you put in a number, follow a rule, and get out another number.

- Write the terms *input* and *output* on the board and have students explain what they mean in their own words.

- Have students work in pairs to create an input-output table with a multiplication rule such as "multiply by 2."

What Can I Do?

Read the question and the response. Then read and discuss the example. Ask:

- *What parts of the table are missing?* (The factor for the rule, one number in the top row, one number in the bottom row.)

- *How can you use the first three columns of numbers to find the rule?* (Look to see how each top number is related to the number beneath it.)

- *How is 2 related to 6?* (Six is 3 times 2.) *How can you get 6 as the output if 2 is the input?* (Multiply 2 times 3.)

Name_____

Tables of Ordered Pairs

Learn

Rule: Multiply by _?_ .

Input	2	3	4	5	?
Output	6	9	12	?	18

What Can I Do?
I want to complete an input and output table.

Look at the first column of numbers. Find the rule. What number times the input gives the output?

Think: _____ × 2 = 6
Since 3 × 2 = 6, the rule is "Multiply by 3."

Look at the next two columns. Check your rule.
3 × 3 = 9   3 × 4 = 12

Look at the fourth column. What is the output for the input 5? Use your rule.
Since 3 × 5 = 15, the output is 15.

Look at the last column. What is the input for the output 18? Use your rule.
Since 3 × 6 = 18, the input is 6.

Try It • Complete the table. Find the unknown output, input, and rule.

1. Rule: Multiply by _5_

Input	3	5	7	8	10
Output	15	25	35	40	50

Find the rule: _5_ × 3 = 15

Check your rule: _5_ × 5 = 25 and

_5_ × 7 = 35

Use your rule: _5_ × 8 = _40_ and

_5_ × _10_ = 50

WHAT IF THE STUDENT CAN'T

Identify the Rows and Columns in a Table

- Use a hundred chart, an addition facts table, or a multiplication facts table. Point out the rows that go across the table and the columns that go up and down.

- Write the terms *row* and *column* on the board. Have students use each term in a sentence.

Complete Number Sentences with Missing Factors

- Write this number sentence on the board:

4 × _?_ = 32

Ask: *How can you find the missing number?* (Think: Four times what number equals 32. Some students may realize that they can divide to find the missing factor.)

- Have students work in pairs. One student suggests a multiplication fact; the partner writes two different missing-factor number sentences using the fact.

Name_____

2. Rule: Multiply by 2.

Input	1	5	8	9	10
Output	2	10	16	18	20

3. Rule: Multiply by 7.

Input	1	4	6	9	20
Output	7	28	42	63	140

4. Rule: Multiply by 6.

Input	3	4	5	9	10
Output	18	24	30	54	60

5. Rule: Multiply by 5.

Input	2	8	10	30	40
Output	10	40	50	150	200

6. Rule: Multiply by _7_.

Input	20	50	60	80	90
Output	140	350	420	560	630

7. Rule: Multiply by _4_.

Input	3	5	7	8	10
Output	12	20	28	32	40

8. Rule: Multiply by _6_.

Input	6	7	8	20	30
Output	36	42	48	120	180

9. Rule: Multiply by _8_.

Input	5	7	9	20	40
Output	40	56	72	160	320

10. Rule: Multiply by _4_.

Input	8	10	20	50	60
Output	32	40	80	200	240

11. Rule: Multiply by _9_.

Input	4	6	50	70	90
Output	36	54	450	630	810

Grade 4, Chapter 5, Cluster B **63**

WHAT IF THE STUDENT CAN'T

Complete Multiplication Facts

- Have students work in pairs using flash cards to find out which facts they do not yet know.

- Provide each student with a multiplication facts table. Students color in the facts they know. Then they write each fact they need to learn on a separate sheet of paper.

Complete the Power Practice

- Copy the first exercise on the board, but leave the entire second row blank. Ask students to tell you how to use the rule to fill in the second row.

- If students are making errors with zeros, they may need a review of multiplying multiples of 10. Use pairs such as 4 x 5, 4 x 50 to emphasize the importance of attaching the final zeros.

USING THE LESSON

- *Which is the fourth column?* (The one with 5 in the top row and the question mark in the bottom row.) *What is missing in this column?* (The output.) *How do you find the missing number?* (Multiply the top number, 5, times 3.) Repeat with similar questions for the fifth column.

Try It

Allow students time to study the problem. Ask:

- *How can you find the rule?* (Look for a way to get the bottom number from the top number.) Once students have identified the rule, ask:

- *How can you use this to find a missing number in the bottom row?* (Multiply the top number times 5.) *How can you use the rule to find a missing number in the top row?* (Think: What number times 5 results in the bottom number?)

Power Practice

- Have the students look over the tables. Ask: *How are the first four tables different from the ones that come after that?* (In the first four tables, the rule is given. In the exercises after that, students must find the rule before they can complete the table.)

- You may want to have students identify the rule for each of the last exercises before they begin work.

USING THE LESSON

Lesson Goal
- Use ordered pairs to graph points on coordinate grids.

What the Student Needs to Know
- Plot points on a number line.
- Use the position words *across*, *up*, *first*, and *second*.
- Count horizontal or vertical units on a square grid.

Getting Started
- Provide students with graph paper. Use centimeter paper so that the squares will be fairly large.
- On the board draw a 5-by-5 graph like those in the lesson. Number the vertical axis, but use the letters A through E for the horizontal axis.

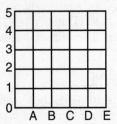

Have a volunteer put a dot to show the location B-2. Write this as (B, 2). Have students mark other locations with dots. Then ask:

- *We've used a letter and a number to describe a location on this grid. How could we use two numbers instead of a letter and a number?* (Replace the letters A through E with the numbers 1 through 5.)
- On the board grid, change the letters A–E to the numbers 1–5. Have students copy this grid on their papers.
- Write these ordered pairs on the board: (4, 4), (2, 2), (3, 3), (5, 5), (1, 1). Have students graph the five points.
- Write the ordered pair (4, 1). Ask: *How is this one different from the ones you just graphed?* (The two numbers are different.) Explain that these are called ordered pairs because the order of the numbers makes a differ-

---

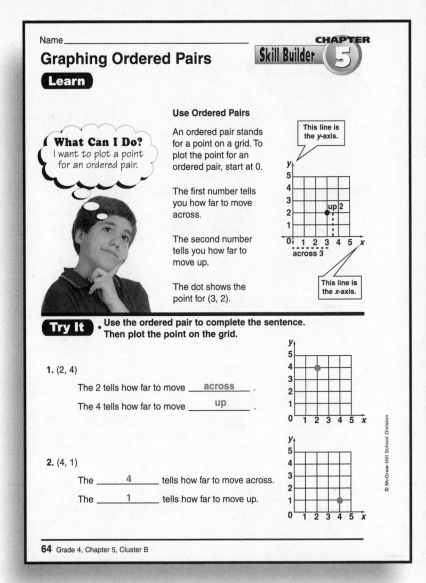

WHAT IF THE STUDENT CAN'T

Plot Points on a Number Line
- Draw a large number line on the board. Label the marks from 0 through 10. Emphasize that the numbers refer to the marks and not to the spaces.
- Mark the point 3 with a large, black dot. Have students take turns coming up to the board and plotting points.

Use the Position Words *Across, Up, First,* and *Second*
- Write each term on the board and give a definition. Have students use the terms in sentences.
- Provide each student with a large 5-by-5 grid like those on the lesson pages. Play a game of "Follow My Clues." Students begin at (0, 0). Give them clues such as "First, go across three spaces. Make an X. Now, go up two spaces. Draw a star where the lines cross."

Name_____

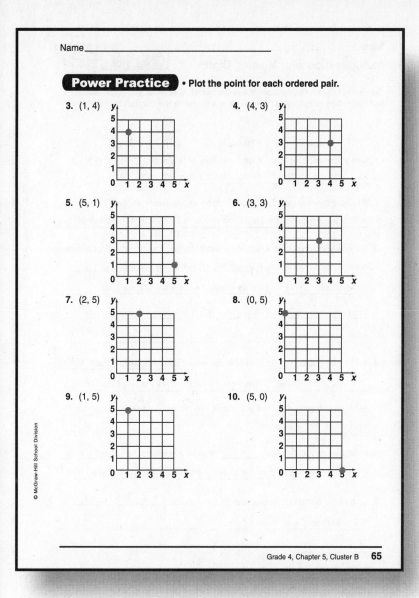

3. (1, 4)
4. (4, 3)
5. (5, 1)
6. (3, 3)
7. (2, 5)
8. (0, 5)
9. (1, 5)
10. (5, 0)

© McGraw-Hill School Division

WHAT IF THE STUDENT CAN'T

Count Horizontal or Vertical Units on a Square Grid

- Draw a large 5-by-5 grid on the board like those on the lesson pages. Demonstrate for students how to count the spaces. Start at (0, 0). Put your finger on the lines as you count across: 1, 2, 3, and so on. Have students take turns coming to the board and practicing this step.

- When the students can count across, have them count up.

- Finally, give students numbers for both counting across *and* counting up; for example, they count 2 spaces across and then go 1 space up.

Complete the Power Practice

- If students are reversing the first and second coordinates, demonstrate again that they count across first.

- If students have trouble when one coordinate is zero, have them think of this as "no spaces." For example, the pair (0, 5) means "go no spaces to the right and then go 5 spaces up."

USING THE LESSON

ence. Graph (4, 1) and (1, 4) for students to illustrate.

- Emphasize these aspects of graphing points: You always start at (0, 0). You first count spaces going across to the right. Then you count spaces going up.

What Can I Do?

Read the question and the response. Then read and discuss the example. Ask:

- *What does it mean to "plot a point?"* (Mark a location with a black dot. Sometimes Xs are used, but dots are seen more frequently.)

- *What is an ordered pair?* (Two numbers inside parentheses that show a location on a grid.)

- Have students graph the ordered pair (2, 3) on their grids. Have them also graph (3, 2) to reinforce the importance of getting the order of the numbers correct.

- If students ask about the terms *x-axis* and *y-axis*, tell them these are terms from algebra. In algebra, a general ordered pair is called (x, y) where the letters x and y stand for any numbers.

Try It

- Do the two exercises together with the class. If students are not certain what to do, have them graph two or three more points on each grid.

Power Practice

- Have the students complete the practice items. Then review each answer.

- For additional practice, you might want to have students graph two more points on each grid. They label the point that is already there with the letter A. Dictate two ordered pairs for students to write beneath the given pair. They graph these points and label them B and C.

CHALLENGE

Lesson Goal

• Use properties of multiplication and digit patterns to solve missing-digit puzzles.

Introducing the Challenge

• Review the vocabulary needed for the lesson by having students use each term in a sentence. Vocabulary used in this lesson includes: *digit, replacement, solution.*

• Write this problem on the board.

      1234
   + 5555
      6789

Ask: *What do you notice about the digits that make up this problem?* (Each of the digits 1 through 9 is used in the problem.)

• To the right of the problem, write this:

       A B C D
     + E E E E
       F G H I

Point out that this is a letter version of the same problem in which A = 1, B = 2, and so on.

Multiplication with Missing Digits **CHALLENGE**

Some digits are missing from these problems. Use what you know about multiplication to help you replace each letter with the correct digit.

$$
\begin{array}{r} 2A \\ \times\ 4 \\ \hline 1B2 \end{array}
\qquad
\begin{array}{r} D9 \\ \times\ C \\ \hline E14 \end{array}
$$

1. Can you replace the letter **A** with a 5? Why or why not? <u>No; there is a 2 in</u> <u>the ones place, and 4 × 5 would put a 0 in the ones place.</u>

2. What are the only two digits you should try as replacements for **A**? Explain. <u>3, 8; 4 × 3 = 12 and 4 × 8 = 32, so either will put a 2 in the ones place.</u>

3. Tell how you can decide which of the two digits you mentioned in your answer to question 2 *cannot* replace **A**. <u>Possible answer: If A were 3, then 10</u> <u>ones would be regrouped as 1 ten. 4 × 2 tens = 8 tens, and</u> <u>8 tens + 1 ten = 9 tens. But there is a 1 in the hundreds place,</u> <u>so A cannot be 3.</u>

4. **A** = <u> 8 </u> **B** = <u> 1 </u> Tell how you know. <u>Since A cannot be 3, then</u> <u>A = 8. 4 × 8 = 32, so 30 ones are regrouped as 3 tens. 4 × 2 tens = 8</u> <u>tens, and 8 tens + 3 tens = 11 tens. Regroup 11 tens as 1 hundred</u> <u>and 1 ten. So, B =1.</u>

5. What digit can replace **C**? <u> 6 </u> How do you know? <u>6 × 9 = 54; 6 is</u> <u>the only number that puts a 4 in the ones place when multiplying by 9.</u>

6. Find all the correct replacement digits for **D** and **E**. <u>If D = 1, then E = 1;</u> <u>if D = 6, then E = 4.</u>

Name_____

	3 3		8H		K3
	× F		× 7		× 5
	26G		JOI		L55

7. Explain how you can tell that **F** cannot be replaced by 1, 2, or 3.

There are no ones to be regrouped. 1 would put a 3 in the tens

place, and neither 2 nor 3 would have a 2 in the hundreds place.

8. F = ___8___   G = ___4___

9. Find all the possible replacements for **H, I,** and **J.**

If H = 6, then I = 2 and J = 6. If H = 7, then I = 9 and J = 6.

10. How can you tell that there is no solution for the last problem above?

No matter what digit K stands for, the product must have a 1 or a 6

in the tens place.

11. Make up a problem in which a 2- or 3-digit number is multiplied by a 1-digit
number and 1 or 2 digits are missing. Explain how your problem can be solved.

Problems and explanations will vary.

12. Make up a multiplication problem that has some missing digits and that cannot
be solved. Explain why your problem has no solution.

Problems and explanations will vary.

© McGraw-Hill School Division

Using the Challenge

- Have a volunteer read the directions aloud. Write the first puzzle on the board for discussion. Students need to understand the following:
- The object of the puzzle is to find the digits that should replace the letters A and B.
- When finished, the problem must be a correct multiplication.
- Students may need help with problem 2. If so, tell them that the clue to finding A is that the ones digit in the answer is 2. There are only two facts with 4 as a factor in which the product ends in two. Ask students what these two facts are. (4 × 3 = 12, 4 × 8 = 32)
- In answering problem 2, students should try both possibilities. Have them try 3 and then tell you why it won't work. (4 × 23 equals 92. But, the product has three digits.)
- The last two problems ask students to create their own missing-digit puzzles. You may want students to work in pairs or small groups for this part of the challenge.

Allow students opportunity to revise puzzles that are flawed.

CHALLENGE

Lesson Goal
- Graph a set of ordered pairs that makes a curve.

Introducing the Challenge
- Review the vocabulary needed for the lesson by having students use each term in a sentence. Vocabulary used in this lesson includes: graph, ordered pair, product, fraction, decimal, straight, curved

- Provide grid paper. Use a size that has about 4 squares to the inch.

- On the board make a 10-by-10 coordinate grid. Have students copy it on their papers.

- Tell students they are to find and graph all the ordered pairs in which the two numbers have a sum of 10. One example is (4, 6).

- When students have finished, tell them to connect the dots with a straight line. (The line should go from (0, 10) down to (10, 0).

- Explain that every point on this line has an ordered pair in which the sum is 10. Have students find one such pair in which the coordinates are fractions or decimals.

Name_____

Graphs That Curve

Many graphs have straight lines. But graphs can also be made up of curved lines. Look at these ordered pairs. Do you see the pattern?

(2, 24) (3, 16) (8, 6) (12, 4)

The numbers in each ordered pair have the same product. When you multiply the numbers you get 48.

1. Find all the different ordered pairs with a product of 48.

2. Mark a dot for each ordered pair. Then connect the dots. You will get a curved graph. The dots for (1, 48) and (48, 1) won't fit on this grid, so you can leave them off the graph.

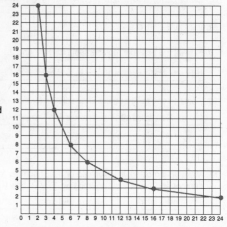

3. Explain why the ordered pair (5, 9.6) belongs on this graph.

   All pairs of factors that have products of 48 will fall on the graph.

   The product of 5 and 9.6 is 48.

4. Find three other ordered pairs that belong on the graph. One number in each pair will be a fraction or a decimal.

   possible answers: (20, 2.4); (40, 1.2); (96, 0.5).

© McGraw-Hill School Division

Name_____

5. Find all the different ordered pairs of whole numbers with a product of 36.

(1, 36); (2, 18); (3, 12); (4, 9); (6, 6)

6. Mark a dot for each ordered pair. Then connect the dots. You will get a curved graph. The dots for (1, 36) and (36, 1) won't fit on this grid, so you can leave them off the graph.

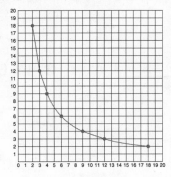

7. Create a set of ordered pairs that will make a curved graph different from the two you have made.

Answers will vary.

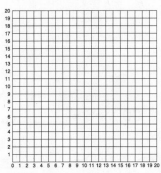

8. Explain how to make a set of ordered pairs that will make a curved graph.

Possible answer: Find all the different ordered pairs of whole

numbers that have the same product. Plot the point for each

ordered pair, and then connect the points.

CHALLENGE

Using the Challenge

- Have a volunteer read the top of page 68 and the first two problems aloud. Check that students know what to do by asking:

- *What are you going to show on the graph?* (Ordered pairs in which the numbers have a product of 48.)

- *How is this different from the graphing we just did?* (Students graphed a function in which they added the coordinates. Now they will multiply the coordinates. The first type of function is linear; the second type is not linear. A linear function is one with a straight line for a graph.)

Multiplication Facts

Find each product.

1. $6 \times 8 =$ _____

2. $7 \times 9 =$ _____

3. $4 \times 6 =$ _____

4. $\begin{array}{r} 5 \\ \times\ 9 \\ \hline \end{array}$

5. $\begin{array}{r} 8 \\ \times\ 3 \\ \hline \end{array}$

6. $\begin{array}{r} 9 \\ \times\ 4 \\ \hline \end{array}$

Multiplying by Powers of Ten

Find each product.

7. $3 \times 100 =$ _____

8. $1,000 \times 6 =$ _____

9. $100 \times 7 =$ _____

10. $4 \times 1,000 =$ _____

Addition Through Thousands

Find each sum.

11. $\begin{array}{r} 812 \\ +\ 4,320 \\ \hline \end{array}$

12. $\begin{array}{r} 78 \\ +\ 250 \\ \hline \end{array}$

13. $\begin{array}{r} 562 \\ +\ 1,940 \\ \hline \end{array}$

Rounding to the Nearest Ten and Hundred

Round each number to the underlined place.

14. 3̲81 _____

15. 4̲5 _____

16. 5̲26 _____

Multiplying by
1-Digit Numbers

Find each product.

17. 38
    × 7

18. 462
    × 30

Using the Distributive Property

Complete each statement.

19. 18 × 26 = (18 × 20) + (18 × ___) _____

20. 34 × 15 = (___ × 15) + (4 × 15) _____

21. 42 × 52 = (40 × 52) + (___ × 52) _____

Addition Through Hundred Thousands

Find each sum.

22.   36,725
    + 129,430

23.   4,291
    + 63,520

24.   8,206
    + 59,320

25.   18,326
    + 461,930

Assessment Goal

This two-page assessment covers skills identified as necessary for success in Chapter 6 Multiply by 2-Digit Numbers. The first page assesses the major prerequisite skills for Cluster A. The second page assesses the major prerequisite skills for Cluster B. When the Cluster A and Cluster B prerequisite skills overlap, the skill(s) will be covered in only one section.

Getting Started

- Allow students time to look over the two pages of the assessment. Point out the labels that identify the skills covered.

- Have students find math vocabulary terms used in the assessment. List vocabulary terms on the board as students identify them. If necessary, review the meanings of all essential math vocabulary.

Introducing the Assessment

- Explain to students that these pages will help you know if they are ready to start a new chapter in their math textbooks.

- Students who have transferred from another school may not have been introduced to some of these skills. Encourage students to do their best and assure them you will help them learn any needed skills.

Cluster A Challenge

Those students who demonstrate mastery of the skills on this page will not need to use the reteaching worksheets. Instead, these students can do the Cluster A Challenge found on pages 78–79.

Name_____

Multiplication Facts

Find each product.

1. $6 \times 8 = $ __48__   2. $7 \times 9 = $ __63__   3. $4 \times 6 = $ __24__

4. 5
   $\times 9$
   ___
   45

5. 8
   $\times 3$
   ___
   24

6. 9
   $\times 4$
   ___
   36

Multiplying by Powers of Ten

Find each product.

7. $3 \times 100 = $ ___300___   8. $1,000 \times 6 = $ ___6,000___

9. $100 \times 7 = $ ___700___   10. $4 \times 1,000 = $ ___4,000___

Addition Through Thousands

Find each sum.

11.   812
    $+ 4,320$
    _____
    5,132

12.   78
    $+ 250$
    _____
    328

13.   562
    $+ 1,940$
    _____
    2,502

Rounding to the Nearest Ten and Hundred

Round each number to the underlined place.

14. 3<u>8</u>1 __400__   15. 4<u>5</u> __50__   16. <u>5</u>26 __500__

CLUSTER A PREREQUISITE SKILLS

The skills listed in this chart are those identified as major prerequisite skills for students' success in the lessons in Cluster A of the chapter. Each skill is covered by one or more assessment items as shown in the middle column. The right column provides the page number for the lessons in this book that reteach the cluster A prerequisite skills.

Skill Name	Assessment Items	Lesson Pages
Multiplication Facts	1-6	70
Multiplying by Powers of 10	7-10	71
Addition through Thousands	11-13	72
Rounding to the Nearest Ten and Hundred	14-16	73

Name _____

Multiplying by 1-Digit Numbers

Find each product.

17. 38
    × 7
    ‾‾‾‾
    266

18. 462
    × 30
    ‾‾‾‾‾
    13,860

Using the Distributive Property

Complete each statement.

19. $18 \times 26 = (18 \times 20) + (18 \times \underline{})$ _____ 6 _____

20. $34 \times 15 = (\underline{} \times 15) + (4 \times 15)$ _____ 30 _____

21. $42 \times 52 = (40 \times 52) + (\underline{} \times 52)$ _____ 2 _____

Addition Through Hundred Thousands

Find each sum.

22. 36,725
    + 129,430
    ‾‾‾‾‾‾‾‾
    166,155

23. 4,291
    + 63,520
    ‾‾‾‾‾‾‾
    67,811

24. 8,206
    + 59,320
    ‾‾‾‾‾‾‾
    67,526

25. 18,326
    + 461,930
    ‾‾‾‾‾‾‾‾
    480,256

© McGraw-Hill School Division

CLUSTER B PREREQUISITE SKILLS

The skills listed in this chart are those identified as major prerequisite skills for students' success in the lessons in Cluster B of the chapter. Each skill is covered by one or more assessment items as shown in the middle column. The right column provides the page numbers for the lessons in this book that reteach the Cluster B prerequisite skills

Skill Name	Assessment Items	Lesson Pages
Multiplying by 1-Digit Numbers	17-18	74
Using the Distributive Property	19-21	75
Addition through Hundred Thousands	22-25	76-77

CHAPTER 6 PRE-CHAPTER ASSESSMENT

Alternative Assessment Strategies

- Oral administration of the assessment is appropriate for younger students or those whose native language is not English. Read the skills title and directions one section at a time. Check students' understanding by asking them to tell you how they will do the first exercise in the group.

- For some skill types you may wish to use group administration. In this technique, a small group or pair of students complete the assessment together. Through their discussion, you will be able to decide if supplementary reteaching materials are needed.

Intervention Materials

If students are not successful with the prerequisite skills assessed on these pages, reteaching lessons have been created to help them make the transition into the chapter.

Item correlation charts showing the skills lessons suitable for reteaching the prerequisite skills are found beneath the reproductions of each page of the assessment.

Cluster B Challenge

Those students who demonstrate mastery of the skills on this page will not need to use the reteaching worksheets. Instead, these students can do the Cluster B Challenge found on pages 80–81.

USING THE LESSON

Lesson Goal
- Complete multiplication facts.

What the Student Needs to Know
- Use repeated addition to show the meaning of multiplication.
- Add 1-digit numbers to 2-digit numbers.
- Subtract 1-digit numbers from 2-digit numbers.

Getting Started
- Draw a large, blank multiplication table on the board.

Have students take turns coming up to the board and filling in squares in the table.

What Can I Do?
Read the question and the response. Then read and discuss the examples. Ask:

- *Five nines equal 45. How can you use this to find six nines?* (Add one more nine.) *Eight sixes equal 48. How can you use this to find nine sixes?* (Add one more six.)
- Write on the board: 10 sevens = ___?___, 9 sevens = ___?___, 8 sevens = ___?___. Point out that 7 is subtracted each time.

Try It
- Show students the first pattern: five eights is 40, one more eight is 48, so six eights is 48.
- Repeat for the next two problems using the phrases "ten sixes" and "five sevens."

Power Practice
- Have the students complete the practice items. Have them tell how they found each fact.

Multiplication Facts

Learn

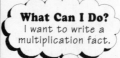
What Can I Do?
I want to write a multiplication fact.

Use a Fact You Know

To find 6 × 9, start with 5 × 9. Add 9.

5 × 9 = 45

45 + 9 = 54 ← 6 × 9

To find 7 × 8, start with 7 × 10. Subtract 7 twice.

7 × 10 = 70

70 − 7 = 63 ← 7 × 9

63 − 7 = 56 ← 7 × 8

Try It • Add or subtract to find the next fact.

1. 5 × 8 = 40

   40 + 8 = ___48___

   6 × 8 = ___48___

2. 6 × 10 = 60

   60 − 6 = ___54___

   6 × 9 = ___54___

3. 7 × 5 = 35

   35 + 7 = ___42___

   7 × 6 = ___42___

Power Practice • Find each product.

4. 4 × 8 = ___32___

5. 7 × 7 = ___49___

6. 9 × 8 = ___72___

7. 9 × 6 = ___54___

8. 8 × 8 = ___64___

9. 6 × 7 = ___42___

10.	11.	12.	13.	14.	15.
7 ×6 = 42	9 ×9 = 81	3 ×7 = 21	6 ×8 = 48	4 ×9 = 36	8 ×7 = 56

© McGraw-Hill School Division

70 Grade 4, Chapter 6, Cluster A

WHAT IF THE STUDENT CAN'T

Use Repeated Addition to Show the Meaning of Multiplication
- Write on the board: 3 × 4. Ask students to show you two addition problems that have the same meaning. They should write 3 + 3 + 3 + 3 and 4 + 4 + 4. If students cannot write the repeated addition problems, they need more work using models of equal groups.

Add 1-Digit Numbers to 2-Digit Numbers
- Use examples such as 56 + 7 to show students how to use the related fact. The reasoning is: 6 + 7 = 13, so 56 + 7 = 63.

Subtract 1-Digit Numbers from 2-Digit Numbers
- Use examples such as 60 − 8 to show students how to use the related fact. The reasoning is:

  10 − 8 = 2, so 60 − 8 = 52.

Complete the Power Practice
- Have students translate problems such as 4 × 8 into two different word forms: four eights, eight fours. The word forms can help students use the addition and subtraction strategies.

Rounding to the Nearest Ten and Hundred

Skill Builder

CHAPTER 6

Learn

What Can I Do?
I want to round to the nearest ten or hundred.

For the Nearest Ten, Use the Ones Digit	For the Nearest Hundred, Use the Tens Digit
8② 2 < 5 82 → 80	4⑦6 7 > 5 476 → 480

Try It · Round each number twice, first to the nearest hundred and then to the nearest ten.

1. 345 __300__ __350__   2. 807 __800__ __810__

3. 182 __200__ __180__   4. 469 __500__ __470__

5. 257 __300__ __260__   6. 836 __800__ __840__

Power Practice · Round each number to the underlined place.

7. 6̲52 __700__   8. 8̲03 __800__   9. 1̲74 __200__

10. 43̲6 __440__   11. 7̲44 __740__   12. 68̲9 __690__

13. 1,5̲38 __1,500__   14. 5,6̲58 __5,700__   15. 8,5̲02 __8,500__

16. 6,52̲6 __6,530__   17. 3,79̲1 __3,790__   18. 5,13̲8 __5,140__

Grade 4, Chapter 6, Cluster A **73**

WHAT IF THE STUDENT CAN'T

Identify the Ones and Tens Digits in a Number

- Use place-value charts and place-value models. Students work in small groups. One student shows a 2-digit or 3-digit number with models; another student write the digits in a place-value chart; a third student writes the standard form for the number.

Identify the Two Multiples of 10 Closest to a Number

- Have students count aloud as a class by tens to 300. Write the numbers in three columns as students count. Give students numbers in this range and have them tell the two closest tens.

Identify the Two Multiples of 100 Closest to a Number

- Have students count aloud by hundreds to 2,000. Write the numbers in two columns on the board.
- Give students numbers up through 2,000 and have them identify the two closest hundreds.

Complete the Power Practice

- Be sure students use the correct digit to decide. They should look at the digit to the right of the underlined digit.

USING THE LESSON

Lesson Goal

- Round to the nearest ten or hundred.

What the Student Needs to Know

- Identify the ones and tens digits in a number.
- Identify the two multiples of 10 closest to a number.
- Identify the two multiples of 100 closest to a number.

Getting Started

- Draw a number line on the board showing the numbers from 260 to 270. Ask: *Which numbers round up to 270?* (265 through 269) *Which numbers round down to 260?* (261 through 264) *Which digit do you use to make your decision when rounding to the nearest ten?* (the ones digit)
- Repeat the questions using a number line with the multiples of ten from 4,500 to 4,600.

What Can I Do?

Read the question. Then read and discuss the examples. If necessary, help students read the > and < symbols. Ask:

- *If you are told to round the number 476, do you know for sure what to do?* (No, you need to know if you should round it to the nearest ten or to the nearest hundred.)

Try It

Do the first exercise with the class. Draw two number lines on the board, one for rounding 345 to the nearest ten; one for rounding it to the nearest hundred. Ask:

- *What are the two tens closest to 345? (340 and 350) What are the two hundreds closest to 345? (300 and 400)* Help students see that they choose between a pair of possible numbers.

Power Practice

- Have the students complete the practice items.

Grade 4, Chapter 6, Cluster A **73**

Lesson Goal
- Multiply 1-digit numbers times 2- and 3-digit numbers.

What the Student Needs to Know
- Complete multiplication facts.
- Identify the ones, tens, and hundreds digits.
- Regroup in multiplication.

Getting Started
- Write these problems on the board:

$$\begin{array}{r} 32 \\ \times\ 4 \\ \hline \end{array} \qquad \begin{array}{r} 32 \\ \times\ 8 \\ \hline \end{array}$$

Ask students to compare the problems. (The top factors are the same; the multipliers are different.)
- Have two volunteers work the problems at the board, explaining their steps as they go. Say:
- *Explain what it means to regroup in this problem.* (The product of the ones digits is 10 or greater, so 1 ten is added to the product of the tens digits.)

What Can I Do?
Read the question and the response. Then read and discuss the example. Ask:
- *Why is regrouping needed when you multiply the ones?* (The product of the ones digit and 4 is 10 or greater.)

Try It
Go over the first step in each exercise, pointing out that regrouping is needed. Ask:
- *What two steps are used when you multiply the tens digit?* (Multiply it by the bottom number; add the number of tens from the regrouping)

Power Practice
- Before students begin, have them look over the exercises and tell you if regrouping is needed. (Regrouping is needed in every exercise.)

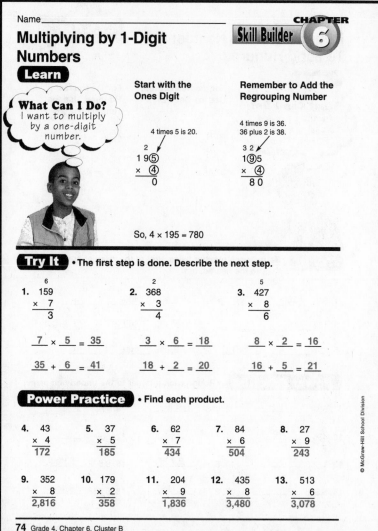

Name_____

Multiplying by 1-Digit Numbers

Learn

What Can I Do? I want to multiply by a one-digit number.

Start with the Ones Digit

4 times 5 is 20.

$$\begin{array}{r} {\scriptstyle 2} \\ 19\text{⑤} \\ \times\ \text{④} \\ \hline 0 \end{array}$$

Remember to Add the Regrouping Number

4 times 9 is 36.
36 plus 2 is 38.

$$\begin{array}{r} {\scriptstyle 3\ 2} \\ 19\text{⑤} \\ \times\ \text{④} \\ \hline 8\ 0 \end{array}$$

So, 4 × 195 = 780

Try It
• The first step is done. Describe the next step.

1. $\begin{array}{r}{\scriptstyle 6}\\159\\ \times\ 7\\ \hline 3\end{array}$ 2. $\begin{array}{r}{\scriptstyle 2}\\368\\ \times\ 3\\ \hline 4\end{array}$ 3. $\begin{array}{r}{\scriptstyle 5}\\427\\ \times\ 8\\ \hline 6\end{array}$

$\underline{\ 7\ } \times \underline{\ 5\ } = \underline{\ 35\ }$ $\underline{\ 3\ } \times \underline{\ 6\ } = \underline{\ 18\ }$ $\underline{\ 8\ } \times \underline{\ 2\ } = \underline{\ 16\ }$

$\underline{\ 35\ } + \underline{\ 6\ } = \underline{\ 41\ }$ $\underline{\ 18\ } + \underline{\ 2\ } = \underline{\ 20\ }$ $\underline{\ 16\ } + \underline{\ 5\ } = \underline{\ 21\ }$

Power Practice
• Find each product.

4. $\begin{array}{r}43\\ \times\ 4\\ \hline 172\end{array}$ 5. $\begin{array}{r}37\\ \times\ 5\\ \hline 185\end{array}$ 6. $\begin{array}{r}62\\ \times\ 7\\ \hline 434\end{array}$ 7. $\begin{array}{r}84\\ \times\ 6\\ \hline 504\end{array}$ 8. $\begin{array}{r}27\\ \times\ 9\\ \hline 243\end{array}$

9. $\begin{array}{r}352\\ \times\ 8\\ \hline 2{,}816\end{array}$ 10. $\begin{array}{r}179\\ \times\ 2\\ \hline 358\end{array}$ 11. $\begin{array}{r}204\\ \times\ 9\\ \hline 1{,}836\end{array}$ 12. $\begin{array}{r}435\\ \times\ 8\\ \hline 3{,}480\end{array}$ 13. $\begin{array}{r}513\\ \times\ 6\\ \hline 3{,}078\end{array}$

WHAT IF THE STUDENT CAN'T

Complete Multiplication Facts
- Post a multiplication fact table. Have each student list those facts he or she is not certain of. Then have students work with partners using flash cards so that students can check their self assessment.

Identify the Ones, Tens, and Hundreds Digits
- Have students write 2- and 3-digit numbers in expanded form and then tell the place names of the digits.

Regroup in Multiplication
- Have students use place-value models to show problems such 3 × 16 and 2 × 39. Students lay out the needed number of groups. Then they model the regrouping process.

Complete the Power Practice
- If students are making errors with basic facts, post a multiplication facts table until they have memorized their facts.
- Check that students are writing the regrouping numbers above the top factor.

Name_____

Using the Distributive Property

Skill Builder CHAPTER **6**

Learn

What Can I Do?
I want to use the Distributive Property for mental math.

Write a Product as a Sum

There are many ways to do this. Examples:

$43 \times \underline{25} = (43 \times \underline{20}) + (43 \times \underline{5})$ ← Think: 25 = 20 + 5

$\underline{43} \times 25 = (\underline{40} \times 25) + (\underline{3} \times 25)$ ← Think: 43 = 40 + 3

Choose a way that helps you use mental math.

$43 \times 25 = (40 \times 25) + (3 \times 25)$
$= (1,000) + (75)$
$= 1,075$

Try It
• Write each product as a sum in two different ways.

1. $58 \times 26 = (58 \times \underline{20}) + (58 \times \underline{6})$

   $58 \times 26 = (\underline{50} \times 26) + (\underline{8} \times 26)$

2. $37 \times 16 = (37 \times \underline{10}) + (37 \times \underline{6})$

   $37 \times 16 = (\underline{30} \times 16) + (\underline{7} \times 16)$

Answers may vary.
Sample answers are given.

Power Practice
• Complete each statement. Use the Distributive Property.

3. $24 \times 53 = (\underline{20} \times 53) + (4 \times 53)$

4. $49 \times 21 = (49 \times 10) + (\underline{49} \times 11)$

5. $52 \times 17 = (50 \times 17) + (2 \times \underline{17})$

6. $95 \times 15 = (95 \times \underline{5}) + (95 \times 10)$

7. $41 \times 68 = (41 \times 60) + (41 \times \underline{8})$

8. $28 \times 55 = (20 \times \underline{55}) + (8 \times 55)$

9. $65 \times 83 = (10 \times 83) + (\underline{55} \times 83)$

10. $63 \times 32 = (\underline{3} \times 32) + (60 \times 32)$

Grade 4, Chapter 6, Cluster B **75**

© McGraw-Hill School Division

WHAT IF THE STUDENT CAN'T

Write a Number as a Sum
• Write a 2-digit number such as 47 on the board. Have students write a sum equal to this number. Point out that an easy sum is the expanded form 40 + 7.
• Have students write the expanded forms for ten more 2-digit numbers.

Use Parentheses to Show Order of Operations
• Remind students to work inside parentheses first. Use an example such as
$(2 \times 3) + (1 \times 4)$.
• Have students work in pairs to create five sample problems that use parentheses.

Use Rectangular Models to Show Products
• Provide graph paper. Have students draw a rectangle with 4 rows and 6 squares in each row. Ask: *How many squares are there in all?* (24 squares) *How does this show the product 4 × 6?* (There are 4 rows of 6; it shows 6 + 6 + 6 + 6.)

Complete the Power Practice
• Emphasize that one factor is not changed—it appears in both parts of the sum. The other factor is broken into two parts.

USING THE LESSON

Lesson Goal
• Use the Distributive Property to write a product as a sum of two other products.

What the Student Needs to Know
• Write a number as a sum.
• Use parentheses to show order of operations.
• Use rectangular models to show products.

Getting Started
• Provide graph paper. Have students draw a rectangle to show the product 2 × 8. Students should draw 2 rows of 8 (or 8 rows of 2). Then ask: *How can you show 8 as a sum?* (Students will give various answers such as 4 + 4 and 3 + 5.)
• On the board show how 2 × 8 equals the sum of two other products. One way is:

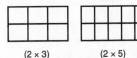

(2 × 3)   (2 × 5)

• Have students draw rectangular models for several other examples of this property.

What Can I Do?
Read the question and the response. Then read and discuss the example.
• *What is another way to show the product 43 × 25 as a sum of two other products?* (Students choose either factor and break it into two parts.)

Try It
• *In the first number sentence, which factor is already there?* (58) *Which factor should you break into a sum?* (26) *How can you write 26 as a sum?* (Many answers are possible. One answer is 20 + 6.)

Power Practice
• Have the students complete the practice items.

Grade 4, Chapter 6, Cluster B **75**

Lesson Goal
- Add whole numbers through 999,999.

What the Student Needs to Know
- Complete addition facts.
- Regroup in an addition problem.
- Read numbers through 999,999.

Getting Started
- Have students write this addition problem in vertical form: four hundred twenty-three thousand, one hundred six plus ten thousand, seven hundred fifty-two.

Students should write:

$$423,106$$
$$+\ 10,752$$

- Watch for students who do not line up the digits properly. The most common error is to write this:

$$423106$$
$$+\ 10752$$

What Can I Do?
Read the question and the response. Then read and discuss the example. Ask:

- *If a student got a sum of over 500,000, what mistake was made?* (The digits were not lined up correctly. The student wrote this:

$$45826$$
$$+\ 134690$$

- *What step will you do first when you add the numbers?* (Add 6 to 0.) *What happens when you add the digits in the tens column?* (The sum is 10 or greater, so you need to regroup.)
- *Do you need to regroup in the hundreds column? Explain why or why not.* (Yes, 8 plus 6 is more than 9. Even if there were no regrouping number from the step before, you would still need to regroup at this step.)

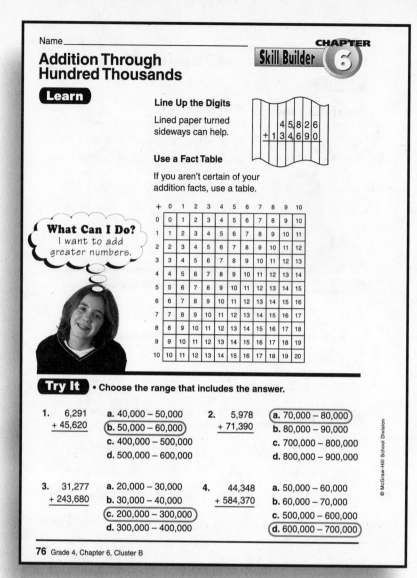

WHAT IF THE STUDENT CAN'T

Complete Addition Facts
- Have students work in pairs using an addition facts table. One student points to a sum in the table; the partner says the fact with that sum.
- Have students work in small groups to share addition fact strategies such as "doubles plus 1." In this strategy, students use a double such as 6 + 6 to find the fact 6 + 7.

Regroup in an Addition Problem
- Provide place-value models. Have students work in pairs adding 2-digit numbers. One student creates a problem; the partner models the sum. Partners confer as needed to carry out any regrouping required in their practice problems.
- Have students work in small groups. One student writes a 2-digit problem that does not require regrouping. Each of the other students must change one digit so that the problem does require regrouping.

Read Numbers Through 999,999
- Have students practice with 5- and 6-digit numbers that end in three zeros such as

Name_____

Finish each addition problem. Remember to regroup.

5.	6.	7.	8.
6,329	4,401	2,875	1,443
+ 45,320	+ 81,760	+ 34,520	+ 63,560
51,649	86,161	37,395	65,003

9.	10.	11.	12.
49,826	37,529	43,108	76,295
+ 267,430	+ 521,360	+ 764,290	+ 331,560
317,256	558,889	807,398	407,855

Power Practice • Find each sum.

13.	14.
23,665	6,325
+ 432,590	+ 42,180
456,255	48,505

15.	16.
42,349	58,917
+ 184,260	+ 603,620
226,609	662,537

17.	18.
4,526	43,294
+ 53,920	+ 735,020
58,446	778,314

19.	20.
37,735	7,103
+ 816,530	+ 77,160
854,265	84,263

21.	22.
46,209	35,872
+ 278,619	+ 409,417
324,828	445,289

Learn with Partners & Parents

Draw the Problem

You and your partner need two sets of 0–9 digit cards.

• Each player makes a game board like this:

• Put the digits cards in a bag. Take turns drawing a card. Write that digit in a box on your game board.

• When all cards have been picked, add your numbers.

• The player with the greater sum gets 1 point. Play until someone has 7 points.

WHAT IF THE STUDENT CAN'T

39,000 and 128,000. Point out that students begin by reading the number before the comma—thirty-nine or one hundred twenty-eight. Then they add the word "thousands."

• When students have mastered saying the word names for these kinds of numbers, have them move on to 5- and 6-digit numbers with no zeros.

Complete the Power Practice

• Make sure that students are beginning at the right in the ones place.

• If students are making errors in basic facts, provide practice with flash cards.

• If students are forgetting to add the regrouping number, have them always write this number above the correct digit in the top addend. You might have them write it with a red pencil for emphasis.

• Remind students to use a comma between the hundreds and thousands digits. This can help students check that they have not omitted a digit in the answer.

Try It

Have students study the first exercise. Ask:

• *What are you to do in the problem?* (Choose one of four possible answers.) *What does each answer show?* (A range of numbers. The – sign means "to" or "through." If necessary, tell students that 2–6 means the numbers 2, 3, 4, 5, and 6.)

• *How many digits will there be in the sum?* (five digits) *Which two answer choices does this eliminate?* (Choices c and d because they have 6-digit numbers.)

• Point out that the answer choice depends on whether or not there is regrouping in the thousands place. If there were no regrouping, the sum would begin with the digit 4. There is regrouping, so the sum will begin with the digit 5.

• Write these problems on the board:

6,291	6,291
+ 45,620	+ 41,620

Ask: *How are these problems different?* (The thousands digits in the bottom numbers are not the same.) *What difference does this make in the sum?* (In the first problem, the sum starts with 5 in the ten thousands place. In the second problem, the sum starts with 4.) Encourage students to do this sort of analysis without actually adding.

Power Practice

• Have the students complete the practice items. For the exercises that are partially done, remind students to go over each exercise to check for regrouping.

Learn with Partners & Parents

• After students have played the game, ask what strategy they discovered. (Possible answer: Put smaller digits in the boxes to the right side of the problem.)

CHALLENGE

Lesson Goal
- Discover patterns in square numbers.

Introducing the Challenge
- Review the vocabulary needed for the lesson by having students use each term in a sentence. Vocabulary used in this lesson includes: *square, diagonal, sum, digit*.

- Provide counters. Have each student make a square array of counters. Students tell you the total number of counters they used. List the numbers on the board.

- Explain that these are called *square numbers*. Each equals the product of a number multiplied by itself.

- Have students write number sentences such as $4 \times 4 = 16$ and describe the parts with the appropriate terms: 16 is a square number, 16 is the square of 4, 4 squared is 16.

CHAPTER 6
CHALLENGE

Square Numbers

To square a number means to multiply it by itself. The square numbers can be drawn as squares. They also form a diagonal in the times table.

16 is a square number.

$4 \times 4 = 16$

○○○○
○○○○
○○○○
○○○○

✗	0	1	2	3	4	5	6	7	8	9	10
0	0	0	0	0	0	0	0	0	0	0	0
1	0	1	2	3	4	5	6	7	8	9	10
2	0	2	4	6	8	10	12	14	16	18	20
3	0	3	6	9	12	15	18	21	24	27	30
4	0	4	8	12	16	20	24	28	32	36	40
5	0	5	10	15	20	25	30	35	40	45	50
6	0	6	12	18	24	30	36	42	48	54	60
7	0	7	14	21	28	35	42	49	56	63	70
8	0	8	16	24	32	40	48	56	64	72	80
9	0	9	18	27	36	45	54	63	72	81	90
10	0	10	20	30	40	50	60	70	80	90	100

Subtract each square number from the next greater square number. Look for the pattern.

0   1   4   9   16   25
  1−0 4−1 9−4 16−9 25−16

1.	2.	3.	4.	5.
1	4	9	16	25
− 0	− 1	− 4	− 9	− 16
1	3	5	7	9

6.	7.	8.	9.	10.
36	49	64	81	100
− 25	− 36	− 49	− 64	− 81
11	13	15	17	19

11. What is the pattern? <u>The differences are the odd numbers.</u>

© McGraw-Hill School Division

Name_____

Use the pattern to find the next ten square numbers. Use the sum of one problem as the top number in the next problem.

12.	100	13.	121	14.	144	15.	169	16.	196
	+ 21		+ 23		+ 25		+ 27		+ 29
	121		144		169		196		225

17.	225	18.	256	19.	289	20.	324	21.	361
	+ 31		+ 33		+ 35		+ 37		+ 39
	256		289		324		361		400

Multiply. Use Problems 12–21 to check your answers.

22.	11	23.	12	24.	13	25.	14	26.	15
	× 11		× 12		× 13		× 14		× 15
	121		144		169		196		225

27.	16	28.	17	29.	18	30.	19	31.	20
	× 16		× 17		× 18		× 19		× 20
	256		289		324		361		400

Square the numbers that end in the digit 5. Look for a pattern to help you.

32.	5	33.	15	34.	25	35.	35	36.	45
	× 5		× 15		× 25		× 35		× 45
	25		225		625		1,225		2,025

37.	55	38.	65	39.	75	40.	85	41.	95
	× 55		× 65		× 75		× 85		× 95
	3,025		4,225		5,625		7,225		9,025

42. What is the pattern? **Possible answer: Multiply the tens digit times the next higher digit. Then write 25 after this product.**

CHALLENGE

Using the Challenge

- Have a volunteer read the top of page 78 aloud. After students have finished this page, have several students describe the pattern they found.

- Challenge students to find ways to display the pattern shown on page 78. For example, they might use a chart with three rows like this:

0	1	4	9	16	25	36	49
	0	1	4	9	16	25	36
	1	3	5	7	9	11	13

- After students have found the pattern for the last set of exercises on page 79, suggest that they make a flow chart to show a method for squaring a number that ends in the digit 5.

- Students may enjoy creating lists of cubic numbers. These equal a factor multiplied by itself three times; for example, $2 \times 2 \times 2 = 8$. While square numbers show the areas of squares, cubic numbers show the volumes of cubes.

CHALLENGE

Lesson Goal
- Identify and apply patterns based on products with repeating digits.

Introducing the Challenge
- Since this lesson involves fairly large numbers, you may want to review reading numbers in the millions.

- Write on the board: 1 × 11, 2 × 11, 3 × 11, 4 × 11. Have students do the multiplication and ask them what pattern is formed. (The multiples of 11: 11, 22, 33, 44, and so on.) Have students continue the pattern through 99.

Name_____

Same-Digit Products

In these problems, the answers use a digit that repeats. Once you find the pattern, you'll be able to write answers without multiplying.

Multiply. Look for patterns.

1. 101	2. 101	3. 101	4. 101	5. 101
× 11	× 22	× 33	× 44	× 55
1,111	2,222	3,333	4,444	5,555

6. 101 × 66 = ___6,666___   7. 101 × 77 = ___7,777___

8. 101 × 88 = ___8,888___   9. 101 × 99 = ___9,999___

10. 37	11. 37	12. 37	13. 37	14. 37
× 3	× 6	× 9	× 12	× 15
111	222	333	444	555

15. 37 × __18__ = 666   16. 37 × __21__ = 777

17. 37 × __24__ = 888   18. 37 × __27__ = 999

19. 10,101	20. 10,101	21. 10,101
× 11	× 22	× 33
111,111	222,222	333,333

22. 10,101 × 44 = ___444,444___

23. 10,101 × 55 = ___555,555___

24. 10,101 × 66 = ___666,666___

25. 10,101 × 77 = ___777,777___

26. 10,101 × 88 = ___888,888___

27. 10,101 × 99 = ___999,999___

80 Grade 4, Chapter 6, Cluster B

Multiply. Look for patterns.

28. 37,037 × 3 111,111	**29.** 37,037 × 6 222,222	**30.** 37,037 × 9 333,333

31. 37,037 × _12_ = 444,444   **32.** 37,037 × _15_ = 555,555

33. 37,037 × _18_ = 666,666   **34.** 37,037 × _21_ = 777,777

35. 37,037 × _24_ = 888,888   **36.** 37,037 × _27_ = 999,999

37. 15,873 × 7 111,111	**38.** 15,873 × 14 222,222	**39.** 15,873 × 21 333,333

40. 15,873 × _28_ = 444,444   **41.** 15,873 × _35_ = 555,555

42. 15,873 × _42_ = 666,666   **43.** 15,873 × _49_ = 777,777

44. 15,873 × _56_ = 888,888   **45.** 15,873 × _63_ = 999,999

46. 12,345,679 × 9 111,111,111	**47.** 12,345,679 × 18 222,222,222	**48.** 12,345,679 × 27 333,333,333

49. 12,345,679 × _36_ = 444,444,444

50. 12,345,679 × _45_ = 555,555,555

51. 12,345,679 × _54_ = 666,666,666

52. 12,345,679 × _63_ = 777,777,777

53. 12,345,679 × _72_ = 888,888,888

54. 12,345,679 × _81_ = 999,999,999

CHALLENGE

Using the Challenge

- Have a volunteer read the directions on page 80 aloud. Have students work the first two exercises. Then ask:
- *What do you notice? What do you think the next answer will be?*
- Have students finish the exercises through number 9. Ask: *How did you use the pattern to help you write the last two or three answers?* (Once students realize the answer has four of the same digits, they can write answers without multiplying. This pattern is based on the fact that the first factor is 101.)
- Have students do exercises 10 and 11. They should notice that the pattern is now three repeating digits.

Place Value

Write the number of hundreds, tens, and ones.

1. 374 = _____ hundreds _____ tens _____ ones

2. 608 = _____ hundreds _____ tens _____ ones

Write the place for each underlined digit.

3. 3<u>8</u>1 _____

4. 19<u>4</u> _____

5. 4,<u>7</u>02 _____

6. 5,2<u>6</u>9 _____

Division Facts

Find each quotient.

7. 35 ÷ 7 = _____

8. 20 ÷ 5 = _____

9. 72 ÷ 8 = _____

10. 36 ÷ 9 = _____

11. 28 ÷ 4 = _____

12. 54 ÷ 6 = _____

Subtracting Whole Numbers

Find each difference.

13. 31
     − 28
     ____

14. 63
     − 56
     ____

15. 52
     − 48
     ____

Name_____

Comparing Money

Compare. Write > or <.

16. $1.19 _____ $1.23   **17.** $0.78 _____ $0.72

Adding Whole Numbers

Find each sum.

18. 9 + 8 + 4 + 6 + 8 = _____

19. 18 + 23 + 17 + 19 + 21 = _____

20. 145 + 172 + 163 = _____

21. 235 + 461 + 378 + 529 = _____

Dividing Whole Numbers and Money

Find each quotient.

22. 84 ÷ 6 = _____

23. 216 ÷ 9 = _____

24. $7\overline{)476}$ **25.** $4\overline{)\$7.04}$

Assessment Goal

This two-page assessment covers skills identified as necessary for success in Chapter 7 Divide by 1-Digit Numbers. The first page assesses the major prerequisite skills for Cluster A. The second page assesses the major prerequisite skills for Cluster B. When the Cluster A and Cluster B prerequisite skills overlap, the skill(s) will be covered in only one section.

Getting Started

- Allow students time to look over the two pages of the assessment. Point out the labels that identify the skills covered.
- Have students find math vocabulary terms used in the assessment. List vocabulary terms on the board as students identify them. If necessary, review the meanings of all essential math vocabulary.

Introducing the Assessment

- Explain to students that these pages will help you know if they are ready to start a new chapter in their math textbooks.
- Students who have transferred from another school may not have been introduced to some of these skills. Encourage students to do their best and assure them you will help them learn any needed skills.

Cluster A Challenge

Those students who demonstrate mastery of the skills on this page will not need to use the reteaching worksheets. Instead, these students can do the Cluster A Challenge found on pages 90–91.

Name _____

Place Value

Write the number of hundreds, tens, and ones.

1. 374 = __3__ hundreds __7__ tens __4__ ones

2. 608 = __6__ hundreds __0__ tens __8__ ones

Write the place for each underlined digit.

3. 3_8_1 ___tens___

4. 19_4_ ___ones___

5. 4,_7_02 ___hundreds___

6. 5,2_6_9 ___tens___

Division Facts

Find each quotient.

7. $35 \div 7 =$ __5__

8. $20 \div 5 =$ __4__

9. $72 \div 8 =$ __9__

10. $36 \div 9 =$ __4__

11. $28 \div 4 =$ __7__

12. $54 \div 6 =$ __9__

Subtracting Whole Numbers

Find each difference.

13.
$$\begin{array}{r} 31 \\ -28 \\ \hline 3 \end{array}$$

14.
$$\begin{array}{r} 63 \\ -56 \\ \hline 7 \end{array}$$

15.
$$\begin{array}{r} 52 \\ -48 \\ \hline 4 \end{array}$$

© McGraw-Hill School Division

81A Use with Grade 4, Chapter 7, Cluster A

CLUSTER A PREREQUISITE SKILLS

The skills listed in this chart are those identified as major prerequisite skills for students' success in the lessons in Cluster A of the chapter. Each skill is covered by one or more assessment items as shown in the middle column. The right column provides the page number for the lessons in this book that reteach the cluster A prerequisite skills.

Skill Name	Assessment Items	Lesson Pages
Place Value	1-6	82-83
Division Facts	7-12	84
Subtracting Whole Numbers	13-15	85

Name_____

Comparing Money

Compare. Write > or <.

16. $1.19 __<__ $1.23   17. $0.78 __>__ $0.72

Adding Whole Numbers

Find each sum.

18. $9 + 8 + 4 + 6 + 8 =$ ____35____

19. $18 + 23 + 17 + 19 + 21 =$ ____98____

20. $145 + 172 + 163 =$ ____480____

21. $235 + 461 + 378 + 529 =$ ____1,603____

Dividing Whole Numbers and Money

Find each quotient.

22. $84 \div 6 =$ ____14____

23. $216 \div 9 =$ ____24____

24. $7\overline{)476}$ 68

25. $4\overline{)\$7.04}$ $1.76

CLUSTER B PREREQUISITE SKILLS

The skills listed in this chart are those identified as major prerequisite skills for students' success in the lessons in Cluster B of the chapter. Each skill is covered by one or more assessment items as shown in the middle column. The right column provides the page numbers for the lessons in this book that reteach the Cluster B prerequisite skills

Skill Name	Assessment Items	Lesson Pages
Comparing Money	16-17	86
Adding Whole Numbers	18-21	87
Dividing Whole Numbes and Money	22-25	88-89

Alternative Assessment Strategies

- Oral administration of the assessment is appropriate for younger students or those whose native language is not English. Read the skills title and directions one section at a time. Check students' understanding by asking them to tell you how they will do the first exercise in the group.

- For some skill types you may wish to use group administration. In this technique, a small group or pair of students complete the assessment together. Through their discussion, you will be able to decide if supplementary reteaching materials are needed.

Intervention Materials

If students are not successful with the prerequisite skills assessed on these pages, reteaching lessons have been created to help them make the transition into the chapter.

Item correlation charts showing the skills lessons suitable for reteaching the prerequisite skills are found beneath the reproductions of each page of the assessment.

Cluster B Challenge

Those students who demonstrate mastery of the skills on this page will not need to use the reteaching worksheets. Instead, these students can do the Cluster B Challenge found on pages 92–93.

USING THE LESSON

Lesson Goal
- Complete expanded forms and identify places of digits.

What the Student Needs to Know
- Identify the digits in a number.
- Use place-value models to show numbers through thousands.
- Use place-value charts to show values of digits.

Getting Started
- Have students work in small groups. Provide place-value models through thousands. One student in each group shows a 4-digit number. Ask:
- *What ten digits are used to make any number?* (0 through 9)
- Draw on the board a place-value chart through thousands:

thousands	hundreds	tens	ones

Have each student copy the chart and write the number he or she has modeled. Point out that the chart shows the place name for each digit.

- *How does the place of a digit change its value?* (A digit in the ones place shows ones, a digit in the tens place shows ten times the digit, a digit in the hundreds place shows one hundred times the digit, and so on.)

What Can I Do?
Read the question and the response. Then read and discuss the examples. Ask:

- *What digits are used in the first number?* (2, 4, and 3) *What is the value of each digit?* (2 hundreds, 4 tens, 3 ones)

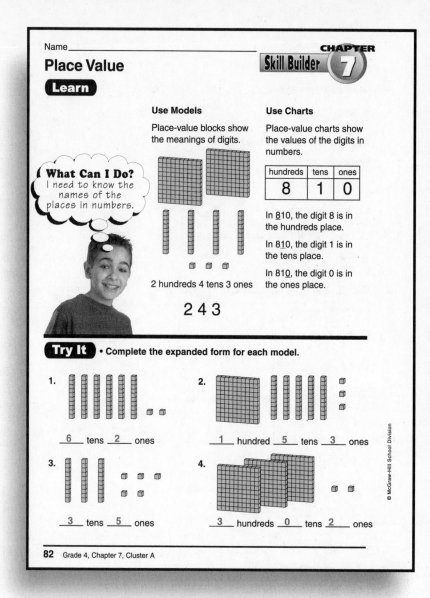

Name_____

Place Value

Skill Builder CHAPTER 7

Learn

Use Models

Place-value blocks show the meanings of digits.

What Can I Do?
I need to know the names of the places in numbers.

2 hundreds 4 tens 3 ones

2 4 3

Use Charts

Place-value charts show the values of the digits in numbers.

hundreds	tens	ones
8	1	0

In 810, the digit 8 is in the hundreds place.

In 810, the digit 1 is in the tens place.

In 810, the digit 0 is in the ones place.

Try It • Complete the expanded form for each model.

1. ___6___ tens ___2___ ones

2. ___1___ hundred ___5___ tens ___3___ ones

3. ___3___ tens ___5___ ones

4. ___3___ hundreds ___0___ tens ___2___ ones

© McGraw-Hill School Division

82 Grade 4, Chapter 7, Cluster A

WHAT IF THE STUDENT CAN'T

Identify the Digits in a Number

- Explain that the numbers 0 through 9 are called digits and they are used to make numbers. Have a student write the ten digits on the board and then make some 2- and 3-digit numbers.
- Provide pairs of students with a set of 0–9 digit cards. Students turn the cards over and mix them up. Each student draws two cards. They make and record two different numbers with the cards. As students write the numbers, ask them to tell you the digits in each number.

Use Place-Value Models to Show Numbers Through Thousands

- Provide place-value models through thousands. Have students pick up one of each type of model and identify it. Show them that ten ones equals one ten, ten tens equals one hundred, and ten hundreds equals one thousand.
- Have students show the number 3,333. Then have them add one tens stick and tell you the new number (3,343). Repeat, having students add or subtract various models and report the new numbers.

Name_____

Write the digit in the ones place.

5. 57 __7__   6. 735 __5__   7. 1,392 __2__

Write the digit in the tens place.

8. 81 __8__   9. 526 __2__   10. 8,405 __0__

Write the digit in the hundreds place.

11. 2,539 __5__   12. 842 __8__   13. 4,106 __1__

Write the digit to answer each question.

14. In 1,426, which digit is in the tens place? __2__

15. In 8,359, which digit is in the ones place? __9__

16. In 2,610, which digit is in the thousands place? __2__

17. In 5,027, which digit is in the hundreds place? __0__

Power Practice • Complete the expanded form for each number.

18. 39 = __3__ tens __9__ ones   19. 51 = __5__ tens __1__ one

20. 60 = __6__ tens __0__ ones   21. 88 = __8__ tens __8__ ones

22. 629 = __6__ hundreds __2__ tens __9__ ones

23. 3,418 = __3__ thousands __4__ hundreds __1__ ten __8__ ones

Write the place for each underlined digit.

24. 3_2_6 __tens__   25. 2,_3_75 __hundreds__   26. 39_7_ __ones__

27. _5_,107 __thousands__   28. 52_1_ __ones__   29. 8_2_ __ones__

30. 81_9_ __ones__   31. _6_04 __hundreds__   32. 6,4_0_8 __tens__

© McGraw-Hill School Division

USING THE LESSON

• Write 243 and 234 on the board. Ask: *How are these numbers the same?* (They both have three digits; they use the same three digits.)

• Ask: *How are the numbers different?* (The digits are not in the same places.) *Compare the values of the digit 4.* (In the first number, it has a value of 4 tens or 40. In the second number, its value is 4 ones.)

• Have students look at the right column at the top of the page. Say: *Read the number in the place-value chart.* (eight hundred ten) *Now show this number with your place-value models.* (8 hundreds squares and 1 tens stick)

Try It

• Provide place-value models for those students who need to model the numbers in the exercises.

• Have a student read the directions on page 82. Check that all students know what to do by asking: *What is an expanded form?* (A way of showing the value of each digit in a number.)

• Before students do exercises 14 through 17 on page 83, check that they have correctly identified the places of the numbers in exercises 5 through 13.

Power Practice

• The last set of exercises has a different format. Ask students to tell you what kind of answer they will write in each blank. (One of the words *ones, tens, hundreds,* or *thousands.*) Then have students complete the practice items.

Learn with Partners & Parents

• Encourage students to use an organized list or make a table to find all the possible 3-digit numbers they can make.

WHAT IF THE STUDENT CAN'T

Use Place-Value Charts to Show Values of Digits

• Students work in pairs. They need two sets of 0–9 digit cards. Have each student copy these three place-value charts:

thousands	hundreds	tens	ones

hundreds	tens	ones

tens	ones

Students turn the digit cards over and mix them up. They take turns drawing cards and writing the digits in their charts. When the charts are complete, students read each number and tell the values of the digits.

Complete the Power Practice

• Students who cannot complete the expanded forms may need more work with place-value models. Have them work in pairs or small groups to show each number with models before they do the exercise.

• For the last group of exercises, have students tell you the ones digit for each number. Repeat with the tens digits and then the hundreds digits.

Lesson Goal

- Complete division facts.

What the Student Needs to Know

- Use counters to show the meaning of division.
- Read a multiplication facts table.
- Use a multiplication fact to write two related division facts.

Getting Started

- Write 32 ÷ 4 on the board. Ask: *What does this mean?* (Divide 32 by 4; divide 32 into 4 equal groups; divide 32 into groups of 4) *What is another way to write this division problem?* (4)$\overline{32}$)
- *Explain your thinking when you do a problem such as 32 ÷ 4.* (Possible strategies: How many times does 4 go into 32? What number times 4 equals 32? How many times can I subtract 4 from 32?)

What Can I Do?

Read the question and the response.

- *If you have not yet memorized the division facts, what can you do?* (Practice using flash cards. Some students may suggest computer software.)
- *Why can you use multiplication to help you do division?* (Multiplication and division are opposite operations. One operation "un-does" the other.)

Try It

- *How can you use the table for exercise 1?* (Find the row with 5 at the left. Go across this row until you get to 20. Look at the top of this column to find the quotient, 4.)

Power Practice

- Have the students complete the practice items. Then review each answer.

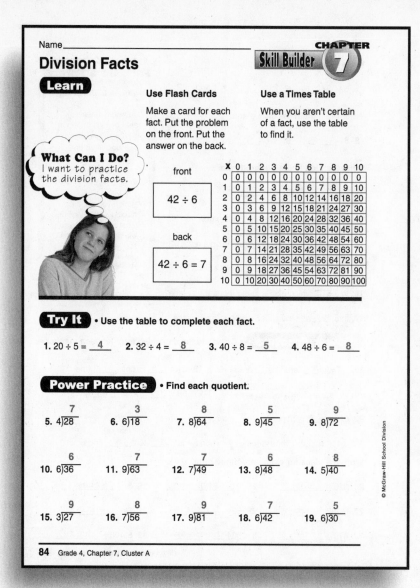

Name_____

Division Facts

Learn

Use Flash Cards
Make a card for each fact. Put the problem on the front. Put the answer on the back.

What Can I Do? I want to practice the division facts.

front
42 ÷ 6

back
42 ÷ 6 = 7

Use a Times Table
When you aren't certain of a fact, use the table to find it.

X	0	1	2	3	4	5	6	7	8	9	10
0	0	0	0	0	0	0	0	0	0	0	0
1	0	1	2	3	4	5	6	7	8	9	10
2	0	2	4	6	8	10	12	14	16	18	20
3	0	3	6	9	12	15	18	21	24	27	30
4	0	4	8	12	16	20	24	28	32	36	40
5	0	5	10	15	20	25	30	35	40	45	50
6	0	6	12	18	24	30	36	42	48	54	60
7	0	7	14	21	28	35	42	49	56	63	70
8	0	8	16	24	32	40	48	56	64	72	80
9	0	9	18	27	36	45	54	63	72	81	90
10	0	10	20	30	40	50	60	70	80	90	100

Try It • Use the table to complete each fact.

1. 20 ÷ 5 = __4__   2. 32 ÷ 4 = __8__   3. 40 ÷ 8 = __5__   4. 48 ÷ 6 = __8__

Power Practice • Find each quotient.

5. 4)$\overline{28}$ — 7
6. 6)$\overline{18}$ — 3
7. 8)$\overline{64}$ — 8
8. 9)$\overline{45}$ — 5
9. 8)$\overline{72}$ — 9

10. 6)$\overline{36}$ — 6
11. 9)$\overline{63}$ — 7
12. 7)$\overline{49}$ — 7
13. 8)$\overline{48}$ — 6
14. 5)$\overline{40}$ — 8

15. 3)$\overline{27}$ — 9
16. 7)$\overline{56}$ — 8
17. 9)$\overline{81}$ — 9
18. 6)$\overline{42}$ — 7
19. 6)$\overline{30}$ — 5

84   Grade 4, Chapter 7, Cluster A

© McGraw-Hill School Division

WHAT IF THE STUDENT CAN'T

Use Counters to Show the Meaning of Division

- Provide pairs of students with 50 counters. One student takes a handful of counters; the partner divides them into 2 equal groups. Students record their work using the ÷ symbol. Repeat using divisors of 3 and 4.

Read a Multiplication Facts Table

- Provide blank multiplication facts tables. Students color a partial row and column for a fact such as 4 × 3. They color the 4-row across to the 12; color the 3-column down to the 12. Repeat with several other facts.

Use a Multiplication Fact to Write Two Related Division Facts

- Write 5 × 6 on the board. Have a volunteer come up and draw a model for the fact. Use the model to write and explain two division facts: 30 ÷ 5 = 6, 30 ÷ 6 = 5.

Complete the Power Practice

- Have students work in pairs using division flash cards to identify which facts they still need to memorize.

Subtracting Whole Numbers

Skill Builder CHAPTER **7**

Learn

What Can I Do?
I want to subtract two-digit numbers.

Start With the Ones
Always begin at the right with the ones digits.

tens	ones
8	5
−8	1
	4

Rename If You Need To

tens	ones
4 5	12 2
−4	8
	4

→ Start here.

Try It • Tell how to rename the top number. Do not subtract.

1. 41 → __3__ tens __11__ ones
   −36

2. 33 → __2__ tens __13__ ones
   −27

3. 25 → __1__ ten __15__ ones
   −16

4. 62 → __5__ tens __12__ ones
   −56

Power Practice • Find each difference.

5. 31
    −25
    ___6___

6. 53
    −48
    ___5___

7. 42
    −36
    ___6___

8. 23
    −15
    ___8___

9. 62
    −54
    ___8___

10. 24
    −18
    ___6___

11. 44
    −35
    ___9___

12. 81
    −72
    ___9___

13. 70
    −64
    ___6___

14. 31
    −24
    ___7___

15. 25
    −16
    ___9___

16. 72
    −63
    ___9___

WHAT IF THE STUDENT CAN'T

Complete Subtraction Facts
• Provide flash cards and addition tables. Students work in pairs to identify the facts they do not know. They color boxes on the addition table to show those facts.

Rename in a Subtraction Problem
• Provide place-value models. Have students show problems such as 42 − 18 in which renaming must be done. Students lay out 4 tens and 2 ones. They cannot take away 8 ones, so they "make a trade" to change 1 ten for 10 ones.

• Students work in pairs, one modeling a problem and the other recording the steps.

Complete the Power Practice
• Remind students that they cannot subtract a greater number from a lesser number. Have them choose an exercise on the page and explain how this error might occur.

USING THE LESSON

Lesson Goal
• Subtract 2-digit numbers.

What the Student Needs to Know
• Complete subtraction facts.
• Rename in a subtraction problem.

Getting Started
• Write these problems on the board:

    63   63
   − 21   − 27

   Ask: *What is different about the problems?* (The number subtracted is not the same.)

• *Will the tens digits of the answers be the same? Why or why not?* (No; in the right problem you will need to rename the top number as 5 tens and 13 ones. When you subtract the tens, the answer will be 3 tens instead of 4 tens.)

What Can I Do?
Read the question and the response. Then read and discuss the examples. Ask:

• *What are the ones digits in the first example? (5, 1) the tens digit? (8, 8) Why do you always start with the ones digits?* (You may need to rename. If you do, the tens digits may be different.)

• *Why are some digits crossed out in the second example?* (This shows the renaming. You can't subtract 8 from 2, so you must rename the top number as 4 tens and 12 ones.)

Try It
Do the first exercise with the students. Point out that 41 equals 4 tens and 1 one, but that is *not* the answer to this problem. If necessary, do the rest of the Try It exercises with the class.

Power Practice
• Have the students complete the practice items.

USING THE LESSON

Lesson Goal
- Compare amounts of money through $9.99.

What the Student Needs to Know
- Tell the meanings of the digits in an amount of money.
- Write amounts less than one dollar in two different ways.
- Use the > and < symbols.

Getting Started
- Dictate these amounts and have students write them using dollar signs and decimal points: four dollars and twenty-three cents, two dollars and thirty cents, six dollars and four cents. ($4.23, $2.30, $6.04) Check that students have included decimal points and have the zeros in the correct places.
- Have students write each of these amounts in two ways: fifty-six cents, eighty cents, nine cents. (56¢, $0.56; 80¢, $0.80; 9¢, $0.09)

What Can I Do?
Read the question and the response. Then read and discuss the examples. Ask:
- *Where do you begin when comparing two amounts of money?* (At the left side; if these digits are the same, compare the next digits.)
- Write the symbols > and < on the board. Ask: *What do these symbols mean?* (greater than, less than) *How do you remember which symbol is which?* (Accept all strategies students suggest.)

Try It
- Have students read the first direction and look at the four exercises. Ask: *In which exercise are the dollars digits different?* (exercise 3) *In which exercise are both the dollars digits and the dimes digits the same?* (exercise 2)

Power Practice
- Have the students complete the practice items.

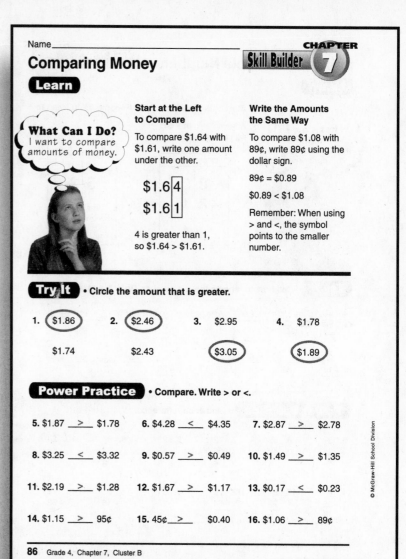

86 Grade 4, Chapter 7, Cluster B

WHAT IF THE STUDENT CAN'T

Tell the Meanings of the Digits in an Amount of Money
- Provide play money for dollars, dimes, and pennies. Students work in pairs. One student puts out an amount of money; the partner writes the total using a dollar sign and decimal point.

Write Amounts Less Than One Dollar in Two Different Ways
- Students work in pairs. One writes ten amounts less than one dollar using the cent sign. The other student writes ten amounts less than one dollar using a dollar sign and decimal point. Students exchange papers and write each amount using the other notation.

Use the > and < Symbols
- Provide pairs of students with a set of 0–9 digit cards and two cards showing the < and > symbols. Students take turns making true number sentences with the cards.

Complete the Power Practice
- Two students work together. They roll a 1–6 number cube three times and make two different money amounts with the resulting digits. They compare the amounts. Have play money available.

Adding Whole Numbers

Learn

Use Ruled Paper

Turn the paper sideways. Write the digits in the correct columns.

Add Each Column

Start at the top. Say the sums to yourself as you add.

What Can I Do? I want to add a list of numbers.

Not Correct

```
  8 9
  1 0 2
+ 7 3
```

Correct

```
    8 9
  1 0 2
+   7 3
```

```
   8 9
 1 0 2
+  7 3
```

— 9 plus 2 is 11.
  11 plus 3 is 14.
— 1 plus 8 is 9.
  9 plus 7 is 16.
— 1 plus 1 is 2.

So the sum is 264. To check, add the columns starting at the bottom.

Try It • Find each sum.

1.	2.	3.	4.	5.	6.
8	4	35	61	348	604
3	12	18	107	49	317
+5	+6	+7	+15	+217	85
16	22	60	183	614	+182
					1,188

Power Practice • Find each sum.

7. $3 + 8 + 7 + 6 + 2 = $ __26__

8. $5 + 1 + 7 + 3 + 1 + 6 + 9 = $ __32__

9. $18 + 9 + 15 + 11 + 8 + 12 = $ __73__

10. $9 + 11 + 8 + 12 + 10 + 8 = $ __58__

11. $23 + 45 + 81 + 65 = $ __214__

12. $56 + 87 + 102 + 93 = $ __338__

13. $91 + 8 + 205 + 47 + 188 = $ __539__

14. $81 + 65 + 46 + 115 + 90 = $ __397__

Grade 4, Chapter 7, Cluster B **87**

WHAT IF THE STUDENT CAN'T

Complete Addition Facts

- Students work in pairs using two sets of 0–9 digit cards. Students turn the cards over and mix them up. Each student draws two cards and says the addition fact.

Add Three 1-Digit Numbers

- Have students add triples that include either 1 or 2; for example, $6 + 2 + 7$, $1 + 4 + 7$. Students first add the two greater numbers; then they add the 1 or the 2.

Regroup in an Addition Problem

- When students add columns of numbers, have them (a) always start at the top of each column and (b) begin by adding the regrouping number to the top digit.

Complete the Power Practice

- Students work in pairs and use lined paper turned sideways. They each write the addends in vertical form, then compare problems before adding. One student adds a column aloud while the partner listens for errors.

USING THE LESSON

Lesson Goal

- Add three or more numbers.

What the Student Needs to Know

- Complete addition facts.
- Add three 1-digit numbers.
- Regroup in an addition problem.

Getting Started

- Dictate these numbers and have students write them as a vertical addition problem: 18, 26, 4, 107, 32. Watch to see if all students line up the digits correctly.

- Ask: *What is the ones digit in each number?* (8, 6, 4, 7, 2) *Why is it important that these digits be lined up?* (Adding these digits is the first step in the problem.)

What Can I Do?

Read the question and the response. Then read and discuss the example. Ask:

- *Where do you begin when adding these numbers?* (At the right with the ones digits.)
- *What are three ways to add the digits in the ones column?* ($9 + 5$, $2 + 12$, $3 + 11$) *Which way is easiest for you?* (Students share opinions.)

Try It

- Have two students do exercise 1 orally. One student starts at the top; the other starts at the bottom.
- Ask: *How can you check the sum of each column?* (If you started at the top to add, start at the bottom to check.)

Power Practice

- Have students look over the exercises. Ask: *What is different about these exercises from those you just did?* (The addends are written across.) *How will you make sure you have the digits in the correct columns?* (Have students share strategies.)

Lesson Goal
- Divide 2- and 3-digit numbers by 1-digit numbers.

What the Student Needs to Know
- Complete multiplication and division facts.
- Subtract 1- and 2-digit numbers.
- Use a dollar sign and decimal point to write an amount of money.

Getting Started
- Have a volunteer write any multiplication fact on the board. Ask: *How can you use this fact to write two division facts?* Have two different students write the division facts. Repeat with several more multiplication facts until you are confident students know the relationship between multiplication and division.
- Write $24 \div 6 = 4$ on the board. Ask: *How can you write this problem in a different way?* (Students should suggest using the $\overline{)}$ notation.) Identify the parts of the division problem: divisor, dividend, quotient, and remainder. In this problem, the remainder is zero.
- Write $6\overline{)29}$ on the board. Ask: *How is this problem different from 24 divided by 6?* (The dividend is 29 and not 24; the remainder will not be zero.) Have a student show how to work the problem on the board. Point out that the quotient is written above the 9 and *not* above the 2.

What Can I Do?
- Read the question and the response. Then read and discuss the examples. Have students identify the divisor, the dividend, and the quotient. Ask: *Is there a remainder when you divide 847 by 7?* (The remainder is zero.)
- At the board, demonstrate for students how to do the steps in 847 divided by 7. As you write, ask students questions such as *What should I do next? What numbers do I multiply? How do I know I have the right digit in the quotient?*

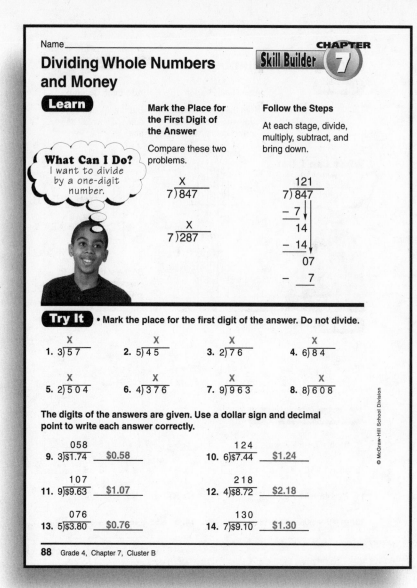

Dividing Whole Numbers and Money

Skill Builder **CHAPTER 7**

Learn

What Can I Do? I want to divide by a one-digit number.

Mark the Place for the First Digit of the Answer

Compare these two problems.

$$7\overline{)847}$$

$$7\overline{)287}$$

Follow the Steps

At each stage, divide, multiply, subtract, and bring down.

$$
\begin{array}{r}
121 \\
7\overline{)847} \\
-7 \\
\hline
14 \\
-14 \\
\hline
07 \\
-7 \\
\hline
\end{array}
$$

Try It • Mark the place for the first digit of the answer. Do not divide.

1. $3\overline{)57}$ 2. $5\overline{)45}$ 3. $2\overline{)76}$ 4. $6\overline{)84}$

5. $2\overline{)504}$ 6. $4\overline{)376}$ 7. $9\overline{)963}$ 8. $8\overline{)608}$

The digits of the answers are given. Use a dollar sign and decimal point to write each answer correctly.

9. $\overset{058}{3\overline{)\$1.74}}$ ___\$0.58___   10. $\overset{124}{6\overline{)\$7.44}}$ ___\$1.24___

11. $\overset{107}{9\overline{)\$9.63}}$ ___\$1.07___   12. $\overset{218}{4\overline{)\$8.72}}$ ___\$2.18___

13. $\overset{076}{5\overline{)\$3.80}}$ ___\$0.76___   14. $\overset{130}{7\overline{)\$9.10}}$ ___\$1.30___

WHAT IF THE STUDENT CAN'T

Complete Multiplication and Division Facts
- Have students work in pairs using multiplication flash cards to identify any unknown facts. Have each student write a short story problem for each unknown fact.
- Provide small groups with multiplication fact tables. One student points to a number in the table. Other students tell two multiplication facts with that product and then tell the two related division facts.

Subtract 1- and 2-Digit Numbers
- Students work in pairs using subtraction flash cards to practice their subtraction facts.
- Have students work in small groups. One student says a subtraction fact. Each of the other students creates a related problem that uses the fact. They do this by changing the tens digit of the first number in the fact. For example, if the first student says $15 - 7 = 8$, the other students can write $25 - 7$, $35 - 7$, and so on.

Name_____

Power Practice • Find each quotient.

	12		25		14
15. 8)96		16. 3)75		17. 7)98	

	17		12		14
18. 4)68		19. 6)72		20. 5)70	

	147		97		219
21. 6)882		22. 2)194		23. 4)876	

	56		266		82
24. 9)504		25. 3)798		26. 7)574	

	85		137		140
27. 3)255		28. 5)685		29. 6)840	

	$0.63		$1.18		$2.07		$3.69
30. 8)$5.04		31. 7)$8.26		32. 4)$8.28		33. 2)$7.38	

© McGraw-Hill School Division

Learn with Partners & Parents

Divvy Up!

Practice dividing by one-digit numbers with a partner. You need one set of digit cards with the digits 0 through 9.

- Turn the cards face-down and mix them up.
- Each partner picks 3 cards.
- Make a division problem with your cards. Divide a one-digit number into a two-digit number.
- Find the answer to your partner's division problem.
- The first player who gets the correct answer scores one point.
- Solve the division problems with paper and pencil first. When you get better at dividing, try to find the answers using mental math.
- For a more difficult game, each partner uses 4 cards to divide a one-digit number into a three-digit number.

WHAT IF THE STUDENT CAN'T

Use a Dollar Sign and Decimal Point to Write an Amount of Money

- Provide play money. Have students work in groups of three. One student lays out an amount of money; another student counts the money; the third student writes the total using a dollar sign and decimal point.

- Have students use newspapers or other advertisements that include many prices. Students work in pairs. One reads a money amount; the partner writes it using a dollar sign and decimal point.

Complete the Power Practice

- Provide more practice with problems that have 1-digit quotients; for example, 35 ÷ 8. Have students first identify the closest division fact. Model for students how to use the fact; for example: *The closest fact to 35 ÷ 8 is 32 ÷ 8. Since 32 ÷ 8 is 4, I will use 4 as the quotient in 35 ÷ 8.*

- Students having extreme difficulties may need to work through some problems with place-value models. Use examples with two-digit dividends and small divisors.

USING THE LESSON

Try It

Have a volunteer read the first direction. Ask:

- *How will you answer each exercise?* (Mark an X over the correct digit in the quotient.)

- *Explain how you will do the first exercise.* (The divisor 3 is less than 5, the first digit in the dividend. So, make an X over the digit 5 in the dividend.)

- On the board draw 15 dimes. Ask: *How much money is this?* (a dollar fifty) *How do you write this amount?* ($1.50) *If you divide this into 3 equal groups, how much will be in each group?* (fifty cents)

- Have a student read the direction for the second group of Try It exercises. Ask: *When you divide money, what kind of answer do you get?* (an amount of money)

- Point out that when the first number in the dividend is less than the 1-digit divisor, you write a zero in the quotient above that digit.

- Remind students to put the decimal in the quotient directly above the decimal point in the dividend.

Power Practice

- Before students begin, ask: *How is the last row of exercises different?* (You are dividing money.) *How will you write these answers?* (Use a dollar sign and decimal point.)

Learn with Partners & Parents

- Decide whether you wish students to practice with 2-digit or 3-digit dividends. One option is for them to alternate.

CHALLENGE

Lesson Goal
- Use mental math to double or halve numbers.

Introducing the Challenge
- Review the vocabulary needed for the lesson by having students use each term in a sentence. Vocabulary used in this lesson includes: double a number, halve a number, odd number.

- Have students count by 2s to 20. Say: *Now multiply each of these numbers by 2: 8, 4, 3, 9, 5, 7, 6. Repeat the exercise using two-digit numbers. Encourage the students to use mental math.*

- Introduce halving numbers with this problem: *If you and a friend are sharing 7 apples, how many apples do each of you get? ($3\frac{1}{2}$ apples) If necessary, draw 7 circles on the board to illustrate dividing the 7 apples into 2 equal groups.*

Name_____

Doubling and Halving

The ability to double numbers or divide them in half is a useful mental math skill. With some practice you should be able to do this quickly and accurately.

Use mental math to double each number. Each group of problems is more difficult than the one before it.

Set A
1. 4 __8__   2. 8 __16__   3. 3 __6__   4. 6 __12__

5. 30 __60__   6. 50 __100__   7. 20 __40__   8. 40 __80__

9. 200 __400__   10. 400 __800__   11. 100 __200__   12. 300 __600__

Set B
13. 14 __28__   14. 22 __44__   15. 13 __26__   16. 31 __62__

17. 42 __84__   18. 12 __24__   19. 33 __66__   20. 21 __42__

21. 34 __68__   22. 23 __46__   23. 41 __82__   24. 32 __64__

Set C
25. 45 __90__   26. 25 __50__   27. 65 __130__   28. 15 __30__

29. 85 __170__   30. 35 __70__   31. 75 __150__   32. 55 __110__

33. 125 __250__   34. 205 __410__   35. 350 __700__   36. 145 __290__

Set D
37. 17 __34__   38. 37 __74__   39. 19 __38__   40. 29 __58__

41. 18 __36__   42. 27 __54__   43. 36 __72__   44. 16 __32__

45. 26 __52__   46. 56 __112__   47. 47 __94__   48. 28 __56__

© McGraw-Hill School Division

Name_____

Now practice halving numbers. To halve a number, divide it by 2.
Odd numbers will have fractional answers.
For example, one-half of 7 equals $3\frac{1}{2}$.

Use mental math to halve each number. Each group of problems is more difficult than the one before it.

Set E

49. 20 _10_   50. 8 _4_   51. 16 _8_   52. 24 _12_

53. 14 _7_   54. 22 _11_   55. 40 _20_   56. 10 _5_

57. 6 _3_   58. 60 _30_   59. 12 _6_   60. 80 _40_

Set F

61. 5 _$2\frac{1}{2}$_   62. 9 _$4\frac{1}{2}$_   63. 3 _$1\frac{1}{2}$_   64. 19 _$9\frac{1}{2}$_

65. 15 _$7\frac{1}{2}$_   66. 23 _$11\frac{1}{2}$_   67. 7 _$3\frac{1}{2}$_   68. 13 _$6\frac{1}{2}$_

69. 27 _$13\frac{1}{2}$_   70. 11 _$5\frac{1}{2}$_   71. 25 _$12\frac{1}{2}$_   72. 29 _$14\frac{1}{2}$_

Set G

73. 64 _32_   74. 108 _54_   75. 44 _22_   76. 86 _43_

77. 84 _42_   78. 42 _21_   79. 102 _51_   80. 62 _31_

81. 48 _24_   82. 68 _34_   83. 82 _41_   84. 46 _23_

Set H

85. 34 _17_   86. 74 _37_   87. 56 _28_   88. 36 _18_

89. 78 _39_   90. 52 _26_   91. 32 _16_   92. 76 _38_

93. 54 _27_   94. 38 _19_   95. 72 _36_   96. 58 _29_

© McGraw-Hill School Division

CHALLENGE

Using the Challenge

- Have one student read the directions for page 90 and another student read the directions for page 91. Check that students know what to do by asking:

- *What are you supposed to do on page 90?* (Multiply each number by 2.) *What are you supposed to do on page 91?* (Divide each number by 2.)

- For Set F, you may want to suggest a strategy. Divide the whole numer by 2. There will be a remainder of 1. Add half the remainder ($\frac{1}{2}$) to the quotient you got by dividing by 2.

- Here is a supplementary activity you can use to reinforce the ideas in this lesson. Have students work in pairs. They write the numbers from 1 through 40 on slips of paper or index cards. They turn the cards over and mix them up. Students take turns drawing a number. If the number is even, students double it. If the number is odd, students halve it.

CHALLENGE

Lesson Goal
• Solving problems using a formula to find speed.

Introducing the Challenge
• Review the vocabulary needed for the lesson by having students use each term in a sentence. Vocabulary used in this lesson includes: distance, time, speed, unit of measure, mile, yard, square yards, square feet, centimeter, meter, kilometer, hour, second, minute.

• Have two students walk across the classroom. One student walks quickly; the other walks slowly. Divide the class in half and have students time the walks in seconds. Ask:

• *What is different about the two walks? (One is faster than the other.) What word is used to describe how quickly something moves? (speed) How can you find the speed at which each person walked? (Accept all suggestions.)*

• After students have done the lesson, you may wish to have them find the speeds of the two walkers in feet per second. To do this, students will need to measure the distance walked in feet.

Speed

Speed is a measure of how fast something moves. To describe speed, you need two measures. Usually the measures are distance and time.

If you divide distance in miles by time in hours, you will get speed in miles per hour.

Find each speed in miles per hour.

1. Mark hiked 12 miles in 2 hours. ____6____ miles per hour

2. Sasha drove 60 miles in 3 hours. ____20____ miles per hour

3. Yvonne walked 8 miles in 4 hours. ____2____ miles per hour

4. Jorge bicycled 15 miles in 3 hours. ____5____ miles per hour

Divide distance by time to find speed. Label the answers with the correct units of measure.

5. Arturo drove 40 kilometers in 2 hours.

____20 kilometers per hour____

6. The plant grew 6 centimeters in 2 days.

____3 centimeters per day____

7. The rocket traveled 600 miles in 3 seconds.

____200 miles per second____

8. Susan read 60 pages of a book in 3 hours.

____20 pages per hour____

9. Harry planted 16 square yards of his garden in 4 hours.

____4 square yards per hour____

10. A factory machine filled 27 boxes in 9 minutes.

____3 boxes per minute____

Name_____

Match each object in Column A with the object in Column B that is moving at the same speed.

<u>B</u> **11.** 30 miles in 2 hours

<u>G</u> **12.** 4 meters per second

<u>E</u> **13.** 20 kilometers per hour

<u>J</u> **14.** 10 yards per minute

<u>A</u> **15.** 10 miles in 2 hours

<u>I</u> **16.** 18 centimeters in 4 seconds

<u>D</u> **17.** 500 yards in 5 days

<u>F</u> **18.** 33 centimeters in 3 minutes

<u>C</u> **19.** 90 kilometers in 3 hours

<u>H</u> **20.** 30 meters in 5 seconds

A. 15 miles in 3 hours

B. 15 miles per hour

C. 60 kilometers in 2 hours

D. 300 yards in 3 days

E. 60 kilometers in 3 hours

F. 55 centimeters in 5 minutes

G. 20 meters in 5 seconds

H. 24 meters in 4 seconds

I. 9 centimeters in 2 seconds

J. 40 yards in 4 minutes

Use what you have learned about speed to solve these problems.

21. Peggy walked 10 miles in 2 hours. If her sister Janice walks at the same speed, how long will it take Janice to walk 15 miles?

<u>   3 hours   </u>

22. Bart painted 120 square feet in 10 minutes. If his friend Marcy works at the same speed, how many square feet can she paint in 20 minutes?

<u>   240 square feet   </u>

23. Hal drove 120 miles in 4 hours to a nearby town. If he drives home in 3 hours, what was his average speed on the trip home?

<u>   40 miles per hour   </u>

24. A factory machine filled 120 bottles in 4 minutes. If a newer machine can fill 200 bottles in the same time, what is the speed of the newer machine?

<u>   50 bottles per minute   </u>

CHALLENGE

Using the Challenge

- Have a volunteer read the top of page 92 and the first directions aloud. After students have completed this page, ask:

- *If the distance is in miles and the time is in minutes, what are the units for speed?* (miles per minute) *What does the word "per" mean?* (in one unit of time; miles per minute means the number of miles covered in 1 minute)

- Have a student read the directions at the top of page 93. Ask students to explain how they will do the first problem. (One strategy is to change 30 miles in 2 hours to the equivalent 15 miles per hour, and then look in the right column for 15 miles per hour.) You may want to suggest that students simplify all the speeds to the smallest unit of time before they do the matching.

- In the matching problems, students may need to use elimination. Point out that they do not have to do the problems in order. They can look for the easiest problems and do them first.

- After students have finished the lesson, they may enjoy finding out how fast they can do various tasks. Provide pairs or groups of students with watches with second hands. When the data have been collected, students can make a class bulletin board showing the speeds they've computed.

Name_____

Dividing by 1-Digit Numbers

Find each quotient.

1. 35 ÷ 7 = _____   **2.** 30 ÷ 4 = _____   **3.** 41 ÷ 8 = _____

4. 24 ÷ 9 = _____   **5.** 36 ÷ 6 = _____   **6.** 19 ÷ 5 = _____

Subtracting Whole Numbers

Find each difference.

7.   73
       − 69
      _____

8.   342
       − 336
      _____

Multiplying Whole Numbers

Find each product.

9.   46
       × 3
      _____

10.   21
        × 6
       _____

Round to the Nearest Ten

Round each number to the nearest ten.

11. 83 _____   **12.** 348 _____   **13.** 6,795 _____

Comparing Whole Numbers

Compare. Use > or <.

14. 48 _____ 54   **15.** 326 _____ 318

Name_____

Multiplication and Division Facts

Find each product or quotient.

16. $4 \times 7 =$ _____

17. $35 \div 5 =$ _____

18. $54 \div 6 =$ _____

19. $7 \times 9 =$ _____

Addition and Subtraction

Find each sum or difference.

20. $25 - 9 =$ _____

21. $14 + 8 =$ _____

22. $7 + 32 =$ _____

23. $19 - 7 =$ _____

Expressions with Parentheses

Find the value of each expression.

24. $3 + (2 \times 8)$ _____

25. $(12 - 4) \div 2$ _____

CHAPTER 8 PRE-CHAPTER ASSESSMENT

Assessment Goal

This two-page assessment covers skills identified as necessary for success in Chapter 8 Divide by 2-Digit Numbers. The first page assesses the major prerequisite skills for Cluster A. The second page assesses the major prerequisite skills for Cluster B. When the Cluster A and Cluster B prerequisite skills overlap, the skill(s) will be covered in only one section.

Getting Started

- Allow students time to look over the two pages of the assessment. Point out the labels that identify the skills covered.

- Have students find math vocabulary terms used in the assessment. List vocabulary terms on the board as students identify them. If necessary, review the meanings of all essential math vocabulary.

Introducing the Assessment

- Explain to students that these pages will help you know if they are ready to start a new chapter in their math textbooks.

- Students who have transferred from another school may not have been introduced to some of these skills. Encourage students to do their best and assure them you will help them learn any needed skills.

Cluster A Challenge

Those students who demonstrate mastery of the skills on this page will not need to use the reteaching worksheets. Instead, these students can do the Cluster A Challenge found on pages 104–105.

Name_____

Dividing by 1-Digit Numbers

Find each quotient.

1. $35 \div 7 =$ __5__   2. $30 \div 4 =$ __7 R2__   3. $41 \div 8 =$ __5 R1__

4. $24 \div 9 =$ __2 R6__   5. $36 \div 6 =$ __6__   6. $19 \div 5 =$ __3 R4__

Subtracting Whole Numbers

Find each difference.

7. 73
   − 69
   ‾‾‾‾
    4

8. 342
   − 336
   ‾‾‾‾
     6

Multiplying Whole Numbers

Find each product.

9. 46
   × 3
   ‾‾‾
   138

10. 21
    × 6
    ‾‾‾
    126

Round to the Nearest Ten

Round each number to the nearest ten.

11. 83 __80__   12. 348 __350__   13. 6,795 __6,800__

Comparing Whole Numbers

Compare. Use > or <.

14. 48 __<__ 54   15. 326 __>__ 318

CLUSTER A PREREQUISITE SKILLS

The skills listed in this chart are those identified as major prerequisite skills for students' success in the lessons in Cluster A of the chapter. Each skill is covered by one or more assessment items as shown in the middle column. The right column provides the page number for the lessons in this book that reteach the cluster A prerequisite skills.

Skill Name	Assessment Items	Lesson Pages
Dividing by 1-Digit Numbers	1-6	94-95
Subtracting Whole Numbers	7-8	96
Multiplying Whole Numbers	9-10	97
Round to the Nearest Ten	11-13	98
Comparing Whole Numbers	14-15	99

Name _____

Multiplication and Division Facts

Find each product or quotient.

16. $4 \times 7 =$ ___28___   **17.** $35 \div 5 =$ ___7___

18. $54 \div 6 =$ ___9___   **19.** $7 \times 9 =$ ___63___

Addition and Subtraction

Find each sum or difference.

20. $25 - 9 =$ ___16___   **21.** $14 + 8 =$ ___22___

22. $7 + 32 =$ ___39___   **23.** $19 - 7 =$ ___12___

Expressions with Parentheses

Find the value of each expression.

24. $3 + (2 \times 8)$ ___19___   **25.** $(12 - 4) \div 2$ ___4___

Use with Grade 4, Chapter 8, Cluster B **93B**

CLUSTER B PREREQUISITE SKILLS

The skills listed in this chart are those identified as major prerequisite skills for students' success in the lessons in Cluster B of the chapter. Each skill is covered by one or more assessment items as shown in the middle column. The right column provides the page numbers for the lessons in this book that reteach the Cluster B prerequisite skills

Skill Name	Assessment Items	Lesson Pages
Multiplication and Division Facts	16-19	100
Addition and Subtraction	20-23	101
Expressions with Parentheses	24-25	102-103

Alternative Assessment Strategies

- Oral administration of the assessment is appropriate for younger students or those whose native language is not English. Read the skills title and directions one section at a time. Check students' understanding by asking them to tell you how they will do the first exercise in the group.

- For some skill types you may wish to use group administration. In this technique, a small group or pair of students complete the assessment together. Through their discussion, you will be able to decide if supplementary reteaching materials are needed.

Intervention Materials

If students are not successful with the prerequisite skills assessed on these pages, reteaching lessons have been created to help them make the transition into the chapter.

Item correlation charts showing the skills lessons suitable for reteaching the prerequisite skills are found beneath the reproductions of each page of the assessment.

Cluster B Challenge

Those students who demonstrate mastery of the skills on this page will not need to use the reteaching worksheets. Instead, these students can do the Cluster B Challenge found on pages 106–107.

Lesson Goal

- Divide two-digit numbers by one-digit numbers.

What the Student Needs to Know

- Complete division facts.
- Complete multiplication facts.
- Subtract one- and two-digit numbers.

Getting Started

- Write these two division problems on the board:

  $28 \div 7 =$ ____

  $30 \div 7 =$ ____

  Ask: *How are the problems the same? How are they different?* (They have the same divisor, 7. They have different dividends.)

- Have two students draw models to show the problems $28 \div 7$ and $30 \div 7$. Point out that the second problem has a remainder or a number left over.

- *How do we write the answer to a division problem when there is a remainder?* (The letter R is used to show the remainder; for example, the answer to $30 \div 7$ is 4 R 2.)

- Write 4 R 2 on the board. Ask: *How do we read this answer?* (4 with a remainder of 2; 4 remainder 2; 4 with 2 left over)

- Write on the board: $30 \div 7$ is 4 R 2. Ask: *What is another way to show this problem?* (Have a student show the vertical division notation.)

- Work the problem $30 \div 7$ for students, showing how 28 is subtracted from 30 to get a remainder of 2.

  $$\begin{array}{r} 4\ R\ 2 \\ 7\overline{)30} \\ -\ 28 \\ \hline 2 \end{array}$$

- Go over the terms used to describe the parts of a division problem: divisor, dividend, product, quotient, remainder.

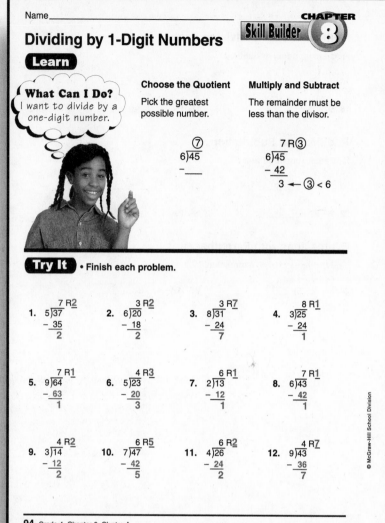

WHAT IF THE STUDENT CAN'T

Complete Division Facts

- Have pairs of students use flash cards to identify which facts still need to be learned.

- Review for students how to use multiplication to find division. For example, to find $42 \div 7$, students can think: "What number times 7 equals 42? Since 6 times 7 is 42, 42 divided by 7 must be 6."

- Have students use counters to practice division facts. For example, to find $72 \div 8$, they use 72 counters and make equal groups of 8 counters. They will find that they can make 9 groups of 8.

Complete Multiplication Facts

- Have pairs of students use flash cards to identify which facts still need to be learned.

- Have students use grid paper to draw rectangles for the facts they still need to learn. Each rectangle stands for two facts; for example, a 5-by-7 rectangle stands for $5 \times 7 = 35$ as well as $7 \times 5 = 35$.

- Have pairs of students work together to practice their facts. Each student needs a set of 0–9 digit cards. Students turn the cards over and each student picks a card. The first student to call out the product gets 1 point.

Divide.

		8 R2			6 R2			5 R7			8 R3
13.	3)26		**14.**	6)38		**15.**	9)52		**16.**	4)35	

		5 R3			5 R1			3 R3			4 R4
17.	8)43		**18.**	2)11		**19.**	5)18		**20.**	7)32	

Power Practice • Find the quotient and remainder.

21. $26 \div 6 = \underline{4 \text{ R2}}$ **22.** $17 \div 3 = \underline{5 \text{ R2}}$ **23.** $24 \div 7 = \underline{3 \text{ R3}}$

24. $28 \div 8 = \underline{3 \text{ R4}}$ **25.** $17 \div 4 = \underline{4 \text{ R1}}$

26. $60 \div 7 = \underline{8 \text{ R4}}$ **27.** $28 \div 5 = \underline{5 \text{ R3}}$

28. $15 \div 2 = \underline{7 \text{ R1}}$ **29.** $70 \div 9 = \underline{7 \text{ R7}}$

30. $51 \div 6 = \underline{8 \text{ R3}}$ **31.** $11 \div 3 = \underline{3 \text{ R2}}$

32. $23 \div 9 = \underline{2 \text{ R5}}$ **33.** $25 \div 4 = \underline{6 \text{ R1}}$

Learn with Partners & Parents

Phone Digit Division

Each person needs 10 cards or slips of paper.

- Write one digit of your phone number on each card.

- Use your telephone digits to make problems like this: ☐☐ ÷ ☐. Use three digits for each problem.

- Make 10 different division problems. Find the quotient for each of your telephone division problems.

© McGraw-Hill School Division

WHAT IF THE STUDENT CAN'T

Subtract One- and Two-Digit Numbers

- Provide pairs of students with one set of 0–9 digit cards. Each student picks two cards. The pair makes as many subtraction problems as they can using the chosen digits.

- Review the regrouping process for students by helping them use place-value model to show subtraction of some two-digit numbers.

Complete the Power Practice

- Check that students are rewriting the problems using the vertical division form:

```
    4 R 2
 7)30
 − 28
    2
```

Many students will make mistakes if they try to do these problems mentally.

- For each problem have students tell you how they decided what quotient to write. It should give a product less than the number they are dividing into.

USING THE LESSON

What Can I Do?

Read the question and the response. Then read and discuss the example. Ask:

- *What happens if the digit in the quotient is not great enough?* (The remainder will be greater than 6.)

- *What happens if the digit in the quotient is too great?* (You won't be able to subtract because the product will be greater than 45.)

Try It

Have students look over the three rows of exercises. Ask:

- *What are you to do in the first row?* (Subtract to find the remainder.)

- *What are you to do in the last two rows?* (Multiply the divisor times the quotient to get a product; subtract that product from the dividend to get the remainder.)

- Have students look at the exercises on the next page. Ask: *How are the first two rows different from the rest of the page?* (These problems are already set up in vertical form.)

Power Practice

- Remind students to first rewrite each problem using the vertical division notation.

- As students work, check that they are correctly translating the horizontal problems into vertical form. In particular, make sure they know which number is the divisor.

Learn with Partners & Parents

- If you do not wish students to use their telephone numbers, have them use a set of 0–9 digit cards.

- This activity can be done individually. If students work in pairs, have them take turns making and solving a problem.

USING THE LESSON

Lesson Goal
- Subtract 2-digit and 3-digit numbers.

What the Student Needs to Know
- Complete subtraction facts.
- Regroup in a subtraction problem.
- Identify the ones, tens, and hundreds digits.

Getting Started
- Write these problems on the board:

74	74
– 23	– 28

  Ask: *How are these problems different?* (The number being subtracted is not the same.) *In which problem will you need to regroup? Why?* (In the right problem because you cannot subtract 8 from 4 in the ones column.)

What Can I Do?
Read the question and the response. Then read and discuss the example. Ask:
- *Which digits are the ones digits?* (7 and 9; the ones on the right far) *What are the digits 3 and 2 called?* (the tens digits) *What happens to the tens digits when you need to regroup in the ones column?* (You subtract one ten from the top tens digit so you can regroup.)
- *Is the problem in the example finished?* (Yes, the final answer is 308.)

Try It
- Have students read the first direction and look over the exercises. Ask: *Which digits will you use to decide if regrouping is needed?* (The ones digits. If the second ones digit is greater than the first, regrouping is needed.)

Power Practice
- Have the students first tell you whether or not regrouping is needed in each exercise.

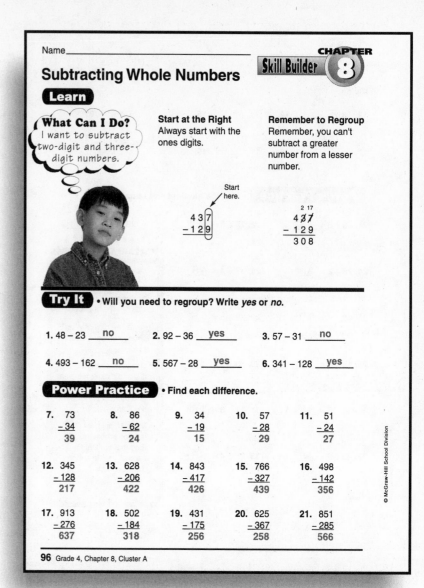

WHAT IF THE STUDENT CAN'T

Complete Subtraction Facts
- Write several subtraction facts on the board. For each fact, show students how to use a related addition fact. For example, for the fact 13 – 8, students think, "What number plus 8 equals 13. Since 8 + 5 = 13, 13 – 8 equals 5."

Regroup in a Subtraction Problem
- Provide place-value models. Have students work in pairs. One student lays out a two-digit number. The other student chooses a number to subtract that will make regrouping necessary.

Identify the Ones, Tens, and Hundreds Digits
- Write 468 on the board. Ask: *How many hundreds are there in this number?* (4) *Which digit shows the number of hundreds?* (the digit 4) Repeat for the tens and ones digits. If necessary, provide place-value models and have students show the numbers.

Complete the Power Practice
- Provide place-value models and have students do several two-digit problems that require regrouping.

Skill Builder **CHAPTER 8**

Multiplying Whole Numbers

Learn

What Can I Do?
I want to multiply one-digit and two-digit numbers.

Start with the ones.

4 times 6 is 24.

2
8⑥
× ④
4

Multiply tens. Add.

4 times 8 is 32.
32 plus 2 is 34.

2
⑧6
× ④
344

Try It • Use the Distributive Property to help you multiply.

1. 8 × 56 = (8 × 50) + (8 × 6) = __400__ + __48__ = __448__

2. 7 × 32 = (7 × 30) + (7 × 2) = __210__ + __14__ = __224__

3. 5 × 63 = (5 × 60) + (5 × 3) = __300__ + __15__ = __315__

4. 9 × 71 = (9 × 70) + (9 × 1) = __630__ + __9__ = __639__

Power Practice • Find each product.

5. 72 × 5 = 360	6. 47 × 6 = 282	7. 36 × 8 = 288	8. 59 × 3 = 177	9. 62 × 9 = 558
10. 81 × 4 = 324	11. 75 × 2 = 150	12. 43 × 7 = 301	13. 67 × 5 = 335	14. 28 × 6 = 168
15. 39 × 7 = 273	16. 46 × 3 = 138	17. 24 × 9 = 216	18. 17 × 4 = 68	19. 37 × 8 = 296

© McGraw-Hill School Division

Grade 4, Chapter 8, Cluster A **97**

WHAT IF THE STUDENT CAN'T

Complete Multiplication Facts

• Post a multiplication facts table. Model for students how to use the table. They find one factor in the left column; the other factor in the top row. Where the row and column meet is the product of the two factors.

Regroup in Multiplication

• Use problems such as 18 × 3 and 24 × 5 that have fairly small numbers. Provide place-value models so that students can show the regrouping process.

Identify the Ones and Tens Digits in a Number

• Have students write 2-digit numbers such as 56 in expanded form. They write the tens and then the ones, as in 56 = 5 tens 6 ones. Then ask students to tell you the tens digit and the ones digit.

Complete the Power Practice

• If students are making errors in basic facts, provide extra practice using rectangle models on grid paper. A student colors in a rectangle and then writes two multiplication facts to show the total number of squares in the rectangle.

USING THE LESSON

Lesson Goal

• Multiply a 1-digit number times a 2-digit number.

What the Student Needs to Know

• Complete multiplication facts.

• Regroup in multiplication.

• Identify the ones and tens digits in a number.

Getting Started

• Write on the board:

31
× 6

Have students identify the ones and tens digits in the top number. Then say: *There are two steps in this problem. What are the two steps?* (Multiply 6 times the ones digit; multiply 6 times the tens digit.)

• Discuss the problem 6 × 37. Ask: *How is this problem different from 6 times 31?* (The ones product is more than 10, so regrouping is needed.) Have a student do the problem at the board.

What Can I Do?

Read the question and the response. Then read and discuss the example. Ask:

• *Which digits do you multiply first?* (the 4 and the 6) *What is their product and where do you write it?* (24; write the 4 ones under the line in the ones place; write the 2 tens above the 8 in the top number.)

• *Explain what is done in the next step.* (Multiply 4 times 8 tens to get 32 tens. Add 2 tens from the regrouping to get 34 tens.)

Try It

• Have students look over the exercises. Point out that these show the two steps in the multiplication in a different way.

Power Practice

• Have the students complete the practice items. Then review each answer.

Grade 4, Chapter 8, Cluster A **97**

Lesson Goal

- Round numbers through thousands to the nearest ten.

What the Student Needs to Know

- Make and read a number line.
- Identify the ones digit.
- Identify the two nearest multiples of 10.

Getting Started

- On the board draw a number line from 130 to 140. Point to 132 and ask: *If you are rounding this number to the nearest ten, what are the two possible choices?* (130 and 140) Point out that the ones digits of both of these are zero.

- *How does a number line help you round a number?* (You can find the two tens nearest to the number. You can see which is nearer to your number.)

What Can I Do?

Read the question and the response. Then read and discuss the rules for rounding. Ask:

- *Why are some of the numbers on the number line inside a circle?* (They are the numbers that round up to 80.)

- *What are the rules for rounding to the nearest ten?* (Look at the ones digit. If it is less than 5, round down. Otherwise, round up.)

Try It

- Explain that students are to complete the blank number line. Ask: *What number will you write on the very left of the number line?* (230) *What number comes next?* (231) *What numbers can this number line help you round?* (numbers from 230 to 240)

Power Practice

- Have the students complete the practice items. Encourage them to draw number lines if they need visual models to help them do the rounding.

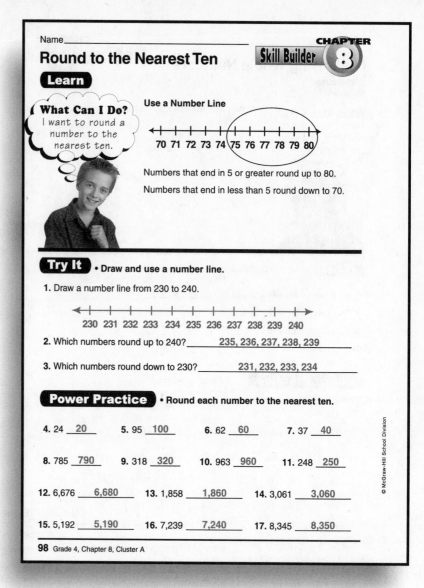

Name_____

Round to the Nearest Ten

Skill Builder

CHAPTER 8

Learn

What Can I Do? I want to round a number to the nearest ten.

Use a Number Line

70 71 72 73 74 75 76 77 78 79 80

Numbers that end in 5 or greater round up to 80.

Numbers that end in less than 5 round down to 70.

Try It • Draw and use a number line.

1. Draw a number line from 230 to 240.

230 231 232 233 234 235 236 237 238 239 240

2. Which numbers round up to 240? __235, 236, 237, 238, 239__

3. Which numbers round down to 230? __231, 232, 233, 234__

Power Practice • Round each number to the nearest ten.

4. 24 __20__   5. 95 __100__   6. 62 __60__   7. 37 __40__

8. 785 __790__   9. 318 __320__   10. 963 __960__   11. 248 __250__

12. 6,676 __6,680__   13. 1,858 __1,860__   14. 3,061 __3,060__

15. 5,192 __5,190__   16. 7,239 __7,240__   17. 8,345 __8,350__

98 Grade 4, Chapter 8, Cluster A

© McGraw-Hill School Division

WHAT IF THE STUDENT CAN'T

Make and Read a Number Line

- Write the term *number line* on the board. Draw a 0–10 number line and point out that it is a line that has numbers on it. The numbers always increase from left to right.

- Have students sketch a few number lines starting at various multiples of 10.

Identify the Ones Digit

- Write 452 on the board. Say: *There are three digits in this number? What are they?* (4, 5, and 2) Have students read the number and then ask: *Which digit tells how many hundreds? tens? ones?*

Identify the Two Nearest Multiples of 10

- Provide tens sticks from a set of place-value models. Students work in pairs. One student takes a handful of tens sticks. The partner writes a number that is 3 more. The students agree on which two tens are closest to the number.

Complete the Power Practice

- Have students work in pairs. The students take turns sketching the number line for each exercise. They circle the number to be rounded and then choose the closer ten on the number line.

Comparing Whole Numbers

Learn

What Can I Do?
I want to compare two whole numbers.

Compare the Digits

If the one number has more digits, it is greater.

123 > 98

> means greater than.

< means less than.

Start at the Left

4|5 8
4|7 1
same

Compare tens digits.

5 < 7, so 458 < 471.

Try It • Circle the number that is greater.

1. 86 or (103)   2. 58 or (85)   3. (426) or 264   4. 327 or (732)

Circle the number that is less.

5. (65) or 116   6. (93) or 96   7. (526) or 562   8. 909 or (99)

Power Practice • Compare. Use > or <.

9. 84 _<_ 86   10. 152 _>_ 105   11. 64 _>_ 58   12. 516 _>_ 496

13. 103 _<_ 130   14. 664 _>_ 646   15. 381 _>_ 318   16. 213 _<_ 231

17. 237 _>_ 232   18. 73 _<_ 105   19. 914 _>_ 419   20. 81 _<_ 813

21. 46 _<_ 64   22. 529 _<_ 532   23. 722 _>_ 702   24. 723 _<_ 728

Grade 4, Chapter 8, Cluster A **99**

WHAT IF THE STUDENT CAN'T

Compare One-Digit Numbers

• Write 8 and 2 on the board. Ask students which number is greater. Write the sentence "Eight is greater than two." Have students change this to math symbols: 8 > 2. Repeat, using the sentence "Two is less than eight."

Use the > and < Symbols

• Write the > and < symbols on the board and review their meanings.

• Provide digit cards and cards with the > and < symbols. Students work in small groups to make and read comparison sentences.

Identify Ones, Tens, and Hundreds Digits

• Provide worksheets with blank place-value charts.

Have pairs use a set of 0–9 digit cards. Students take turns drawing cards and writing digits in a chart. When the charts are complete, students read the numbers and tell the place names of the digits.

Complete the Power Practice

• Provide place-value models. Have students work in pairs to show the numbers.

USING THE LESSON

Lesson Goal

• Compare 2- and 3-digit whole numbers.

What the Student Needs to Know

• Compare 1-digit numbers.

• Use the > and < symbols.

• Identify ones, tens, and hundreds digits.

Getting Started

• Write 17 on the board. Say: *Name a number less than 17. What math sentence can you write to show your number is less than 17?* (If students choose 13, for example, they write 13 < 17.)

• *Now write a math sentence that show 17 is greater than your number.* (For example, 17 > 13)

What Can I Do?

Read the question and the response. Then read and discuss the examples. Ask:

• *What numbers are being compared in the first example?* (123 and 98) *Which number is greater and how do you know?* (123, because it has more digits)

• *In the second example, do you use the hundreds digits?* (Yes, you check and find out the hundreds digits are the same. Then you compare the tens digits.)

Try It

• Have students read the directions for the two sets of exercises.

• Then have students find those exercises in which the two numbers have a different number of digits. Ask: *Why are these exercises easier than the others?* (The number with more digits is always greater. You don't have to actually read the numbers or look at the digits.)

Power Practice

• Remind students that the smaller, pointed part of the > or < symbol points at the number that is less.

Grade 4, Chapter 8, Cluster A **99**

USING THE LESSON

Lesson Goal
• Complete multiplication and division facts.

What the Student Needs to Know
• Read a multiplication facts table.
• Explain the meaning of multiplication or division.

Getting Started
• Draw a large, blank times table on the board. Have students take turns filling in products. For each number, they should say four facts, two multiplication and two division.
• Draw a line diagonally down a facts table through the square numbers 0, 1, 4, 9, 16, and so forth. Ask: *How does the table show each fact twice?* (The top right is a reflection of the bottom left. For example, 4 × 5 and 5 × 4 are both given in the table.) Point out that this cuts the number of facts to be learned almost in half.

What Can I Do?
• Read the question and the response. Ask: *What does the table show?* (The multiplication facts through 10 times 10.) *Which facts do you already know?* (Students will probably know the facts with factors through 5. They may still need practice with the 6s, 7s, 8s, and 9s.)
• *How can you use multiplication to help do division?* (Think of a missing factor; for example, "What number times 2 equals 18?" This kind of reasoning gives the quotient for 18 ÷ 2.)

Try It
• Have a volunteer read the first direction. Ask: *How will you make the facts for Exercise 1?* (Start with the product, 54. Divide it by each of the two factors, 6 and 9.)

Power Practice
• Remind students to watch the operation signs.

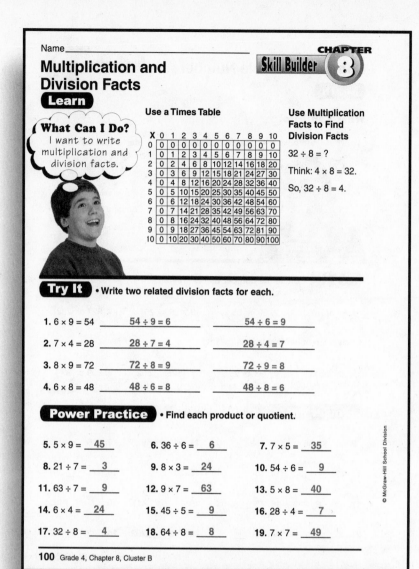

Multiplication and Division Facts

Learn

What Can I Do?
I want to write multiplication and division facts.

Use a Times Table

X	0	1	2	3	4	5	6	7	8	9	10
0	0	0	0	0	0	0	0	0	0	0	0
1	0	1	2	3	4	5	6	7	8	9	10
2	0	2	4	6	8	10	12	14	16	18	20
3	0	3	6	9	12	15	18	21	24	27	30
4	0	4	8	12	16	20	24	28	32	36	40
5	0	5	10	15	20	25	30	35	40	45	50
6	0	6	12	18	24	30	36	42	48	54	60
7	0	7	14	21	28	35	42	49	56	63	70
8	0	8	16	24	32	40	48	56	64	72	80
9	0	9	18	27	36	45	54	63	72	81	90
10	0	10	20	30	40	50	60	70	80	90	100

Use Multiplication Facts to Find Division Facts

$32 \div 8 = ?$

Think: $4 \times 8 = 32$.

So, $32 \div 8 = 4$.

Try It • Write two related division facts for each.

1. $6 \times 9 = 54$ $54 \div 9 = 6$ $54 \div 6 = 9$

2. $7 \times 4 = 28$ $28 \div 7 = 4$ $28 \div 4 = 7$

3. $8 \times 9 = 72$ $72 \div 8 = 9$ $72 \div 9 = 8$

4. $6 \times 8 = 48$ $48 \div 6 = 8$ $48 \div 8 = 6$

Power Practice • Find each product or quotient.

5. $5 \times 9 = \underline{45}$ 6. $36 \div 6 = \underline{6}$ 7. $7 \times 5 = \underline{35}$

8. $21 \div 7 = \underline{3}$ 9. $8 \times 3 = \underline{24}$ 10. $54 \div 6 = \underline{9}$

11. $63 \div 7 = \underline{9}$ 12. $9 \times 7 = \underline{63}$ 13. $5 \times 8 = \underline{40}$

14. $6 \times 4 = \underline{24}$ 15. $45 \div 5 = \underline{9}$ 16. $28 \div 4 = \underline{7}$

17. $32 \div 8 = \underline{4}$ 18. $64 \div 8 = \underline{8}$ 19. $7 \times 7 = \underline{49}$

© McGraw-Hill School Division

WHAT IF THE STUDENT CAN'T

Read a Multiplication Facts Table
• Write 5 × 7 on the board. Model for students how to find the 5 row, go across until you are under the 7, and read the product.
• Write 42 ÷ 6 on the board. Model for students how to find the 6 row, go across until you find the 42, and read the quotient at the top of that column.

Explain the Meaning of Multiplication or Division
• Draw this model on the board:

Have students explain how the model shows multiplication. (There are 3 groups of 5; 3 × 5 = 15.) Repeat for division. (15 Xs divided into 3 groups; 15 ÷ 3 = 5)

Complete the Power Practice
• If students miss only the division exercises, have them draw grouping models.
• If students miss both multiplication and division, provide practice with flash cards.

Name_____

Addition and Subtraction

Skill Builder

CHAPTER 8

Learn

What Can I Do?
I want to add and subtract one-digit numbers.

Use Related Facts

$34 + 8 = ?$

Think: $4 + 8 = 12$.

So, $34 + 8 = 42$.

$71 - 7 = ?$

Think: $11 - 7 = 4$.

So, $71 - 7 = 64$.

Try It • Write the related fact for each problem.

1. $47 + 6 = ?$

   $7 + 6 = 13$

2. $49 + 9 = ?$

   $9 + 9 = 18$

3. $85 + 8 = ?$

   $5 + 8 = 13$

Power Practice • Find each sum or difference.

4. $65 + 9 = \underline{74}$

5. $18 + 6 = \underline{24}$

6. $78 + 9 = \underline{87}$

7. $97 - 8 = \underline{89}$

8. $33 - 7 = \underline{26}$

9. $75 - 7 = \underline{68}$

10. $69 + 7 = \underline{76}$

11. $52 - 6 = \underline{46}$

12. $27 + 8 = \underline{35}$

13. $43 - 9 = \underline{34}$

14. $49 + 9 = \underline{58}$

15. $44 - 8 = \underline{36}$

16. $25 - 9 = \underline{16}$

17. $86 - 7 = \underline{79}$

18. $61 - 9 = \underline{52}$

19. $58 + 8 = \underline{66}$

20. $86 + 7 = \underline{93}$

21. $39 + 6 = \underline{45}$

Grade 4, Chapter 8, Cluster B **101**

WHAT IF THE STUDENT CAN'T

Complete Addition Facts

- Have pairs of students use addition flash cards to find out which facts still need to be learned.
- Have students write and illustrate a story problem for each fact they need to practice.

Complete Subtraction Facts

- Have pairs of students use subtraction flash cards to find out which facts still need to be learned.

Add or Subtract Tens

- Provide tens sticks from a set of place-value models. Students work in pairs. Each

takes a handful of tens sticks. The students work together to add the two numbers. Then they subtract to find out how many more. As students work, ask: *How many tens do each of you have? How many tens do you have together? How many more tens do you have?*

Complete the Power Practice

- Have students work in pairs. One student tells the related addition or subtraction fact for an exercise. The partner uses the fact to find the sum or difference.

USING THE LESSON

Lesson Goal

- Add or subtract a 1-digit number to a 2-digit number.

What the Student Needs to Know

- Complete addition facts.
- Complete subtraction facts.
- Add or subtract tens.

Getting Started

- Write on the board:

  $6 + 8 = 14$

  $16 + 8 = 24$

  $26 + 8 = 34$

  Ask students to describe the pattern. (The ones digits are always 6 and 8. The tens digit increases by one. The value of the tens place increases by 10.) Discuss how knowing 6 plus 8 can help you find the other sums.

- Write on the board:

  $13 - 7 = 6$

  $43 - 7 = ?$

  Discuss how knowing the fact 13 – 7 can help you find other differences.

What Can I Do?

Read the question and the response. Then read and discuss the examples. Ask:

- *Are there other ways to do problems of this type?* (Yes, write the problems in vertical form and use regrouping.)
- *What advantages does this strategy have?* (Possible answer: It is easier to use this strategy when using mental math.)

Try It

Check that all students know what is meant by "the related fact." Ask:

- *How do you create the related fact?* (Use only the ones digits.)

Power Practice

- Have the students complete the practice items. Remind them to notice the operation signs.

Lesson Goal
- Find the value of expressions that use parentheses.

What the Student Needs to Know
- Complete addition and subtraction facts.
- Complete multiplication and division facts.
- Add 1- and 2-digit numbers.

Getting Started
- Write on the board: $2 \times 8 - 3$. Ask students to find the value of the expression. They will probably subtract 3 from 16 to get 13. Then ask: *Could there be a different value for this expression?* (Students may suggest subtracting 3 from 8 first. If they do this, they will get 10 rather than 13. Remind them such a solution does not follow the order of operation.)
- Write on the board:

  $(2 \times 8) - 3$

  $2 \times (8 - 3)$

Remind students that the curved symbols are called parentheses. Ask: *How does using parentheses make it clear what to do?* (The parentheses show what operation to do first. In $(2 \times 8) - 3$, students multiply before subtracting. In $2 \times (8 - 3)$, they subtract before multiplying.)

- Point out that two steps are needed to do this problem. Show students how to write the steps:

  $(2 \times 8) - 3 =$

  $16 - 3 =$

  13

What Can I Do?
Read the question and the response. Then read and discuss the examples. Ask:

- *What operation should you do first in each example?* (the one in parentheses)
- Have students finish each example to find the number that equals the original expression.

Name_____

CHAPTER 8

Expressions with Parentheses *Skill Builder*

Learn

What Can I Do? I want to solve problems that have parentheses.

Work Inside Parentheses First

These examples show how to begin.

$3 \times (9 - 2)$	$(3 \times 9) - 2$
$= 3 \times 7$	$= 27 - 2$
$= 21$	$= 25$
$(6 + 8) \div 2$	$6 + (8 \div 2)$
$= 14 \div 2$	$= 6 + 4$
$= 7$	$= 10$

Try It • Fill in the blanks to find the value of each expression.

1. $(7 - 2) \times 4 =$

$\underline{5} \times \underline{4} = \underline{20}$

2. $8 + (15 \div 3) =$

$\underline{8} + \underline{5} = \underline{13}$

3. $(16 - 8) \div 2 =$

$\underline{8} \div \underline{2} = \underline{4}$

4. $3 + (2 \times 6) =$

$\underline{3} + \underline{12} = \underline{15}$

5. $(4 \times 6) - 5 =$

$\underline{24} - \underline{5} = \underline{19}$

6. $(24 \div 4) \times 3 =$

$\underline{6} \times \underline{3} = \underline{18}$

7. $9 \div (3 + 6) =$

$\underline{9} \div \underline{9} = \underline{1}$

8. $6 \times (12 - 5) =$

$\underline{6} \times \underline{7} = \underline{42}$

9. $7 + (12 \div 6) =$

$\underline{7} + \underline{2} = \underline{9}$

10. $(25 \div 5) + 2 =$

$\underline{5} + \underline{2} = \underline{7}$

11. $(17 - 8) \div 3 =$

$\underline{9} \div \underline{3} = \underline{3}$

12. $18 - (15 \div 3) =$

$\underline{18} - \underline{5} = \underline{13}$

13. $8 \times (11 - 2) =$

$\underline{8} \times \underline{9} = \underline{72}$

14. $9 - (6 \div 2) =$

$\underline{9} - \underline{3} = \underline{6}$

15. $(13 - 6) + 4 =$

$\underline{7} + \underline{4} = \underline{11}$

© McGraw-Hill School Division

102 Grade 4, Chapter 8, Cluster B

WHAT IF THE STUDENT CAN'T

Complete Addition and Subtraction Facts

- Provide pairs of students with flash cards to identify facts that still needed to be memorized.
- Post an addition facts table. Model for students how to use it to find addition or subtraction fact answers. To find $5 + 6$, students find the 5 row, go across until they are under the 6, and read the sum. To find $14 - 8$, students find the 8 row, go across to the 14, then find the difference at the top of the column.

Complete Multiplication and Division Facts

- Provide pairs of students with flash cards to identify facts that still needed to be memorized.
- Post a multiplication facts table. Model for students how to use it to find multiplication or division fact answers. To find 5×6, students find the 5 row, go across until they are under the 6, and read the product. To find $48 \div 8$, students find the 8 row, go across to the 48, then find the quotient at the top of the column.

Name_____

Fill in the blanks to finish each problem.

16. $2 + (6 \times 3) = 2 + \underline{18} = \underline{20}$ **17.** $(2 + 6) \times 3 = \underline{8} \times 3 = \underline{24}$

18. $9 - (2 \times 4) = 9 - \underline{8} = \underline{1}$ **19.** $(9 - 2) \times 4 = \underline{7} \times 4 = \underline{28}$

20. $12 \div (4 + 2) = 12 \div \underline{6} = \underline{2}$ **21.** $(12 \div 4) + 2 = \underline{3} + 2 = \underline{5}$

22. $8 + (12 \div 4) = 8 + \underline{3} = \underline{11}$ **23.** $(8 + 12) \div 4 = \underline{20} \div 4 = \underline{5}$

24. $4 \times (8 - 5) = 4 \times \underline{3} = \underline{12}$ **25.** $(4 \times 8) - 5 = \underline{32} - 5 = \underline{27}$

Power Practice • Find the value of each expression.

26. $18 - (6 + 5) = \underline{7}$ **27.** $(12 \div 2) + 4 = \underline{10}$

28. $(9 + 6) \div 3 = \underline{5}$ **29.** $(12 + 9) - 2 = \underline{19}$

30. $(18 \div 6) - 2 = \underline{1}$ **31.** $4 \times (7 + 3) = \underline{40}$

32. $4 + (3 \times 7) = \underline{25}$ **33.** $(8 + 1) \times 5 = \underline{45}$

34. $15 - (12 \div 3) = \underline{11}$ **35.** $20 - (15 \div 5) = \underline{17}$

36. $(6 + 9) - 4 = \underline{11}$ **37.** $7 \times (8 - 3) = \underline{35}$

38. $5 \times (8 \div 2) = \underline{20}$ **39.** $(15 - 10) \div 5 = \underline{1}$

40. $(8 \times 3) - 7 = \underline{17}$

41. $16 \div (1 + 3) = \underline{4}$

42. $(15 - 7) \times 2 = \underline{16}$

43. $3 + (2 \times 9) = \underline{21}$

44. $(14 \div 7) \times 2 = \underline{4}$

Learn with Partners & Parents

The Four Threes
• Use four 3s to make problems like this:
  $(3 \times 3) - (3 + 3)$ $(33 \div 3) + 3$
• Use parentheses in every problem.
• Make at least ten different problems. Find the answer to each problem.

WHAT IF THE STUDENT CAN'T

Add 1- and 2-Digit Numbers

• Remind students of how to use a related fact when adding or subtracting a 1-digit number. For example, to find $43 + 8$, students use the fact $3 + 8 = 11$. They add 1 to the 4 tens in 43 to get a sum of 51.

• Provide place-value models so that students can show addition and subtraction problems that involve regrouping.

Complete the Power Practice

• Check that students know which operation to do first by having them explain how they worked two or three of the problems.

• Discourage students from using mental math until you and they are confident they can do so without making errors.

Try It

• Have students look over the exercises on page 102. Ask: *In the first exercise, how will you use the top problem to fill in the blanks?* (Subtract inside the parentheses to get 5 for the first blank. Bring down the 4 for the second blank.)

• Have students tell you what operation is done first for each exercise on page 102.

• Have students look over the remaining Try It exercises on the top of page 103. Ask: *How will you fill in the blanks for each exercise?* (One number will be the answer to the problem inside parentheses. The other number will be brought down. The final answer can then be found.)

• Have students tell you the two operations needed for each exercise; for example, "I will multiply and then add."

Power Practice

• Have the students complete the practice items. Students can try doing the problems mentally. If they find this too difficult, have them write the first step beneath each problem.

Learn with Partners & Parents

• Students can use any of the four operations—addition, subtraction, multiplication, and division. They can also combine the digits to make two-digit numbers.

CHALLENGE

Lesson Goal

- Solve division puzzles based on missing digits.

Introducing the Challenge

- Review the vocabulary needed for the lesson by having students use each term in a sentence. Vocabulary used in this lesson includes: *digit, quotient, product, dividend, divisor.*

- Write this puzzle on the board:

Have students identify the divisor, dividend, and quotient in the problem. Then ask:

- *What digit goes in the tens place in the quotient? Explain how you know.* (The first product is 8 and 1 times 8 is 8.)

- *How do you know that the three empty boxes must have the same number?* (When you divide, you bring down digits from the dividend. So, the missing digit in the dividend must match the digit directly below it. There is no remainder, so the last number must be the same as the one above it.) *What is the missing digit for these three boxes? How do you know?* (The digit is 6 because 2 times 8 is 16.)

Division with Missing Digits

In this kind of puzzle you are to write one digit in each box.

$$\begin{array}{r} \boxed{1}\boxed{0}\;5 \\ 5\overline{)5\,\boxed{2}\,5} \\ -\underline{5} \\ \boxed{2}\;5 \\ -\underline{\boxed{2}\;5} \\ 0 \end{array}$$

1. How do you know the first digit of the quotient must be 1?

   The first product is 5, and 1 times 5 is 5.

2. What is the product in the last row? How do you know?

   It is 25 because the last digit of the quotient is 5.

3. What digit goes in the second-to-last row? How do you know?

   The digit 2. There is no remainder, so the second-to-last row

   must be the same as the last row. It must also be 25.

4. Complete the dividend. How do you know what digit goes in the box?

   The dividend is 525 because of the 25s in the last two rows.

5. Complete the quotient. How do you know what number goes in the box?

   Since 525 divided by 5 is 105, the quotient must be 105.

Name_____

This puzzle is more difficult. The 1s and 8s are given.
Find the other digits.

```
              9 0 8 0 9
      1 2 ) 1 0 8 9 7 0 9
          - 1 0 8
              9 7
            - 9 6
              1 0 9
            - 1 0 8
                  1
```

6. There are 5 digits in the quotient, but only 3 subtracted products. So, 2 digits in the quotient are zeros. Which digits are zeros?

the second and fourth digits

7. The divisor times 8 is a two-digit number, but the first product is three digits. So, the first digit of the quotient is greater than 8. What is the digit? **9**

8. The second digit in the dividend is zero. Use this to find the divisor. Explain.

Since 108 divided by 9 is 12, the divisor must be 12.

9. Why can you guess that the last digit of the quotient must be the same as the first digit?

It looks like the product will be 108, and 108 divided by 9 is 12.

10. Use what you know about division to finish the problem.

The quotient is 90,809 R1. The dividend is 1,089,709.

Using the Challenge

- Have students look over the directions for both pages. Point out that there are two different puzzles.

- The questions beneath each puzzle provide clues to guide students through the solution. Some students may want to try solving the puzzles without using the clues in the questions.

- Another approach is for a student to solve the second puzzle using the questions for help. Then the student tries the first puzzle without using the questions.

- These types of puzzles are appropriate for small group work. Form the groups with students of similar abilities so that one student doesn't give away the puzzle answer too quickly.

- When students have finished the puzzles, they may enjoy creating puzzles of their own similar to the one on page 104. Have students work in pairs. Each creates a puzzle; then they trade and try to solve. Allow time for revisions if the first attempts are flawed.

CHALLENGE

Lesson Goal

- Solve puzzles using parentheses and combinations of operations.

Introducing the Challenge

- Review the vocabulary needed for the lesson by having students use each term in a sentence. Vocabulary used in this lesson includes: operation, parentheses, expression, digit.

- Write on the board: $3 + 3 + 3$. Have students find the sum. Then change the first plus sign to a times sign. Ask: *If you use parentheses, can you make this have two different values?*
  (Yes, $3 \times (3 + 3) = 18$, $(3 \times 3) + 3 = 12$)

- Have students change the operation signs and the position of the parentheses to make different values. Compile the class results on the board.

- Summarize by pointing out that three threes can equal many different numbers. The value of the expression depends on the operation signs used.

Name_____

Digit Puzzles

CHALLENGE CHAPTER 8

In these puzzles, the challenge is to find different ways to make a given number. You can use the four operations: addition, subtraction, multiplication, and division. You will also need to use parentheses.

Find the value of each expression. Remember to do the operations inside the parentheses first.

1. $(3 \times 1) - (4 - 2) = \underline{\ 1\ }$ 2. $(4 - 3) + (2 - 1) = \underline{\ 2\ }$

3. $(4 - 3) + (2 \times 1) = \underline{\ 3\ }$ 4. $(4 - 2) + (3 - 1) = \underline{\ 4\ }$

5. $13 - (2 \times 4) = \underline{\ 5\ }$ 6. $4 + (3 + 1) - 2 = \underline{\ 6\ }$

7. $3 \times (4 - 1) - 2 = \underline{\ 7\ }$ 8. $14 - (2 \times 3) = \underline{\ 8\ }$

9. $4 + 2 + (3 \times 1) = \underline{\ 9\ }$ 10. $(4 + 3) + (2 + 1) = \underline{\ 10\ }$

11. What pattern do you see in these problems?

   Possible answer: The values increase by 1s from 1 through 10.

   In each problem, the digits 1, 2, 3, and 4 are each used one time.

Write each number using the digits 1, 2, 3, and 4. Use each digit only once.

12. $11 = \underline{\ (3 \times 4) - (2 - 1)\ }$ 13. $12 = \underline{\ (3 \times 4) \times (2 - 1)\ }$

14. $13 = \underline{\ (3 \times 4) + (2 - 1)\ }$ 15. $14 = \underline{\ (3 \times 4) + (2 \times 1)\ }$

16. $15 = \underline{\ 2 \times (3 + 4) + 1\ }$ 17. $16 = \underline{\ (4 \times 2) \times (3 - 1)\ }$

18. $17 = \underline{\ 3 \times (2 + 4) - 1\ }$ 19. $18 = \underline{\ (2 \times 3) \times (4 - 1)\ }$

20. $19 = \underline{\ 3 \times (2 + 4) + 1\ }$ 21. $20 = \underline{\ 21 - (4 - 3)\ }$

22. $21 = \underline{\ (3 + 4) \times (2 + 1)\ }$ 23. $22 = \underline{\ 21 + (4 - 3)\ }$

24. $23 = \underline{\ 31 - (4 \times 2)\ }$ 25. $24 = \underline{\ (2 + 4) \times (3 + 1)\ }$

26. $25 = \underline{\ (2 + 3) \times (4 + 1)\ }$ For 12 – 26, sample answers are given.

© McGraw-Hill School Division

106 Grade 4, Chapter 8, Cluster B

Name_____

Write each number using four fours.

27. $1 = \underline{\;\;(4 \div 4) \times (4 \div 4)\;\;}$ **28.** $2 = \underline{\;\;(4 \div 4) + (4 \div 4)\;\;}$

29. $3 = \underline{\;\;(4 + 4 + 4) \div 4\;\;}$ **30.** $6 = \underline{\;\;(4 + 4) \div 4 + 4\;\;}$

31. $7 = \underline{\;\;(4 + 4) - (4 \div 4)\;\;}$ **32.** $8 = \underline{\;\;(4 + 4) + (4 - 4)\;\;}$

33. $9 = \underline{\;\;(4 + 4) + (4 \div 4)\;\;}$ **34.** $12 = \underline{\;\;4 - (4 \div 4) \times 4\;\;}$

35. $15 = \underline{\;\;(4 \times 4) - (4 \div 4)\;\;}$ **36.** $16 = \underline{\;\;4 + 4 + 4 + 4\;\;}$

37. $17 = \underline{\;\;(4 \times 4) + (4 \div 4)\;\;}$ **38.** $20 = \underline{\;\;4 + (4 \div 4) \times 4\;\;}$

Write each number using four fives.

39. $1 = \underline{\;\;(5 \div 5) \times (5 \div 5)\;\;}$ **40.** $2 = \underline{\;\;(5 \div 5) + (5 \div 5)\;\;}$

41. $9 = \underline{\;\;(5 + 5) - (5 \div 5)\;\;}$ **42.** $10 = \underline{\;\;(5 + 5) + (5 - 5)\;\;}$

43. $11 = \underline{\;\;(5 + 5) + (5 \div 5)\;\;}$ **44.** $15 = \underline{\;\;(5 \times 5) - (5 + 5)\;\;}$

Write each number using five fives.

45. $3 = \underline{\;\;5 - (5 \div 5) - (5 \div 5)\;\;}$ **46.** $4 = \underline{\;\;5 - (5 \div 5) + (5 - 5)\;\;}$

47. $5 = \underline{\;\;(5 \times 5) \div 5 + (5 - 5)\;\;}$ **48.** $6 = \underline{\;\;5 + (5 - 5) + (5 \div 5)\;\;}$

49. $7 = \underline{\;\;5 + (5 \div 5) + (5 \div 5)\;\;}$ **50.** $14 = \underline{\;\;(5 + 5 + 5) - (5 \div 5)\;\;}$

51. $15 = \underline{\;\;(5 + 5 + 5) + (5 - 5)\;\;}$ **52.** $16 = \underline{\;\;(5 + 5 + 5) + (5 \div 5)\;\;}$

CHALLENGE

Using the Challenge

- Have students do the first ten exercises. Discuss the pattern students found. Then have a student read the top section of the page. Check that students know what to do by asking:

- *For exercises 12–26, what operations can you use?* (addition, subtraction, multiplication, division) *What digits must be used in each problem?* (1, 2, 3, 4; Each digit must be used once and only once.)

- Draw students' attention to Exercise 5. Point out that the digits 1 and 3 are used to make the 2-digit number 13. This technique is also allowed in solving these puzzles.

- First, have students try problem 12. Then have them share solutions and strategies. Possible ways of making 11 include:

$$(3 \times 4) - (2 - 1)$$
$$4 + (3 \times 2) + 1$$
$$(4 \times 2) + (3 \times 1)$$
$$42 - 31$$

Measuring to the Nearest $\frac{1}{2}$, $\frac{1}{4}$, $\frac{1}{8}$ Inch

Measure each line segment to the nearest $\frac{1}{2}$ inch.

1. _____

2. _____

Measure each line segment to the nearest $\frac{1}{4}$ inch.

3. _____

4. _____

Measure each line segment to the nearest $\frac{1}{8}$ inch.

5. _____

6. _____

Reading Weight Shown on a Scale

Each scale shows pounds and ounces. Write the weight shown.

7.

8.

9.

_____   _____   _____

Multiplication and Division

Find each product or quotient.

10. 12
  $\times$ 12

11. 24
  $\times$ 16

12. $36\overline{)180}$

13. $3\overline{)108}$

Name_____

Measuring to the Nearest Centimeter

Measure each line segment to the nearest centimeter.

14. ————

_____

15. ——

_____

16. ——

_____

Reading a Thermometer

Write the Celsius temperature and the Fahrenheit temperature shown on each thermometer.

17.

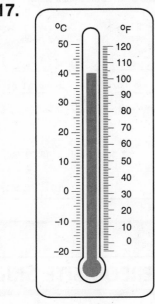

___ °C, ___ °F

18.

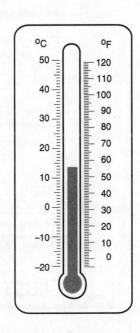

___ °C, ___ °F

19.

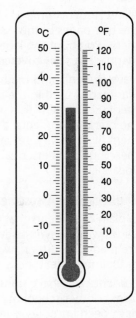

___ °C, ___ °F

Multiply and Divide by 10, 100, 1,000

Find each product or quotient.

20. 3 × 100

_____

21. 200 × 10

_____

22. 50 × 1,000

_____

23. 9,000 ÷ 1,000

_____

24. 7,000 ÷ 100

_____

25. 40 ÷ 10

_____

Assessment Goal

This two-page assessment covers skills identified as necessary for success in Chapter 9 Measurement. The first page assesses the major prerequisite skills for Cluster A. The second page assesses the major prerequisite skills for Cluster B. When the Cluster A and Cluster B prerequisite skills overlap, the skill(s) will be covered in only one section.

Getting Started

- Allow students time to look over the two pages of the assessment. Point out the labels that identify the skills covered.

- Have students find math vocabulary terms used in the assessment. List vocabulary terms on the board as students identify them. If necessary, review the meanings of all essential math vocabulary.

Introducing the Assessment

- Explain to students that these pages will help you know if they are ready to start a new chapter in their math textbooks.

- Students who have transferred from another school may not have been introduced to some of these skills. Encourage students to do their best and assure them you will help them learn any needed skills.

Cluster A Challenge

Those students who demonstrate mastery of the skills on this page will not need to use the reteaching worksheets. Instead, these students can do the Cluster A Challenge found on pages 118–119.

Name_____

Measuring to the Nearest $\frac{1}{2}$, $\frac{1}{4}$, $\frac{1}{8}$ Inch

Measure each line segment to the nearest $\frac{1}{2}$ inch.

1. _____
   2 in.

2. _____
   $2\frac{1}{2}$ in.

Measure each line segment to the nearest $\frac{1}{4}$ inch.

3. _____
   $2\frac{1}{2}$ in.

4. _____
   $\frac{3}{4}$ in.

Measure each line segment to the nearest $\frac{1}{8}$ inch.

5. _____
   $2\frac{5}{8}$ in.

6. _____
   2 in.

Reading Weight Shown on a Scale

Each scale shows pounds and ounces. Write the weight shown.

7.
   65 lb

8.
   8 lb 8 oz

9.
   2 lb 2 oz

Multiplication and Division

Find each product or quotient.

10. $\begin{array}{r} 12 \\ \times\ 12 \\ \hline 144 \end{array}$

11. $\begin{array}{r} 24 \\ \times\ 16 \\ \hline 384 \end{array}$

12. $36\overline{)180}$ with quotient 5

13. $3\overline{)108}$ with quotient 36

© McGraw-Hill School Division

107A Use with Grade 4, Chapter 9, Cluster A

CLUSTER A PREREQUISITE SKILLS

The skills listed in this chart are those identified as major prerequisite skills for students' success in the lessons in Cluster A of the chapter. Each skill is covered by one or more assessment items as shown in the middle column. The right column provides the page number for the lessons in this book that reteach the cluster A prerequisite skills.

Skill Name	Assessment Items	Lesson Pages
Measuring to the Nearest $\frac{1}{2}$, $\frac{1}{4}$, $\frac{1}{8}$ Inch	1-6	108-109
Reading Weight Shown on a Scale	7-9	110-111
Multiplication and Division	10-13	112-113

Name_____

Measuring to the Nearest Centimeter

Measure each line segment to the nearest centimeter.

14. ———   15. ——   16. ——
    2cm   1 cm   1 cm

Reading a Thermometer

Write the Celsius temperature and the Fahrenheit temperature shown on each thermometer.

17. 18. 19.

<u>40</u> °C, <u>104</u> °F   <u>14</u> °C, <u>57</u> °F   <u>30</u> °C, <u>86</u> °F

Multiply and Divide by 10, 100, 1,000

Find each product or quotient.

20. 3 × 100	21. 200 × 10	22. 50 × 1,000
300	2,000	50,000

23. 9,000 ÷ 1,000	24. 7,000 ÷ 100	25. 40 ÷ 10
9	70	4

© McGraw-Hill School Division

Use with Grade 4, Chapter 9, Cluster B **107B**

CHAPTER 9 PRE-CHAPTER ASSESSMENT

Alternative Assessment Strategies

- Oral administration of the assessment is appropriate for younger students or those whose native language is not English. Read the skills title and directions one section at a time. Check students' understanding by asking them to tell you how they will do the first exercise in the group.
- For some skill types you may wish to use group administration. In this technique, a small group or pair of students complete the assessment together. Through their discussion, you will be able to decide if supplementary reteaching materials are needed.

Intervention Materials

If students are not successful with the prerequisite skills assessed on these pages, reteaching lessons have been created to help them make the transition into the chapter.

Item correlation charts showing the skills lessons suitable for reteaching the prerequisite skills are found beneath the reproductions of each page of the assessment.

CLUSTER B PREREQUISITE SKILLS

The skills listed in this chart are those identified as major prerequisite skills for students' success in the lessons in Cluster B of the chapter. Each skill is covered by one or more assessment items as shown in the middle column. The right column provides the page numbers for the lessons in this book that reteach the Cluster B prerequisite skills

Skill Name	Assessment Items	Lesson Pages
Measuring to the Nearest Centimeter	14-16	114
Reading a Thermometer	17-19	115
Multiply and Divide by 10, 100, 1,000	20-25	116-117

Cluster B Challenge

Those students who demonstrate mastery of the skills on this page will not need to use the reteaching worksheets. Instead, these students can do the Cluster B Challenge found on pages 120–121.

Grade 4, Chapter 9, Cluster B **107D**

Lesson Goal

- Measure line segments to the nearest inch, half inch, quarter inch, and eighth inch.

What the Student Needs to Know

- Identify inch and half inch markings.
- Identify quarter inch and eighth inch markings.
- Identify sixteenth inch markings.

Getting Started

Ask students to look at the labeled ruler. Say:

- *On an inch ruler, the longest lines are inch marks. What inch markings are shown on this ruler?* (0 and 1)

- *The second longest mark is the half-inch mark. It is half way between the inch marks. Point to the half-inch mark.*

- *The next longest lines are quarter-inch marks. What are the labels on the quarter-inch marks?* ($\frac{1}{4}$ and $\frac{3}{4}$)

- *The shortest lines are sixteenth-inch marks. Between what two marks is the $\frac{5}{16}$ inch mark?* ($\frac{1}{4}$ and $\frac{3}{8}$)

What Can I Do?

Read the question and the response. Then read and discuss the examples. Ask:

- *Why is it important to line one end of the line up with the zero point on the ruler?* (If one end of the line is on the zero mark, the other end lines up with the mark that shows the line's length.)

- *How can you use the quarter-inch mark help you decide if the length is closer to 3 inches or to $3\frac{1}{2}$ inches?* (The quarter-inch mark shows half way between 3 and $3\frac{1}{2}$ inches. If the length is on the left of the quarter-inch mark, it is closer to 3 inches. If the length is on the right side of the quarter-inch mark, it is closer to $3\frac{1}{2}$ inches.)

Name_____

Measuring to the Nearest $\frac{1}{2}$, $\frac{1}{4}$, $\frac{1}{8}$ Inch

Learn

What Can I Do? I want to measure a line segment.

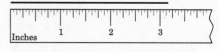

Measure to the Nearest $\frac{1}{2}$ Inch

The marks that are between the inch marks help you measure lengths less than an inch (in.). The smallest marks are sixteenth-inch marks.

Line the zero mark on the ruler up with the left end of the line segment.

Think: The other end is between the 3-inch and $3\frac{1}{2}$-inch marks.

Use the quarter-inch mark to decide if the length is closer to 3 inches or to $3\frac{1}{2}$ inches.

Think: To the nearest half inch, the line segment is 3 inches long.

Measure to the Nearest $\frac{1}{4}$ Inch

Think: I can use the eighth-inch mark to decide if the line is closer to 3 or $3\frac{1}{4}$ inches long. To the nearest $\frac{1}{4}$ inch the line segment is $3\frac{1}{4}$ inches long.

Measure to the Nearest $\frac{1}{8}$ Inch

Think: I can use the sixteenth-inch mark to decide if the line is closer to $3\frac{1}{8}$ or $3\frac{1}{4}$ inches long. To the nearest $\frac{1}{8}$ inch the line segment is $3\frac{1}{8}$ inches long.

WHAT IF THE STUDENT CAN'T

Identify Inch and Half-Inch Markings

- Point out that inch marks are numbered. Have students point to inch marks you name. For example: "three inches."

- Tell students that they can identify the half-inch mark because it is the longest mark between the two inch marks. Have them point out half-inch marks you name. For example: "two and one-half inches."

Identify Quarter-Inch and Eighth- Inch Markings

- Show students the quarter-inch marks between 0 and 1. Name them as you point them out. Then read the quarter-inch marks between 1 and 2. Finally have students point out and name the quarter-inch marks between 2 and 3, and between 3 and 4.

- Have students point out quarter-inch and eighth-inch marks as you name them. For example: "$2\frac{7}{8}$ inches."

Name_____

Try It • Measure the line segment.

━━━━━━━━━━━━

|‖‖‖‖‖‖‖‖‖‖‖‖‖‖‖‖‖‖‖‖‖‖‖‖‖‖‖‖‖‖‖‖‖
Inches   1   2

1. To the nearest $\frac{1}{2}$ inch the length is __2__ inches.

2. To the nearest $\frac{1}{4}$ inch the length is __$2\frac{1}{4}$__ inches.

3. To the nearest $\frac{1}{8}$ inch the length is __$2\frac{1}{4}$__ inches.

Power Practice • Use an inch ruler. Measure each line segment to the nearest $\frac{1}{2}$ inch.

4. ━━━━━━━━   __2__ inches

5. ━━━━━━   __$1\frac{1}{2}$__ inches

Use an inch ruler. Measure each line segment to the nearest $\frac{1}{4}$ inch.

6. ━━━━━━━━━   __$2\frac{1}{4}$__ inches

7. ━━━   __$\frac{1}{2}$__ inch

Use an inch ruler. Measure each line segment to the nearest $\frac{1}{8}$ inch.

8. ━━━━━   __$1\frac{1}{8}$__ inches

9. ━━━━━━━━━   __$2\frac{3}{4}$__ inches

© McGraw-Hill School Division

Grade 4, Chapter 9, Cluster A **109**

WHAT IF THE STUDENT CAN'T

Identify Sixteenth-Inch Markings

• Remind students that sixteenth-inch markings are the smallest markings on the ruler. Ask them to point out the sixteenth-inch mark between two numbers. For example: "between $2\frac{1}{2}$ and $2\frac{5}{8}$."

Complete the Power Practice

• Discuss each incorrect answer. Have students show you how they arrived at the answer. Stress the importance of lining up the left end of the line with the zero mark on the ruler.

• Some students may benefit from coloring paper rulers so that each fractional mark is a different color. For example: color inch marks red, half-inch marks blue, quarter-inch marks yellow, eighth-inch marks green.

USING THE LESSON

• *What if the end of the line was exactly above the $3\frac{1}{8}$ inch mark; would you say the line was 3 inches or $3\frac{1}{4}$ inches long to the nearest quarter inch?* (Either answer could be correct, but usually the higher measurement is used.)

Try It

• Have students explain how they find the length to each fraction of an inch. First, they should name the two measures the length is between. Then they point out the halfway mark between the two points. Finally, they decide which measure the length is closer to.

Power Practice

• Remind students to line the left side of each line up with the zero point on the ruler.

• Select some of the exercises and ask volunteers to show how they found the lengths.

• Invite students to describe any problems they had measuring the lines or any measuring tips they might have for their classmates.

• Ask students to explain how they could measure the line if their ruler did not have a zero mark.

Lesson Goal
• Read weight shown on a scale.

What the Student Needs to Know
• Read a number line.
• Read a scale.
• Recognize the relationship between pounds and ounces.

Getting Started
• Have students skip count to 16 by twos, fours, and eights and list the numbers.
• Have a volunteer draw a number line from 0 to 16 with ones marked. Then have another volunteer erase numbers so the number line shows 0 to 16 with multiples of 2 labeled. Have another volunteer erase numbers so that only multiples of 4 are labeled. Ask students to locate 7 on each of the number lines.

What Can I Do?
Read the question and the response. Then read and discuss the examples. Ask:

• *What marker shows the weight on the scale?* (Students will point to the indicator line on the scale.)
• *How can you tell that the weight is between 80 and 90 pounds?* (The marker is between the numbers 80 and 90 on the scale.)
• *How can you check to be sure that each of the small marks shows one pound?* (Count by ones from 80. If you count 90 at the 90 mark, the marks show 1 pound.)
• *How many marks are there between each pound mark?* (15)
• *If there were 7 marks between each pound mark, what would each mark show?* (2 ounces)

Name_____

Reading Weight
Shown on a Scale

Learn

What Can I Do?
I want to read the weight shown on a scale.

Read Weight in Pounds

Pounds

First look at the numbers.

Think: The weight is between 80 and 90 pounds.

Then figure out what the marks in between the numbers show.

Think: There are 9 marks between 80 and 90, so each mark shows 1 pound. The weight is 6 marks past 80, or 86 pounds.

Read Weight in Pounds and Ounces
Sometimes the units used will be written on the scale.

Think: The numbers on this scale show pounds (lb). The marks in between show ounces (oz).

The grapes weigh 3 pounds, 7 ounces, or 3 lb 7 oz.

Remember: There are 16 oz in 1 lb.

Pounds/Ounces

© McGraw-Hill School Division

WHAT IF THE STUDENT CAN'T

Read a Number Line
• Use a number line with tens labeled. Have students count by ones to name the points between the labeled tens. Then name a number and have students point to it on the number line.
• Provide an unnumbered number line and have students label it.

Read a Scale
• Provide practice reading scales in the form of number lines with different multiples labeled. For instance show a number line with multiples of 8 labeled. Ask students to

find 24, and then to find 12 on the number line.
• Have students label similar number lines using skip counting by various numbers such as 2, 10, and 25. Then have the students name the scale they would use to locate a given number such as 88. Some scales will not include this number while others will. Ask students to explain how they would estimate where the number is located on the scale.

Name_____

Try It • Read the weight shown on each scale.

1. The fish weighs between

   __3__ pounds and __4__ pounds.

2. Each mark shows __1__ oz.

3. The fish weighs __3__ lb __2__ oz.

The weight of each ⊙ (lb.) is 1 lb.

The weight of each ⊙ (oz) is 1 oz.

4. The rock weighs __1__ lb __5__ oz.

Power Practice • Read the weight shown on each scale.

5.

Pounds

99 lb

6.

Pounds/Ounces

1 lb 8 oz

7.

Pounds/Ounces

4 lb 1 oz

8.

Pounds/Ounces

8 lb 2 oz

© McGraw-Hill School Division

Try It

• Check to see that students can locate the mark that indicates the weight. Have them point out where they will read the weight from the scale.

• Have a volunteer describe how a balance scale shows weight. Ask how the scale will look if not enough weights have been placed on the scale.

• Tell students to suppose they do not have any pound weights. Ask how they could use ounce weights to weigh the rock in pounds and ounces.

Power Practice

• For each exercise, ask a volunteer to explain how he or she decided what weight was shown on the scale. Each explanation should include a description of the markings and their meaning.

WHAT IF THE STUDENT CAN'T

Recognize the Relationship Between Pounds and Ounces

• Remind students that there are 16 ounces in a pound. Have them draw a number line and number it from 1 to 64. They should label this scale ounces. Then have them use a different color marker to color each 16th mark. They can then number the marks from 1 to 4 and label this scale *pounds*. The number line will illustrate the relationship between pounds and ounces.

Complete the Power Practice

• Discuss each incorrect answer with the student. Ask the student to point out where on the scale the weight is indicated. Then ask him or her to tell how the scale measures weight and explain how they read the scale.

USING THE LESSON

Lesson Goal
- Multiply and divide numbers with more than one digit.

What the Student Needs to Know
- Recall multiplication facts.
- Multiply by a 1-digit number.
- Divide by a 1-digit number.

Getting Started
- Have students multiply some 2-digit numbers by 1-digit numbers. Include examples with and without renaming. For example: 4 × 42 (168), 5 × 28 (140), 3 × 77 (231).
- Have students multiply some 1-digit numbers by multiples of 10. For example: 30 × 31 (930), 40 × 17 (680), 20 × 22 (440)
- Ask students where to place the first digit of the quotient for each of these examples: 46 ÷ 5 (over the 6), 75 ÷ 3 (over the 7), 626 ÷ 8 (over the 2).

What Can I Do?
Read the question and the response. Then read and discuss the examples. Ask:

- *How is multiplying by two digits like multiplying by one digit?* (To multiply by two digits you multiply by each of the digits separately. Then you add the products.)
- *When you multiply 16 × 35, why do you think 10 × 35 rather than 1 × 35?* (The one is in the tens place, so it stands for 10.)
- *How do you decide where to place the first digit in a quotient?* (Look for the first number that the divisor can be divided into.)
- *How do you know if the number you choose for the quotient is too great?* (You will not be able to subtract.)
- *How do you know if the number you choose for the quotient is not great enough?* (When you subtract, the remainder will be greater than the divisor.)

Multiplication and Division

Learn

What Can I Do? I want to multiply and divide numbers with more than one digit.

Multiply

Find 16 × 35.

Think: I can multiply by one digit at a time and then add the products.

Multiply by the ones digit.	Multiply by the tens digit.	Add the products.
3 35 × 16 ――― 210	³ 35 × 16 ――― 210 + 350	³ 35 × 16 ――― 210 + 350 ――― 560

Think:
6 × 5 = 30
6 × 30 = 180
180 + 30 = 210

Think:
10 × 5 = 50
10 × 30 = 300
300 + 50 = 350

Divide

Find 156 ÷ 12.

Think: I cannot divide 12 into 1. I can divide 12 into 15, so I will start there.

Decide where to place the first digit. Then divide and subtract.	Bring down the next digit. Divide.
1 12)156 − 12 ―― 3	13 12)156 − 12↓ ―― 36 − 36 ―― 0

© McGraw-Hill School Division

WHAT IF THE STUDENT CAN'T

Recall Multiplication Facts
- Remind students that they can draw a rectangle, use repeated addition, use facts they know, or skip count to find products they have forgotten.
- Demonstrate how students can break down a fact they cannot remember into two simpler facts. For example to find 8 × 3, they can find (4 × 3) + (4 × 3).

Multiply by a One-Digit Number
- Have students use place-value models to find some products. Review the process of renaming ones as tens and tens as hundreds.
- Ask students to write the multiplication exercise as they use place-value models to find a product. Review the placement of renamed digits. Then have students multiply by one digit without using the models.

Name _____

Try It • Complete. Find each product or quotient.

1.
$$\begin{array}{r} \overset{1}{12} \\ \times\ 6 \\ \hline 72 \end{array}$$

2.
$$\begin{array}{r} \overset{2}{36} \\ \times\ 24 \\ \hline 144 \\ +\ 720 \\ \hline 864 \end{array}$$

3.
$$\begin{array}{r} 24 \\ \times\ 12 \\ \hline 288 \end{array}$$

4.
$$\begin{array}{r} \overset{3}{5{,}280} \\ \times\ 4 \\ \hline 21{,}120 \end{array}$$

5. $3\overline{)81}$ → 27

6. $16\overline{)64}$ → 4 -64

7. $36\overline{)108}$ → 3

8. $12\overline{)360}$ → 30

Power Practice • Find each product or quotient.

9.
$$\begin{array}{r} 32 \\ \times\ 8 \\ \hline 256 \end{array}$$

10.
$$\begin{array}{r} 16 \\ \times\ 9 \\ \hline 144 \end{array}$$

11.
$$\begin{array}{r} 31 \\ \times\ 12 \\ \hline 372 \end{array}$$

12.
$$\begin{array}{r} 1{,}760 \\ \times\ 3 \\ \hline 5{,}280 \end{array}$$

13.
$$\begin{array}{r} 32 \\ \times\ 15 \\ \hline 480 \end{array}$$

14.
$$\begin{array}{r} 108 \\ \times\ 6 \\ \hline 648 \end{array}$$

15.
$$\begin{array}{r} 12 \\ \times\ 7 \\ \hline 84 \end{array}$$

16.
$$\begin{array}{r} 48 \\ \times\ 36 \\ \hline 1{,}728 \end{array}$$

17. $4\overline{)96}$ → 24

18. $12\overline{)72}$ → 6

19. $16\overline{)122}$ → 7 R10

20. $8\overline{)128}$ → 16

21. $3\overline{)123}$ → 41

22. $36\overline{)216}$ → 6

23. $24\overline{)168}$ → 7

24. $3\overline{)5{,}280}$ → 1,760

© McGraw-Hill School Division

Grade 4, Chapter 9, Cluster A **113**

USING THE LESSON

Try It

• Be sure students understand that when they multiply 36 × 24, the ones digit for the second multiplication is 0 since they are multiplying by 20.

• You may want to work with the class to decide where to put the first digit in each quotient before they begin the exercises.

Power Practice

• Review each answer with the students. Have volunteers describe how they solved any problems that are missed by several students.

• Ask students to share their methods for selecting digits to try in the quotient. Encourage students who are not immediately successful at selecting the correct digit to adjust their estimates. Point out that with practice their estimating skills will improve.

WHAT IF THE STUDENT CAN'T

Divide by a One–Digit Number

• Have students use place-value models to find some quotients that involve dividing two or more digits by one digit. Review how to rename tens as ones and hundreds as tens.

• Ask students to write down the division exercise as they use place-value models to solve a problem. Encourage them to explain how they identify whether or not they can divide using the models and help them translate their model to the written problem.

Complete the Power Practice

• Discuss each incorrect answer. If it is practical have students use place-value materials to model the problem. If not, have them model a simpler problem writing their steps down as they go. Then have them try the more difficult problem.

Lesson Goal

- Measure line segments to the nearest centimeter.

What the Student Needs to Know

- Identify the markings on a centimeter ruler.
- Identify the mark half way between two consecutive centimeter markings on a ruler.

Getting Started

Show a number line with tens numbered and marks for the ones digits. Have students locate a number you name on the number line. For example:

- Point to 56 on this number line.

What Can I Do?

Read the question and the response. Then read and discuss the examples. Ask:

- What if the end of the line was exactly above the mark that is half way between 5 and 6 centimeters; would you say that to the nearest centimeter the line is 5 or 6 centimeters long? (Either answer is acceptable, but usually the greater measurement is used.)

Try It

As you review student measurements point out that, to the nearest centimeter, both lines are 4 cm long. Ask:

- What are the longest and shortest length lines that to the nearest centimeter measure 4 centimeters? (4.4 cm and 3.5 cm)

Power Practice

- Remind students to line up the zero point on their rulers with the left end of each line.
- Have students measure each line segment. Then review each answer.

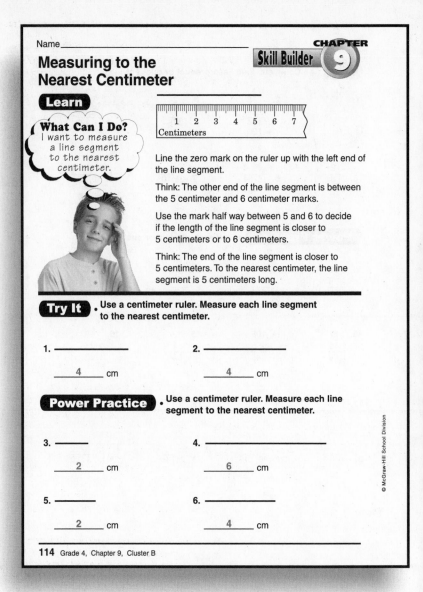

Measuring to the Nearest Centimeter

Learn

What Can I Do? I want to measure a line segment to the nearest centimeter.

Line the zero mark on the ruler up with the left end of the line segment.

Think: The other end of the line segment is between the 5 centimeter and 6 centimeter marks.

Use the mark half way between 5 and 6 to decide if the length of the line segment is closer to 5 centimeters or to 6 centimeters.

Think: The end of the line segment is closer to 5 centimeters. To the nearest centimeter, the line segment is 5 centimeters long.

Try It Use a centimeter ruler. Measure each line segment to the nearest centimeter.

1. _____
   _____4_____ cm

2. _____
   _____4_____ cm

Power Practice Use a centimeter ruler. Measure each line segment to the nearest centimeter.

3. ——
   _____2_____ cm

4. ——————————
   _____6_____ cm

5. ————
   _____2_____ cm

6. ——————
   _____4_____ cm

114 Grade 4, Chapter 9, Cluster B

WHAT IF THE STUDENT CAN'T

Identify the Markings on a Centimeter Ruler

- Point out that centimeters are numbered. The longest marks on the centimeter ruler show centimeters. Name a centimeter marking and have students point it out. For example: Locate the 8 centimeter mark on your ruler.
- Tell students that the shortest markings on the centimeter ruler show millimeters. The slightly longer mark is the 5 millimeter mark half way between any two centimeter measures.

Identify the Halfway Mark Between Two Centimeter Marks

- Have students point out the mark half way between two centimeter measures you name. For example: Point to the mark that is half way between 6 and 7 cm.

Complete the Power Practice

- Check that students line up the left end of each line segment with the zero point on the ruler.
- Have students identify the two centimeters each measurement is between and which it is closer to.

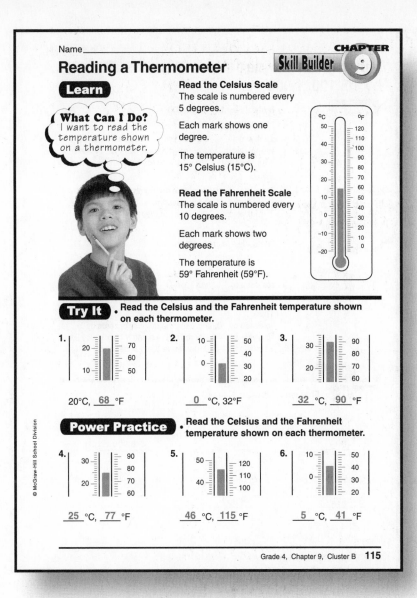

Name_____

Reading a Thermometer

Learn

What Can I Do?
I want to read the temperature shown on a thermometer.

Read the Celsius Scale
The scale is numbered every 5 degrees.

Each mark shows one degree.

The temperature is 15° Celsius (15°C).

Read the Fahrenheit Scale
The scale is numbered every 10 degrees.

Each mark shows two degrees.

The temperature is 59° Fahrenheit (59°F).

Try It . Read the Celsius and the Fahrenheit temperature shown on each thermometer.

1. 20°C, __68__ °F

2. __0__ °C, 32°F

3. __32__ °C, __90__ °F

Power Practice . Read the Celsius and the Fahrenheit temperature shown on each thermometer.

4. __25__ °C, __77__ °F

5. __46__ °C, __115__ °F

6. __5__ °C, __41__ °F

© McGraw-Hill School Division

Grade 4, Chapter 9, Cluster B   **115**

WHAT IF THE STUDENT CAN'T

Read a Number Scale with Multiples of 5 Labeled

• Ask students to skip count by 5s. Then have them read a number on the number scale and count by ones to the next multiple of 5.

• Say a number and have students locate it on the number scale. For example say: *Point to 18 on the number scale.*

Read a Number Scale with Multiples of 10 Labeled

• Ask students to skip count by 10s. Then have them locate a number you name on the number scale. For example, say: *Point to 26 on the number scale.*

Complete the Power Practice

• Cover one of the temperature scales so students can focus on the other. Have them identify the marked number of degrees that the temperature falls between. Then have students count on to find the temperature.

Lesson Goal
• Read temperatures in degrees Celsius and in degrees Fahrenheit.

What the Student Needs to Know
• Read a number scale in which multiples of 5 are labeled.
• Read a number scale in which multiples of 10 are labeled.

Getting Started
Have students read the degree labels on the Celsius scale. 0 degrees, 5 degrees, 10 degrees, etc. Ask:
• *How many marks are shown between each of the numbered marks on the Celsius scale? (4) How many degrees does each mark stand for? (1 degree)*

Have students to read the degree labels on the Fahrenheit scale. 0 degrees, 10 degrees, 20 degrees, etc. Ask:
• *How many marks are shown between each of the numbered marks on the Fahrenheit scale? (4) How many degrees does each mark stand for? (2 degrees)*

What Can I Do?
Read the question and the response. Then read and discuss the examples. Ask:
• *If the temperature is between two marks on the Fahrenheit scale, how can you decide how many degrees is shown? (Each mark on the Fahrenheit scale shows two degrees, so you can skip count by twos to find the values of the marks on each side of the temperature shown. The temperature is then the number between those two numbers.)*

Try It
• Remind students that the Celsius scale is on the left side of the thermometer and the Fahrenheit scale is on the right side.

Power Practice
• Remind students that they will be finding two temperatures for each thermometer.

Grade 4, Chapter 9, Cluster B   **115**

USING THE LESSON

Lesson Goal
- Multiply and divide by 10, 100, and 1,000.

What the Student Needs to Know
- Understand and apply the identity property for multiplication.
- Understand and apply the identity property for division
- Recognize place value through ten thousands.

Getting Started
- Ask students to find these products: 6×1, 2×1, 8×1, 10×1.
- Have students find these quotients: $6 \div 1$, $2 \div 1$, $8 \div 1$, $10 \div 1$.

What Can I Do?
Read the question and the response. Then read and discuss the examples. Ask:
- *Look at the first column of multiplication exercises. If 10 is one factor, what is true about the product?* (The product has 1 more zero than the other factor.)
- *Look at the second column of multiplication exercises. If 100 is one factor, what is true about the product?* (The product has 2 more zeros than the other factor.)
- *Look at the third column of multiplication exercises. If 1,000 is one factor, what is true about the product?* (The product has 3 more zeros than the other factor.)
- *What pattern do you see in the first column of division exercises?* (When you divide by 10, the quotient has one less zero than the dividend.)
- *What pattern do you see in the second column of division exercises?* (When you divide by 100, the quotient has two fewer zeros than the dividend.)
- *What pattern do you see in the third column of division exercises?* (When you divide by 1,000, the quotient has three fewer zeros than the dividend.)

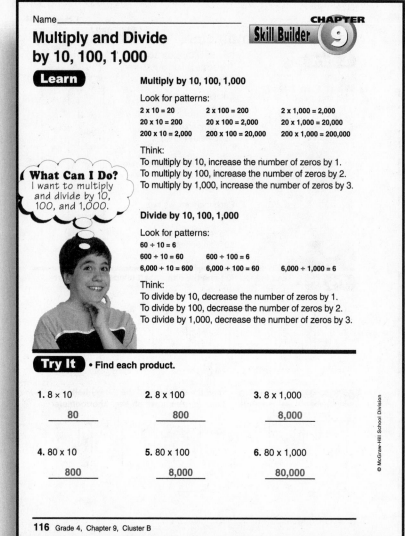

Multiply and Divide by 10, 100, 1,000

Learn

Multiply by 10, 100, 1,000

Look for patterns:

$2 \times 10 = 20$	$2 \times 100 = 200$	$2 \times 1{,}000 = 2{,}000$
$20 \times 10 = 200$	$20 \times 100 = 2{,}000$	$20 \times 1{,}000 = 20{,}000$
$200 \times 10 = 2{,}000$	$200 \times 100 = 20{,}000$	$200 \times 1{,}000 = 200{,}000$

Think:
To multiply by 10, increase the number of zeros by 1.
To multiply by 100, increase the number of zeros by 2.
To multiply by 1,000, increase the number of zeros by 3.

What Can I Do?
I want to multiply and divide by 10, 100, and 1,000.

Divide by 10, 100, 1,000

Look for patterns:

$60 \div 10 = 6$

$600 \div 10 = 60$	$600 \div 100 = 6$	
$6{,}000 \div 10 = 600$	$6{,}000 \div 100 = 60$	$6{,}000 \div 1{,}000 = 6$

Think:
To divide by 10, decrease the number of zeros by 1.
To divide by 100, decrease the number of zeros by 2.
To divide by 1,000, decrease the number of zeros by 3.

Try It • Find each product.

1. 8×10 80	**2.** 8×100 800	**3.** $8 \times 1{,}000$ 8,000
4. 80×10 800	**5.** 80×100 8,000	**6.** $80 \times 1{,}000$ 80,000

© McGraw-Hill School Division

116 Grade 4, Chapter 9, Cluster B

WHAT IF THE STUDENT CAN'T

Recall the Identity Property for Multiplication
- Ask students to find some products such as 5×1, 1×9, 54×1, and so on in which 1 is a factor. Then have them write their own multiplication problems with 1 as a factor.
- Have students solve this riddle. *If you multiply any number by this digit, the product is the same as the number. What is the digit?* (1)
- Have a volunteer state a rule about multiplying by 1. (1 times any number is that number.)

Recall the Identity Property for Division
- Ask students to find some quotients such as $5 \div 1$, $11 \div 1$, $34 \div 1$, and so on in which 1 is the divisor. Then have them write their own division problems with 1 as a divisor.
- Have students solve this riddle. *If you divide any number by this digit, the quotient is the same as the number. What is the digit?* (1)
- Have a volunteer state a rule about dividing by 1. (The quotient of any number divided by 1 is that number.)

Name_____

7. 800 x 10	8. 800 x 100	9. 800 x 1,000
8,000	80,000	800,000

Find each quotient.

10. 150 ÷ 10	11. 1,500 ÷ 10	12. 15,000 ÷ 10
15	150	1,500

13. 1,500 ÷ 100	14. 15,000 ÷ 100	15. 15,000 ÷ 1,000
15	150	15

Power Practice • Find each product or quotient.

16. 9 x 10	17. 50 x 100	18. 17 x 1,000
90	5,000	17,000

19. 300 ÷ 100	20. 7,000 ÷ 10	21. 35,000 ÷ 1,000
3	700	35

22. 6 x 1,000	23. 800 x 10	24. 100 x 100
6,000	8,000	10,000

25. 90 ÷ 10	26. 4,000 ÷ 1,000	27. 19,000 ÷ 100
9	4	190

28. 3,000 x 100	29. 700 x 1,000	30. 4,000 x 10
300,000	700,000	40,000

© McGraw-Hill School Division

Try It

- Have students predict the number of zeros in each product.
- Ask students if they can state a rule for determining the number of zeros each product will have. (Add the number of zeros in the two factors.)
- Ask students if they can figure out a way to make each division into division by 1. (Count the number of zeros in the divisor. Cross out that number of zeros in both the divisor and the dividend.)

Power Practice

- Caution students to watch the operation signs as they are doing the problems.
- Have the students solve each problem. Then review the answers.
- Ask students to share their techniques for multiplying with 10, 100, and 1,000 as one factor.
- Ask students to share their techniques for dividing by 10, 100, and 1,000.

WHAT IF THE STUDENT CAN'T

Use Place Value to Ten Thousands

- Use a place-value chart. Write a number in the chart and ask the student to identify the digit in a place you name. For example: *What digit is in thousands place?*
- Write a number in a place-value chart. Ask the student to name the place for a given digit. For example: *In what place is the 6?*
- Write numbers such as 70,000, 9,000, and so on and ask students to read them.

Complete the Power Practice

- For any incorrect multiplication answer, have student draw an arrow to each zero in both factors. Then ask how many zeros will be in the product. For any incorrect division answer, have student cross out the zeros in the divisor and then cross out the same number in the dividend.Then ask how many zeros will be in the quotient.

CHALLENGE

Lesson Goal

- To find perimeter by measuring side lengths to the nearest $\frac{1}{2}$ inch.

Introducing the Challenge

- Be sure each student has an inch ruler.
- Review measuring to the nearest $\frac{1}{2}$ inch with students.
- Remind students that they can use quarter-inch marks to help them measure to the nearest half-inch.

Using the Challenge

- Explain to students that they will be finding the perimeter, or distance around, some geometric figures by measuring the lengths of the sides of the figures and then adding to find the sum of the measurements.
- You may want to suggest that students letter or number the sides of the geometric figures or that they make a mark through sides as they measure them to keep track of which sides they have measured.
- Have students complete the Challenge. Then review student measurements and perimeter lengths.
- Encourage students to compare the figures they drew for the *Draw Your Own Figure* problem. Ask volunteers to explain how they drew their figures. Help students make the generalization that many shapes can have the same perimeter.

Name_____

Measuring Perimeter

The distance around a figure is its perimeter. Find the perimeter of the triangle.

1. Measure each side of the triangle to the nearest half inch.

   The side lengths are:

   ___3___ inches

   ___2___ inches

   ___$4\frac{1}{2}$___ inches

2. Add the side lengths to find the perimeter.

   The perimeter is:

   ___$9\frac{1}{2}$___ inches

Find the perimeter. Measure each side to the nearest half inch.

3. The side lengths are:

   ___2___ inches

   ___2___ inches

   ___2___ inches

   ___5___ inches

4. The perimeter is:

   ___11___ inches

118 Grade 4, Chapter 9, Cluster A

Name_____

Measure each side to the nearest half inch. Find the perimeter.

5. The side lengths are:

_____3_____ inches

_____2_____ inches

_____2_____ inches

_____3_____ inches

____$1\frac{1}{2}$____ inches

6. The perimeter is:

____$11\frac{1}{2}$____ inches

Draw your own figure.

7. Draw a figure that has a perimeter of ten inches.

Figures will vary.

8. What are the lengths of the sides of your figure?

Side lengths will vary._____

Grade 4, Chapter 9, Cluster A **119**

CHALLENGE

Lesson Goal

- To discover the relationship between Celsius and Fahrenheit temperature by drawing a Celsius/Fahrenheit thermometer.

Introducing the Challenge

- Have students skip count by 5's beginning at 0, at 2, and at 3.
- Have students skip count by 9's beginning at 0, at 2, and at 5.
- Ask students to identify this pattern and to find the next number in the pattern: 25, 34, 43, 52, ... (add 9, 61).
- Ask students to identify this pattern and to continue the pattern: 18, 23, 28, 33, ... (add 5, 38, 43, 48, 53).

Using the Challenge

- Tell students that in this Challenge, they will use patterns to draw the scales for a Celsius/Fahrenheit thermometer.
- Have students complete the Challenge. Then lead a discussion in which students identify any difficulties they had and share their methods for labeling the Fahrenheit scale.

CHALLENGE CHAPTER 9

Draw a Celsius/Fahrenheit Thermometer

Follow the steps on the next page to draw a Celsius/Fahrenheit Thermometer.

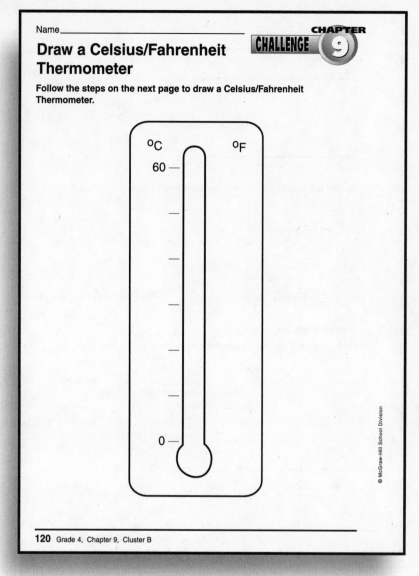

Name_____

1. Start with the Celsius scale. Count by tens to complete the scale shown in the drawing. What numbers will you use to label the scale?

   0, 10, 20, 30, 40, 50, 60

2. Draw a line halfway between each of the marks given on the drawing. Put in numbers so your scale is numbered by fives. What numbers will you put in?

   5, 15, 25, 35, 45, 55

This table shows Fahrenheit temperatures for some Celsius temperatures.

0°C	5°C	10°C	15°C	20°C
32°F	41°F	50°F	59°F	68°F

3. What is the pattern for degrees Celsius? _____Add 5 degrees_____

4. What is the pattern for degrees Fahrenheit? _____Add 9 degrees_____

5. Complete this sentence: As the Celsius temperature increases by 5 degrees, the Fahrenheit temperature increases by __9__ degrees.

6. Use the pattern to complete this table.

25°C	30°C	35°C	40°C	45°C	50°C	55°C	60°C
77°F	86°F	95°F	104°F	113°F	122°F	131°F	140°F

7. Explain how you can use the temperatures in the table to label the Fahrenheit scale on your thermometer by tens. Then label the scale.

   Possible answer: Label points across from those on the Celsius scale. Draw eight equally spaced marks between each label to show degrees. Locate and label 40, 50, 60, 70, 80, 90, 100, 110, 120, 130, 140.

CHALLENGE

Name_____

Identify Pyramids and Prisms

Write the name of each figure.

1.

_____

2.

_____

3.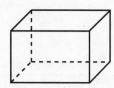

_____

Identify Basic Shapes

Write the name of each shape.

4.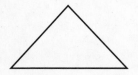

_____

5.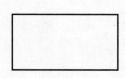

_____

6.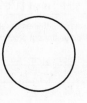

_____

Identify Sides and Angles of Polygons

Write the number of sides and angles for each polygon. Then name the polygon.

7.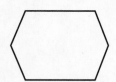

Sides _____

Angles _____

Name _____

8.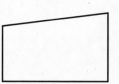

Sides _____

Angles _____

Name _____

9.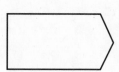

Sides _____

Angles _____

Name _____

Name_____

Geometric Patterns

Draw what the next shape in this pattern could be.

10.

Congruence

Are the shapes congruent? Write *yes* or *no*.

11. 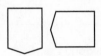   12.

_____   _____

Adding Three or More Numbers

Find each sum.

13.   4
     2
 + 8

14. 14
    5
   10
+ 15

15.   3
  22
   4
 + 1

Using Formulas

Use the formulas.

16. Formula $T = 3m$.

   Find T for $m = 7$.

   $T =$ _____

17. Formula $P = n + w$.

   Find P for $n = 3$ and $w = 7$.

   $P =$ _____

Multiplying Three Numbers

Find each product.

18. $3 \times 3 \times 6 =$ _____   19. $4 \times 2 \times 10 =$ _____   20. $5 \times 5 \times 5 =$ _____

CHAPTER 10 PRE-CHAPTER ASSESSMENT

Assessment Goal

This two-page assessment covers skills identified as necessary for success in Chapter 10 Geometry. The first page assesses the major prerequisite skills for Cluster A. The second page assesses the major prerequisite skills for Cluster B. When the Cluster A and Cluster B prerequisite skills overlap, the skill(s) will be covered in only one section.

Getting Started

- Allow students time to look over the two pages of the assessment. Point out the labels that identify the skills covered.

- Have students find math vocabulary terms used in the assessment. List vocabulary terms on the board as students identify them. If necessary, review the meanings of all essential math vocabulary.

Introducing the Assessment

- Explain to students that these pages will help you know if they are ready to start a new chapter in their math textbooks.

- Students who have transferred from another school may not have been introduced to some of these skills. Encourage students to do their best and assure them you will help them learn any needed skills.

Cluster A Challenge

Those students who demonstrate mastery of the skills on this page will not need to use the reteaching worksheets. Instead, these students can do the Cluster A Challenge found on pages 130–131.

Name_____

Identify Pyramids and Prisms

Write the name of each figure.

1.
square prism

2.
triangular pyramid

3.
rectangular prism

Identify Basic Shapes

Write the name of each shape.

4.
triangle

5.
rectangle

6.
circle

Identify Sides and Angles of Polygons

Write the number of sides and angles for each polygon. Then name the polygon.

7.

Sides ____6____

Angles ____6____

Name ___hexagon___

8.

Sides ____4____

Angles ____4____

Name ___quadrilateral___

9.

Sides ____5____

Angles ____5____

Name ___pentagon___

121A Use with Grade 4, Chapter 10, Cluster A

CLUSTER A PREREQUISITE SKILLS

The skills listed in this chart are those identified as major prerequisite skills for students' success in the lessons in Cluster A of the chapter. Each skill is covered by one or more assessment items as shown in the middle column. The right column provides the page number for the lessons in this book that reteach the cluster A prerequisite skills.

Skill Name	Assessment Items	Lesson Pages
Identify Pyramids and Prisms	1-3	122
Identify Basic Shapes	4-6	123
Identify Sides and Angles of Polygons	7-9	124

Name_____

Geometric Patterns

Draw what the next shape in this pattern could be.

10.

Congruence

Are the shapes congruent? Write *yes* or *no*.

11.   12.

　　　yes　　　　　　　　　　　no

Adding Three or More Numbers

Find each sum.

13.　4　　　　　14.　14　　　　　15.　　3
　　　2　　　　　　　　5　　　　　　　22
　+ 8　　　　　　　10　　　　　　　 4
　 14　　　　　 + 15　　　　　　+ 1
　　　　　　　　　 44　　　　　　　 30

Using Formulas

Use the formulas.

16. Formula $T = 3m$.　　　　17. Formula $P = n + w$.

Find T for $m = 7$.　　　　Find P for $n = 3$ and $w = 7$.

$T = $ _21_　　　　　　$P = $ _10_

Multiplying Three Numbers

Find each product.

18. $3 \times 3 \times 6 = $ _54_　　19. $4 \times 2 \times 10 = $ _80_　　20. $5 \times 5 \times 5 = $ _125_

Use with Grade 4, Chapter 10, Cluster B　**121B**

© McGraw-Hill School Division

CLUSTER B PREREQUISITE SKILLS

The skills listed in this chart are those identified as major prerequisite skills for students' success in the lessons in Cluster B of the chapter. Each skill is covered by one or more assessment items as shown in the middle column. The right column provides the page numbers for the lessons in this book that reteach the Cluster B prerequisite skills

Skill Name	Assessment Items	Lesson Pages
Geometric Patterns	10	125
Congruence	11-12	126
Adding Three or More Numbers	13-15	127
Using Formulas	16-17	128
Multiplying Three Numbers	18-20	129

Alternative Assessment Strategies

- Oral administration of the assessment is appropriate for younger students or those whose native language is not English. Read the skills title and directions one section at a time. Check students' understanding by asking them to tell you how they will do the first exercise in the group.

- For some skill types you may wish to use group administration. In this technique, a small group or pair of students complete the assessment together. Through their discussion, you will be able to decide if supplementary reteaching materials are needed.

Intervention Materials

If students are not successful with the prerequisite skills assessed on these pages, reteaching lessons have been created to help them make the transition into the chapter.

Item correlation charts showing the skills lessons suitable for reteaching the prerequisite skills are found beneath the reproductions of each page of the assessment.

Cluster B Challenge

Those students who demonstrate mastery of the skills on this page will not need to use the reteaching worksheets. Instead, these students can do the Cluster B Challenge found on pages 132–133.

Lesson Goal
- To name pyramids and prisms.

What the Student Needs to Know
- Identify a solid shape.
- Identify the base or bases of a solid figure.
- Identify the sides of a solid figure.

Getting Started
- Show students models of prisms and pyramids. Ask them to group the models in as many different ways as they can. Possible groupings include: shapes with points and shapes without points, shapes with triangles and shapes without triangles, shapes with rectangles and shapes without rectangles, etc.

What Can I Do?
Read the question and the response. Then read and discuss the examples. Ask:
- *How can you tell a prism from a pyramid?* (A pyramid has 1 base, a prism has 2 bases.)
- *How are the sides of a pyramid different from the sides of a prism?* (The sides of a pyramid are triangular; the sides of a prism are rectangular.)

Try It
- Ask students to point to the base or bases of each figure.
- Advise students that the word that tells the shape of the base is an adjective, so instead of saying triangle pyramid, we say triangular pyramid. Instead of saying rectangle prism, we say rectangular prism.

Power Practice
- Remind students that each figure is named with two words, the first tells the shape of the base and the second tells the name of the figure.

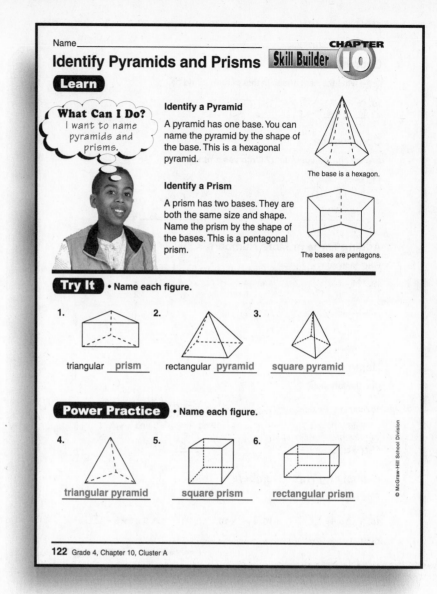

Name_____

Identify Pyramids and Prisms Skill Builder CHAPTER 10

Learn

What Can I Do? I want to name pyramids and prisms.

Identify a Pyramid
A pyramid has one base. You can name the pyramid by the shape of the base. This is a hexagonal pyramid.

The base is a hexagon.

Identify a Prism
A prism has two bases. They are both the same size and shape. Name the prism by the shape of the bases. This is a pentagonal prism.

The bases are pentagons.

Try It • Name each figure.

1. triangular __prism__
2. rectangular __pyramid__
3. square pyramid

Power Practice • Name each figure.

4. triangular pyramid
5. square prism
6. rectangular prism

© McGraw-Hill School Division

122 Grade 4, Chapter 10, Cluster A

WHAT IF THE STUDENT CAN'T

Identify a Solid Shape
- Show a group of solid and plane shapes and have the student separate them and then explain the difference between the two.

Identify the Base or Bases of a Solid Shape
- Ask students to share their tips for determining how many bases a figure has and for identifying the base or bases.

Identify the Sides of a Solid Figure
- Use models of three-dimensional figures. Point out the base or bases on a model. Then ask the student to point to and count the sides. Next have the student identify both the bases and the sides of some solid figures.

Complete the Power Practice
- Use models of the solids. Have the student identify the bases and name the shape of the bases. Then ask the student to identify each shape as either a pyramid or prism.

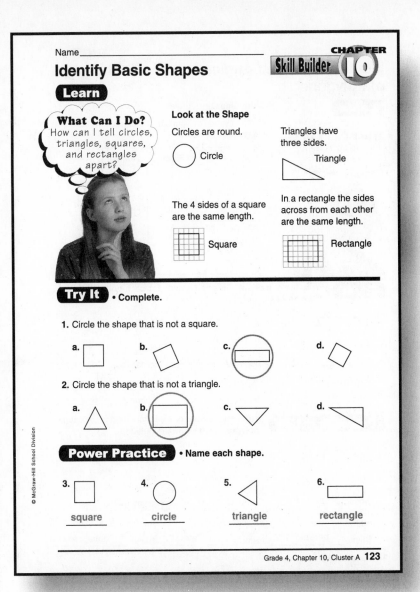

Name_____

Identify Basic Shapes

Learn

What Can I Do?
How can I tell circles, triangles, squares, and rectangles apart?

Look at the Shape

Circles are round.

◯ Circle

Triangles have three sides.

△ Triangle

The 4 sides of a square are the same length.

⬚ Square

In a rectangle the sides across from each other are the same length.

▭ Rectangle

Try It • Complete.

1. Circle the shape that is not a square.

   a. ☐   b. ◇   c. ▭ (circled)   d. ◇

2. Circle the shape that is not a triangle.

   a. △   b. ☐ (circled)   c. ▽   d. ◁

Power Practice • Name each shape.

3. ☐ square

4. ◯ circle

5. ◁ triangle

6. ▭ rectangle

© McGraw-Hill School Division

WHAT IF THE STUDENT CAN'T

Identify Straight Sides

- Provide the student with a straight edge or ruler. Tell the student that if he or she can line the straight edge up along a side, the side is straight. Have the student cut out items from a catalog or magazine and use a heavy marker to outline the straight sides.

Identify Sides Across from Each Other

- Provide models of squares and rectangles. Use several of the models to illustrate sides across from each other. Then choose a model and ask the student to identify the sides across from each other.

Complete the Power Practice

- Use objects in the room such as a sheet of paper, a coin, and a desk top, to illustrate shapes. Trace each shape with your finger and name it. Then ask the student to describe the shape.

USING THE LESSON

Lesson Goal

- To identify basic shapes.

What the Student Needs to Know

- Identify straight sides.
- Identify sides across from each other.

Getting Started

- Provide students with a group of models of these geometric shapes: circles, triangles, squares, and rectangles. Ask the students to sort the shapes. Then have them to tell what properties they used to do the sort. A possible sort is round shapes, three-sided shapes, four-sided shapes.

What Can I Do?

Read the question and the response. Then read and discuss the examples. Ask:

- *How can you tell that the four sides of the square shown are the same length?* (The square is shown on grid paper and all four sides of the square are the same number of units long.)
- *For the rectangle shown, how can you tell that the sides across from each other are the same length?* (The sides across from each other are the same number of grid paper units long.)

Try It

Before students begin, ask:

- *How can you tell if a shape is not a square?* (The sides are not all the same length.)
- *How can you tell if a shape is not a triangle?* (It does not have three sides.)

Power Practice

- Have the students complete the practice. Then have volunteers explain how they named each shape.

Lesson Goal
- Classify polygons by the number of sides and angles.

What the Student Needs to Know
- Identify a polygon.
- Count the sides and angles of a polygon.

Getting Started
- Tell students that poly- means much or many. A polygon is a figure with three or more straight sides.
- Show the students models or pictures of two-dimensional shapes and ask them to identify each shape as *a polygon* or *not a polygon*.

What Can I Do?
Read the question and the response. Then read and discuss the examples. Ask:
- *What do you notice about the number of sides and the number of angles in each polygon?* (They are the same.)

Try It
Point out that the directions call the shapes in the exercises polygons. Ask:
- *Do you think that all of the sides of a polygon must be the same length? Explain.* (No, the polygons shown do not have same length sides.)
- *Do you think that all of the angles of a polygon must be the same size? Explain.* (No, the polygons shown do not have angles that are the same size.)

Power Practice
- Suggest that students might mark off each side and angle as they count it.
- Tell them to use the chart at the top of the page to help them name the polygons.

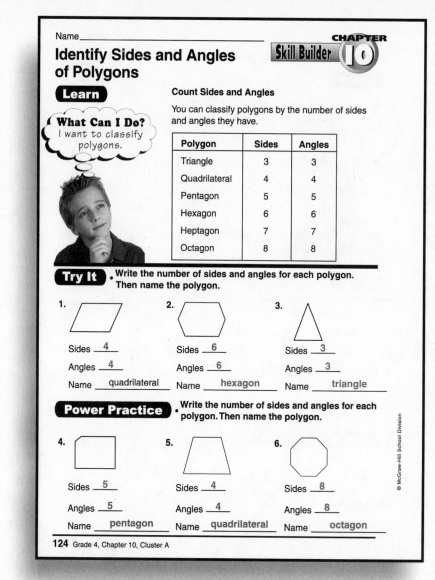

Name_____

Skill Builder CHAPTER **10**

Identify Sides and Angles of Polygons

Learn

What Can I Do? I want to classify polygons.

Count Sides and Angles

You can classify polygons by the number of sides and angles they have.

Polygon	Sides	Angles
Triangle	3	3
Quadrilateral	4	4
Pentagon	5	5
Hexagon	6	6
Heptagon	7	7
Octagon	8	8

Try It • Write the number of sides and angles for each polygon. Then name the polygon.

1.
Sides __4__
Angles __4__
Name ___quadrilateral___

2.
Sides __6__
Angles __6__
Name ___hexagon___

3.
Sides __3__
Angles __3__
Name ___triangle___

Power Practice • Write the number of sides and angles for each polygon. Then name the polygon.

4.
Sides __5__
Angles __5__
Name ___pentagon___

5.
Sides __4__
Angles __4__
Name ___quadrilateral___

6.
Sides __8__
Angles __8__
Name ___octagon___

124 Grade 4, Chapter 10, Cluster A

© McGraw-Hill School Division

WHAT IF THE STUDENT CAN'T

Identify a Polygon
- Show the student a number of different polygons. For each, point out that it has three or more sides and that the sides are straight.
- Have the student identify figures you hold up as *a polygon* or *not a polygon*.

Count the Number of Sides and Angles of a Polygon
- Tell students to put their finger on the first side they count as they say "one." Then have them count clockwise around the figure to determine the number of sides. As they count, have them put a line through each side so they don't count a line twice.
- Have students use the technique above to count angles.

Complete the Power Practice
- Remind the student that the number of sides and the number of angles in a polygon are the same. Tell the student to count both the sides and the angles and to check that the counts match to be sure that he or she has counted correctly.

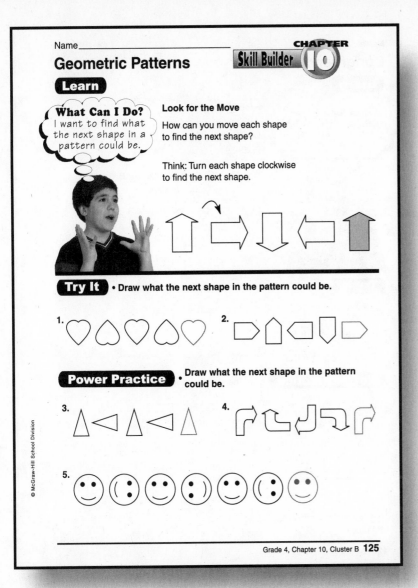

Name_____

Geometric Patterns

Skill Builder **CHAPTER 10**

Learn

What Can I Do?
I want to find what the next shape in a pattern could be.

Look for the Move

How can you move each shape to find the next shape?

Think: Turn each shape clockwise to find the next shape.

Try It
• Draw what the next shape in the pattern could be.

1.

2.

Power Practice
• Draw what the next shape in the pattern could be.

3.

4.

5.

Grade 4, Chapter 10, Cluster B **125**

© McGraw-Hill School Division

WHAT IF THE STUDENT CAN'T

Identify a Pattern

• Tell the student that when the same movement or group of movements happens over and over again, the movements create a pattern.

• Have the student do some movement patterns. For example, *turn right, turn right, turn right...* or *sit down, stand up, sit down, stand up,...*

• Model several patterns using physical objects and verbally stating the movements. Then have the student to model a pattern as you describe it. For example *turn up, turn down, turn up, turn down.* Ask the student to continue the pattern.

Complete the Power Practice

• Suggest that the student draw or cut out a shape like the first shape in each pattern. He or she can then move the shape to model the pattern and to determine the next shape in the pattern.

USING THE LESSON

Lesson Goal

• Find the next shape in a geometric pattern.

What the Student Needs to Know

• Identify a pattern.

Getting Started

Ask students to find the next number in each of these patterns.

• 3, 6, 9, 12, ... (15)
• 45, 35, 25, 15, ... (5)
• 2, 4, 8, 16, ... (32)

What Can I Do?

Read the question and the response. Then read and discuss the example. Ask:

• *How can you move the second arrow in the pattern to get the third arrow?* (Turn it clockwise.)

• *How can you move the third arrow in the pattern to get the fourth arrow?* (Turn it clockwise.)

• *What is the pattern?* (Turn each shape clockwise to get the next shape.)

Try It

• Suggest that students can use their pencils to model the pattern. The pointed end of the pencil could be the top of the heart and the point of the arrow.

• Have volunteers model each pattern physically, describe the movements, and show what the next shape in the pattern could be.

Power Practice

• Point out that it may be helpful to model the pattern.

• Have volunteers describe each pattern verbally and explain how they found the next shape in the pattern.

Grade 4, Chapter 10, Cluster B **125**

USING THE LESSON

Lesson Goal
- Identify congruent figures.

What the Student Needs to Know
- Understand the meaning of "flip".
- Understand the meaning of "slide".
- Understand the meaning of "turn".

Getting Started
- Have students sort a set of attribute blocks by size.
- Have students sort a set of attribute blocks by shape.
- Ask students to identify any pairs or groups of blocks that are the same size and shape.

What Can I Do?
Read the question and the response. Then read and discuss the examples. Ask:
- *Are congruent shapes the same size? How do you know?* (Yes, to fit exactly over one another they must be the same size.)
- *Are congruent shapes the same shape? How do you know?* (Yes, to fit exactly over one another they must be the same shape.)

Try It
Be sure students understand the directions. Ask:
- *If you write yes, what does it mean about the two shapes?* (They are congruent.)
- *How will you decide if the shapes are congruent?* (Figure out if they will exactly fit over each other.)

Power Practice
- Remind students that the shapes must be able to fit exactly over one another to be congruent.
- Have volunteers explain why the shapes in Exercises 3 and 6 are not congruent.

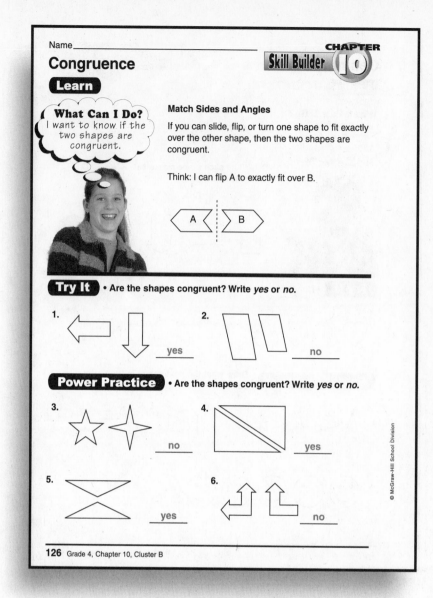

WHAT IF THE STUDENT CAN'T

Understand the Meaning of "Flip"
- Draw a line on a sheet of paper and model flipping a pencil or other object over the line. Ask the student to model flipping his or her hand over the line.

Understand the Meaning of "Slide"
- Model repeated slide movements of a scalene triangle or other object. Verbalize each movement. Ask the student to model sliding his or her feet.

Understand the Meaning of "Turn"
- Model turning an object in quarter turns. Describe each turn as you make it. Ask the student to follow your directions to model turning. For example: *Turn left, turn right, turn left.*

Complete the Power Practice
- Have the student trace the first shape in each exercise and cut it out. Then have the student try to fit the shape exactly over the second shape.

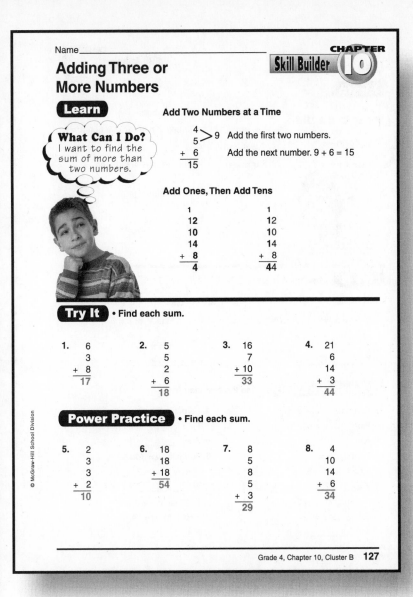

Name_____

Adding Three or More Numbers

Learn

What Can I Do?
I want to find the sum of more than two numbers.

Add Two Numbers at a Time

$$\begin{array}{r} 4 \\ 5 \end{array}\!\!\Big\rangle 9 \quad \text{Add the first two numbers.}$$
$$\begin{array}{r} + 6 \\ \hline 15 \end{array} \quad \text{Add the next number. } 9 + 6 = 15$$

Add Ones, Then Add Tens

$$\begin{array}{r} 1 \\ 12 \\ 10 \\ 14 \\ + 8 \\ \hline 4 \end{array} \qquad \begin{array}{r} 1 \\ 12 \\ 10 \\ 14 \\ + 8 \\ \hline 44 \end{array}$$

Try It • Find each sum.

1. $\begin{array}{r} 6 \\ 3 \\ + 8 \\ \hline 17 \end{array}$ 2. $\begin{array}{r} 5 \\ 5 \\ 2 \\ + 6 \\ \hline 18 \end{array}$ 3. $\begin{array}{r} 16 \\ 7 \\ + 10 \\ \hline 33 \end{array}$ 4. $\begin{array}{r} 21 \\ 6 \\ 14 \\ + 3 \\ \hline 44 \end{array}$

Power Practice • Find each sum.

5. $\begin{array}{r} 2 \\ 3 \\ 3 \\ + 2 \\ \hline 10 \end{array}$ 6. $\begin{array}{r} 18 \\ 18 \\ + 18 \\ \hline 54 \end{array}$ 7. $\begin{array}{r} 8 \\ 5 \\ 8 \\ 5 \\ + 3 \\ \hline 29 \end{array}$ 8. $\begin{array}{r} 4 \\ 10 \\ 14 \\ + 6 \\ \hline 34 \end{array}$

WHAT IF THE STUDENT CAN'T

Recall Addition Facts

- Remind students that they can use objects or place-value models to show addition. They can also start with one of the numbers and count on to find the sum or count on using a number line.

- Suggest that students make flash cards for any facts they do not know and use the cards to learn these facts.

Rename Ones as Tens

- Have students use place-value models to show addition with renaming. Show them how to record renaming ones as tens by writing the tens digit above the digits in the tens column.

Complete the Power Practice

- Review 2-addend addition with students. Have them use place-value models to show 2-digit addition if necessary. Then move to modeling 3-digit addition. Have them record their work on paper.

USING THE LESSON

Lesson Goal

- Find the sum of three or more numbers.

What the Student Needs to Know

- Recall addition facts.
- Rename ones as tens.

Getting Started

- Call out some addition facts and ask students to give their sums.

What Can I Do?

Read the question and the response. Then read and discuss the examples. Ask:

- *In the first example, could you add 5 + 6 first? Would the sum of the three numbers be the same?* (Yes. You can add numbers in any order.)

- *In the second example, what sum could you find first to make adding the ones easy?* (Add 2 + 8 = 10. Then 4 + 10 = 14.)

Try It

- Tell students to write the sum of two numbers to the right to keep track, as in the Learn section.

- Remind students that when they add 2-digit numbers they should add the ones digits and then write the tens digit from the sum above the column of tens digits.

- Review students' answers. Ask volunteers to show how they solved each problem.

Power Practice

- Review students' answers. Ask volunteers to show how they solved each problem.

Lesson Goal
• Use a formula.

What the Student Needs to Know
• Substitute numbers for letters in a formula.
• Perform basic mathematical operations.

Getting Started
Ask students to solve each equation.
• $P = 7 + 5$ ($P = 12$)
• $W = 32 \div 4$ ($W = 8$)
• $M = 9 \times 3$ ($M = 27$)
• $S = 14 - 8$ ($S = 6$)

What Can I Do?
Remind students that in mathematics letters are often used to represent numbers.

Read the question and the response. Then read and discuss the examples. Ask:
• *What is another way to write m times n?* ($m \times n$)
• *What is another way to write S = mn?* ($S = m \times n$).

Try It
• Tell students that to solve each formula they will use numbers to replace letters in the formula.
• Ask students to identify the letter they are solving for in each formula.
• Ask students to identify the operation they will use to solve each formula.

Power Practice
• Alert students that to solve the formula for Exercise 6 they will need to use more than one operation. Ask them to identify the operations they will use and to tell which operation they will do first.
• Select formulas and have volunteers show how they solved them.

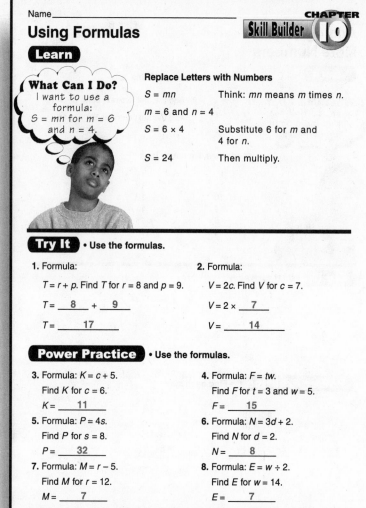

Name _____

Using Formulas

Learn

What Can I Do?
I want to use a formula: $S = mn$ for $m = 6$ and $n = 4$.

Replace Letters with Numbers

$S = mn$	Think: mn means m times n.
$m = 6$ and $n = 4$	
$S = 6 \times 4$	Substitute 6 for m and 4 for n.
$S = 24$	Then multiply.

Try It • Use the formulas.

1. Formula:
   $T = r + p$. Find T for $r = 8$ and $p = 9$.
   $T = \underline{\ 8\ } + \underline{\ 9\ }$
   $T = \underline{\ 17\ }$

2. Formula:
   $V = 2c$. Find V for $c = 7$.
   $V = 2 \times \underline{\ 7\ }$
   $V = \underline{\ 14\ }$

Power Practice • Use the formulas.

3. Formula: $K = c + 5$.
   Find K for $c = 6$.
   $K = \underline{\ 11\ }$

4. Formula: $F = tw$.
   Find F for $t = 3$ and $w = 5$.
   $F = \underline{\ 15\ }$

5. Formula: $P = 4s$.
   Find P for $s = 8$.
   $P = \underline{\ 32\ }$

6. Formula: $N = 3d + 2$.
   Find N for $d = 2$.
   $N = \underline{\ 8\ }$

7. Formula: $M = r - 5$.
   Find M for $r = 12$.
   $M = \underline{\ 7\ }$

8. Formula: $E = w \div 2$.
   Find E for $w = 14$.
   $E = \underline{\ 7\ }$

WHAT IF THE STUDENT CAN'T

Substitute Numbers for Letters in a Formula
• Use arrows to illustrate the substitution. For example:
  Formula: $R = k + t$.
  Find R for $k = 3$ and $t = 2$.
  $R = k + t$
  $\quad\ \downarrow\ \ \downarrow$
  $R = \underline{3} + \underline{2}$
• Begin with formulas that require only one substitution. For example:
  Formula: $J = v - 3$
  Find J for $v = 6$.

Perform Basic Mathematical Operations
• Write equations that can be solved using basic facts. For example: $B = 5 + 5$.
• Have students make flash cards for any basic facts they are still unsure of. Have pairs of students review the flash cards with each other. Continue practice with the facts daily until students are sure of them.

Complete the Power Practice
• Discuss each incorrect answer. Have the student name the operation he or she will use and tell what numbers he or she will use in the calculation.

Name_____

Multiplying Three Numbers

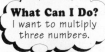

Learn

What Can I Do?
I want to multiply three numbers.

Multiply Two Numbers at a Time

$3 \times 8 \times 5$

Think: You can multiply the numbers in any order.

$$\begin{array}{r} 3 \\ \times\ 8 \\ \hline 24 \end{array}$$ Multiply the first two numbers.

$$\begin{array}{r} \times\ 5 \\ \hline 120 \end{array}$$ Then multiply by the third number.

Try It • Find each product.

1. $2 \times 3 \times 5$

$$\begin{array}{r} 2 \\ \times\ 3 \\ \hline 6 \\ \times\ 5 \\ \hline 30 \end{array}$$

2. $7 \times 6 \times 2$

$$\begin{array}{r} 7 \\ \times\ 6 \\ \hline 42 \\ \times\ 2 \\ \hline 84 \end{array}$$

3. $4 \times 4 \times 4$

$$\begin{array}{r} 4 \\ \times\ 4 \\ \hline 16 \\ \times\ 4 \\ \hline 64 \end{array}$$

Power Practice • Find each product.

4. $4 \times 2 \times 7 = \underline{56}$

5. $3 \times 3 \times 8 = \underline{72}$

6. $5 \times 2 \times 5 = \underline{50}$

7. $6 \times 3 \times 5 = \underline{90}$

8. $4 \times 6 \times 10 = \underline{240}$

9. $3 \times 4 \times 9 = \underline{108}$

Grade 4, Chapter 10, Cluster B **129**

WHAT IF THE STUDENT CAN'T

Recall Multiplication Facts
• Remind students that they can use models, repeated addition, skip counting, or a number line to find any products they cannot recall.

Multiply Two Factors
• Provide place-value models and show students how to model multiplication and how to record the multiplication.
• Review renaming ones as tens and where to write the tens digit in the multiplication problem.

Complete the Power Practice
• Be sure students know their multiplication facts.
• Discuss each incorrect answer and ask students to share their techniques for multiplying three digits. Have volunteers show the steps they used to solve the problems.

Lesson Goal
• Find the product for three factors.

What the Student Needs to Know
• Recall multiplication facts.
• Multiply two factors.

Getting Started
Ask students to find these products.
• 9×7 (63)
• 14×4 (56)
• 4×3 (12)
• 12×6 (72)

What Can I Do?
Read the question and the response. Then read and discuss the examples. Ask:
• *Does it matter which two numbers you multiply first?* (No. You can multiply any two of the three factors first.)
• *How could you check that your multiplication is correct?* (Possible answer: Multiply the factors in a different order.)

Try It
• Have volunteers show how they solved each problem.
• Ask students if there are any problems they could have solved more easily by changing the order in which they multiplied.

Power Practice
• Tell students that they may find it easier to solve some of these problems if they multiply the digits in a different order from the order given.
• Have the students complete the practice. Then review each answer.

CHALLENGE

Lesson Goal
Explore properties of polygons using pentominoes.

Introducing the Challenge
- Ask students how many sides a pentagon has. (5)
- Tell them that in this challenge they are going to work with shapes made up of 5 squares. The shapes are called pentominoes.
- To be a pentomino, the five squares must share at least one side with another square.

Using the Challenge
- Be sure students understand the difference between five-square shapes that are pentominoes and those that are not. Show other examples if needed. Have students explain the difference between a pentominoe and a five-square shape that is not a pentominoe.
- Ask students to point to three pentominoes that are shown on the page.
- You may want to have students work in pairs to find the remaining pentominoes.
- It will be much easier for students to experiment with arranging pentominoes if they cut them out.
- Review the definitions of square and rectangle with students. A square has four sides the same length. A rectangle has opposite sides the same length.

Pentominoes

A pentomino is made up of five squares.

These are pentominoes.

These are not pentominoes.

There are 12 different pentominoes.

These are all the same pentomino. They have the same shape.

1. Draw the nine pentominoes not shown on this page.

Name_____

2. Arange five pentominoes to make a square. You may want to trace and cut out your pentominoes.

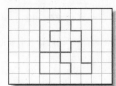

Answers will vary.
Possible answer given.

3. Use some of your pentominoes to make a rectangle.

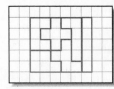

Answers will vary.
Possible answer given.

4. Draw the outline of a shape that can be made with pentominoes. Challenge a classmate to arrange pentominoes to make the shape.

Answers will vary.

CHALLENGE

Lesson Goal

To provide practice adding three addends.

Introducing the Challenge

- Tell students that magic squares have been found that are over 2,000 years old.

- Inform students that in this lesson they will be working with three-by-three magic squares, but magic squares are often four-by-four or larger.

Using the Challenge

- Explain to the students that they can use what they discover by answering questions 1–4 to arrange the numbers 1 through 9 in a magic square for Exercise 5.

- Advise students to use what they discover by answering questions 6 and 7 to help them make their own magic square in Exercise 8.

- Ask students how they can be sure they have created a magic square. (The sum of each row, column, and diagonal in the square is the same number.)

Name_____

Magic Squares

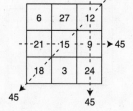

This is a magic square. The sum of the numbers in each row, column, and diagonal is 45.

Look at the magic square.

1. What is the middle number? __15__

2. What is the sum of the numbers above and below the middle number? __30__

3. What is the sum of the numbers on each side of the middle number? __30__

4. What is the sum of the numbers along the diagonal on each side of the middle number? __30__

5. Make slips of paper like these.

1	2	3	4	5

6	7	8	9

Arrange the numbers in a magic square.

Hint: Put 5 in the middle square.

Possible Answer:

8	1	6
3	5	7
4	9	2

© McGraw-Hill School Division

Name_____

6. Add 2 to each number in your magic square.
Write the numbers in this square.
Did you make a new magic square?

_____yes_____

Possible Answer:

10	3	8
5	7	9
6	11	4

7. Multiply each number in your magic square by 2.
Write the numbers in this square.
Did you make a new magic square?

_____yes_____

Possible Answer:

16	2	12
6	10	14
8	18	4

8. Make your own magic square.
What is your magic sum?

_____

Answers will vary. They will most likely be formed by
adding a number to each number in their magic
square or by multiplying each number in their magic
square by the same number.

© McGraw-Hill School Division

Grade 4, Chapter 10, Cluster B **133**

Name_____

Comparing Parts to the Whole or the Group

Use the drawing to answer each question.

1. How many animals are there? _____

2. How many of the animals are cows? _____

3. How many of the animals are chickens? _____

Write numbers to complete each statement.

4. _____ out of the _____ animals are cows.

5. _____ out of the _____ animals are chickens.

Write Two Fractions

Write a fraction to complete the statement.

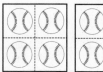

6. _____ of the sheets are baseball stickers.

7. _____ of the stickers are baseballs.

Compare Shaded Parts of Equal Regions

**Write the fraction for the shaded part of each figure.
Then write >, <, or = to compare the shaded areas.**

8.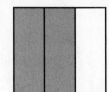

9.

____ ◯ ____   ____ ◯ ____

Name_____

Numbers and Fractions

Use the drawing to answer the questions.

10. How many of the dogs are white? _____

11. What fraction of the dogs is white? _____

Possible Events

List the possible events.

12. Draw a ball from the box. What color ball could you get?

_____

13. Spin this spinner. What number could you get?

_____

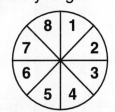

Equivalent Fractions

Write the numerator or denominator to find equivalent fractions.

14. $\dfrac{1}{4} = \dfrac{}{12}$ **15.** $\dfrac{12}{18} = \dfrac{}{3}$ **16.** $\dfrac{21}{24} = \dfrac{7}{}$

Ordering Parts

Write the fraction for the part of the spinner that is each color.

17. black ____   **18.** white ____   **19.** gray ____

20. List the parts of the spinner in order

from greatest to least. _____

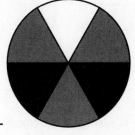

Assessment Goal

This two-page assessment covers skills identified as necessary for success in Chapter 11 Fractions and Probability. The first page assesses the major prerequisite skills for Cluster A. The second page assesses the major prerequisite skills for Cluster B. When the Cluster A and Cluster B prerequisite skills overlap, the skill(s) will be covered in only one section.

Getting Started

- Allow students time to look over the two pages of the assessment. Point out the labels that identify the skills covered.

- Have students find math vocabulary terms used in the assessment. List vocabulary terms on the board as students identify them. If necessary, review the meanings of all essential math vocabulary.

Introducing the Assessment

- Explain to students that these pages will help you know if they are ready to start a new chapter in their math textbooks.

- Students who have transferred from another school may not have been introduced to some of these skills. Encourage students to do their best and assure them you will help them learn any needed skills.

Cluster A Challenge

Those students who demonstrate mastery of the skills on this page will not need to use the reteaching worksheets. Instead, these students can do the Cluster A Challenge found on pages 144–145.

Name_____

CHAPTER 11 What Do I Need To Know?

Comparing Parts to the Whole or the Group

Use the drawing to answer each question.

1. How many animals are there? ___10___

2. How many of the animals are cows? ___5___

3. How many of the animals are chickens? ___3___

Write numbers to complete each statement.

4. ___5___ out of the ___10___ animals are cows.

5. ___3___ out of the ___10___ animals are chickens.

Write Two Fractions

Write a fraction to complete the statement.

6. $\frac{2}{3}$ of the sheets are baseball stickers.

7. $\frac{8}{12}$ of the stickers are baseballs.

Compare Shaded Parts of Equal Regions

Write the fraction for the shaded part of each figure. Then write >, <, or = to compare the shaded areas.

8.

9.

$\frac{1}{2}$ $<$ $\frac{2}{3}$ $\frac{3}{4}$ $=$ $\frac{6}{8}$

© McGraw-Hill School Division

133A Use with Grade 4, Chapter 11, Cluster A

CLUSTER A PREREQUISITE SKILLS

The skills listed in this chart are those identified as major prerequisite skills for students' success in the lessons in Cluster A of the chapter. Each skill is covered by one or more assessment items as shown in the middle column. The right column provides the page number for the lessons in this book that reteach the cluster A prerequisite skills.

Skill Name	Assessment Items	Lesson Pages
Compare Parts of to the Whole or the Group	1-5	134-135
Write Two Fractions	6-7	136-137
Compare Shaded Parts of Equal Regions	8-9	138

Name_____

Numbers and Fractions

Use the drawing to answer the questions.

10. How many of the dogs are white? ___4___

11. What fraction of the dogs is white? ___$\frac{4}{7}$___

Possible Events

List the possible events.

12. Draw a ball from the box. What color ball could you get?

___black, white, gray___

13. Spin this spinner. What number could you get?

___1, 2, 3, 4, 5, 6, 7, 8___

Equivalent Fractions

Write the numerator or denominator to find equivalent fractions.

14. $\frac{1}{4} = \frac{3}{12}$ 15. $\frac{12}{18} = \frac{2}{3}$ 16. $\frac{21}{24} = \frac{7}{8}$

Ordering Parts

Write the fraction for the part of the spinner that is each color.

17. black ___$\frac{2}{6}$___ 18. white ___$\frac{1}{6}$___ 19. gray ___$\frac{3}{6}$___

20. List the parts of the spinner in order

from greatest to least. ___gray, black, white___

Use with Grade 4, Chapter 11, Cluster B **133B**

Alternative Assessment Strategies

- Oral administration of the assessment is appropriate for younger students or those whose native language is not English. Read the skills title and directions one section at a time. Check students' understanding by asking them to tell you how they will do the first exercise in the group.

- For some skill types you may wish to use group administration. In this technique, a small group or pair of students complete the assessment together. Through their discussion, you will be able to decide if supplementary reteaching materials are needed.

Intervention Materials

If students are not successful with the prerequisite skills assessed on these pages, reteaching lessons have been created to help them make the transition into the chapter.

Item correlation charts showing the skills lessons suitable for reteaching the prerequisite skills are found beneath the reproductions of each page of the assessment.

CLUSTER B PREREQUISITE SKILLS

The skills listed in this chart are those identified as major prerequisite skills for students' success in the lessons in Cluster B of the chapter. Each skill is covered by one or more assessment items as shown in the middle column. The right column provides the page numbers for the lessons in this book that reteach the Cluster B prerequisite skills

Skill Name	Assessment Items	Lesson Pages
Numbers and Fractions	10-11	139
Possible Events	12-13	140
Equivalent Fractions	14-16	141
Ordering Parts	17-20	142-143

Cluster B Challenge

Those students who demonstrate mastery of the skills on this page will not need to use the reteaching worksheets. Instead, these students can do the Cluster B Challenge found on pages 146–147.

Lesson Goal

- Compare a part to the whole object or group.

What the Student Needs to Know

- Identify the part.
- Identify the whole.
- Show a relationship between the part and the whole.

Getting Started

Ask students to count the number of people in the class. Then ask questions such as:

- *How many out of the ___ people in the class wear glasses?*
- *How many out of the ___ people in the class are girls?*
- *How many out of the ___ people in the class are wearing a sweater?*
- *How many out of the ___ people in the class have black shoes?*
- Have students make up and answer questions about how many out of the total number in the group meet a given condition.

What Can I Do?

Read the question and the response. Then read and discuss the examples. Ask:

- *How many out of the 8 pieces of pizza are left?* (7)
- *How many out of the 6 animals are octopuses?* (3)
- *How is comparing parts of a whole like comparing parts of a group?* (For both you compare the number of parts to the total number.)

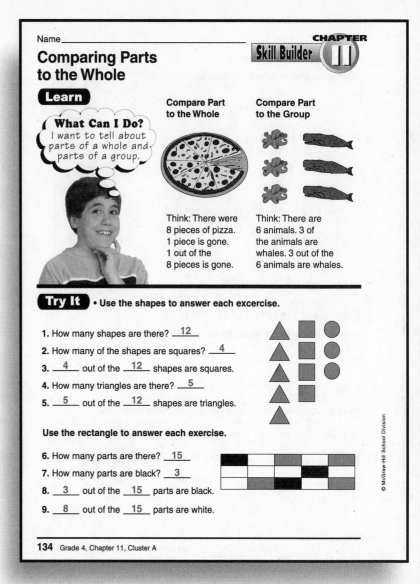

Comparing Parts to the Whole

Learn

What Can I Do?
I want to tell about parts of a whole and parts of a group.

Compare Part to the Whole

Think: There were 8 pieces of pizza. 1 piece is gone. 1 out of the 8 pieces is gone.

Compare Part to the Group

Think: There are 6 animals. 3 of the animals are whales. 3 out of the 6 animals are whales.

Try It • Use the shapes to answer each excercise.

1. How many shapes are there? __12__
2. How many of the shapes are squares? __4__
3. __4__ out of the __12__ shapes are squares.
4. How many triangles are there? __5__
5. __5__ out of the __12__ shapes are triangles.

Use the rectangle to answer each exercise.

6. How many parts are there? __15__
7. How many parts are black? __3__
8. __3__ out of the __15__ parts are black.
9. __8__ out of the __15__ parts are white.

© McGraw-Hill School Division

134   Grade 4, Chapter 11, Cluster A

WHAT IF THE STUDENT CAN'T

Identify the Whole

- Show students a group of objects and explain that the whole group is all of the objects in the group. Explain that the whole group can be described using the total number of objects. Have students tell you how many objects are in the group.
- Show students an object divided into pieces. Explain that in this case the whole is an object that is divided into a number of pieces. The total number of pieces can be used to describe the whole. Have students tell you the total number of pieces.

Identify the Part

- Use concrete materials such as attribute blocks. Select a group of blocks and have students count them. Then ask students to count the blocks in the group that have a given characteristic. For example, ask: *How many of the blocks are red?* Explain that the red blocks are part of the total number of blocks. Repeat for other attributes.

Name_____

Power Practice • Use the balls to answer each excercise.

10. How many balls are there? __14__

11. How many baseballs are there? __4__

12. __4__ out of the __14__ balls are baseballs.

13. __5__ out of the __14__ balls are footballs.

14. __3__ out of the __14__ balls are bowling balls.

Use the pie to answer each exercise.

15. Into how many equal pieces was the pie cut? __8__

16. __2__ out of __8__ pieces of pie were eaten.

17. __6__ out of __8__ pieces of pie are left.

Use the instruments to answer each exercise.

18. How many instruments are there? __8__

19. __3__ out of the __8__ instruments are guitars.

20. __1__ out of the __8__ instruments is a piano.

Lesson Goal
- Write two fractions for a picture.

What the Student Needs to Know
- Recognize that a picture or model can show more than one relationship.
- Write a fraction for a picture or model.

Getting Started
List the days of the week. Ask students to use the names of the days to write fractions.

- *What fraction of the names begin with the letter T?* ($\frac{2}{7}$)
- *What fraction of the names ends with the letters DAY?* ($\frac{7}{7}$)
- *What fraction of the names has at least one N in it?* ($\frac{3}{7}$)
- *What fraction of the letters in the word Wednesday is Ds?* ($\frac{2}{9}$)
- Have students make up some other "what fraction" problems using the names of the days of the week.

What Can I Do?
Read the question and the response. Then read and discuss the examples. Ask:

- *What does the 2 in the fraction $\frac{1}{2}$ show?* (The total number of packages of juice)
- *What does the 1 in the fraction $\frac{1}{2}$ show?* (The number of packages of juice that are orange juice)
- *What does the 8 in the fraction $\frac{4}{8}$ show?* (The total number of bottles of juice)
- *What does the 4 in the fraction $\frac{4}{8}$ show?* (The number of bottles of juice that are orange juice)
- *What do both $\frac{1}{2}$ and $\frac{4}{8}$ tell about the juice?* (The amount of orange juice compared to the total amount of juice.)

Write Two Fractions

Learn

What Can I Do?
I want to tell what part of the juice is orange juice.

Write Two Fractions

Write a fraction for the packages.
Think: There are 2 packs of juice.

1 pack is orange juice.
1 out of 2 packs is orange juice.
$\frac{1}{2}$ of the juice is orange juice.

Write a fraction for the bottles.
Think: There are 8 bottles of juice.

4 of the bottles are orange juice.
4 out of 8 bottles are orange juice.
$\frac{4}{8}$ of the juice is orange juice.

Try It • Write numbers and fractions to complete each statement.

1. There are ___3___ packages of tapes.

2. ___2___ of the packages are 60-minute tapes.

3. ___2___ out of ___3___ packages are 60-minute tapes.

4. $\frac{2}{3}$ of the packages are 60-minute tapes.

5. ___6___ out of ___9___ tapes are 60-minute tapes.

6. $\frac{6}{9}$ of the tapes are 60-minute tapes.

136 Grade 4, Chapter 11, Cluster A

© McGraw-Hill School Division

WHAT IF THE STUDENT CAN'T

Recognize That a Picture or Model Can Show More Than One Relationship

Have students use their two hands as models. Ask them these questions.

- *How many hands do you have?*
- *How many are left hands?*
- *How many fingers do you have?*
- *How many of your fingers are on your left hand?*

Write a Fraction for a Picture or Model

- Ask the students to draw 3 same size squares. Have them color two of the squares red and the other square blue. Ask them to draw a fraction bar and write the number of squares below the bar. Tell them that this number is the denominator of the fraction. Ask them to write the number of red squares above the fraction bar. Tell them that this is the numerator of the fraction. Ask them to read the fraction and tell what the fraction describes.

Name_____

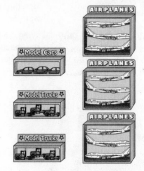

7. $\frac{3}{6}$ of the packages are airplanes.

8. $\frac{9}{18}$ of the models are airplanes.

9. $\frac{2}{6}$ of the packages are trucks.

10. $\frac{6}{18}$ of the models are trucks.

11. $\frac{1}{6}$ of the packages are cars.

12. $\frac{3}{18}$ of the models are cars.

13. $\frac{3}{8}$ of the strips are flag stamps.

14. $\frac{12}{32}$ of the stamps show flags.

15. $\frac{1}{8}$ of the strips are flower stamps.

16. $\frac{4}{32}$ of the stamps show flowers.

17. $\frac{4}{8}$ of the strips are lighthouse stamps.

18. $\frac{16}{32}$ of the stamps show lighthouses.

Grade 4, Chapter 11, Cluster A **137**

© McGraw-Hill School Division

WHAT IF THE STUDENT CAN'T

• Then ask them to divide each square into 4 equal parts. Use the steps above to help them write a fraction for the part that is red.

Complete the Power Practice

Discuss each incorrect answer. For each, help the student find the numerator and the denominator by asking him or her to name the number of example items and the total number of items.

Try It
Have students complete the exercises. Then ask:

• *What does the fraction in exercise 4 compare?* (The number of packages of 60-minute tapes to the total number of packages of tapes)

• *What does the fraction in exercise 6 compare?* (The number of 60-minute tapes to the total number of tapes)

• *What do both fractions tell about the tapes?* (The part that is 60 minute compared to the total)

Power Practice
Have students look at the vehicles shown and answer these questions.

• *How many packages are there?* (6)

• *How many of the packages are airplanes?* (3)

• *How many models are there?* (18)

• *How many of the models are airplanes?* (9)

• *How many of the packages are trucks?* (2)

• *How many of the models are trucks?* (6)

Have students look at the stamps. Ask these questions.

• *How many strips of stamps are there?* (8)

• *How many of the strips show flags?* (3)

• *How many stamps are there?* (32)

• *How many of the stamps show flags?* (12)

Lesson Goal
- Compare shaded parts of equal regions.

What the Student Needs to Know
- Write a fraction for the shaded part of a region.
- Use the symbols >, <, and = to show comparison.

Getting Started
Ask students to tell which of these numbers is greater.
- 7 or 5
- 23 or 15
- 77 or 75
- 426 or 264

Ask students to tell which of these numbers is less.
- 14 or 18
- 42 or 38
- 155 or 163
- 684 or 648

What Can I Do?
Read the question and the response. Then read and discuss the examples. Ask:
- *How can you tell that $\frac{4}{5}$ is greater than $\frac{1}{2}$?* (The two rectangles are the same size. The one that is $\frac{4}{5}$ shaded has a greater area shaded than the one that is $\frac{1}{2}$ shaded.)

Try It
- Remind students that the open part of the inequality sign faces the greater fraction.
- Point out that in each exercise, the two shapes are the same, so the one that is most shaded shows the greatest fraction.

Power Practice
- Tell students that they can use the table at the top of the page to help them remember the meaning of each sign.
- Have students complete the practice items. Then review each answer.

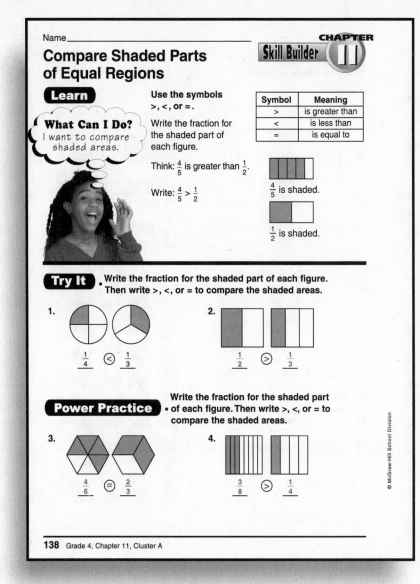

WHAT IF THE STUDENT CAN'T

Write a Fraction for the Shaded Part of a Region
- Have students draw a fraction bar. Then have them count the number of shaded parts and write that number as the numerator. Next, have them count the total number of parts and write that number as the denominator.

Use the Symbols <, >, and = to Show Comparison
- Remind the students that the big end or open end of the inequality sign faces the greater fraction and the point faces the lesser fraction.

Complete the Power Practice
- Help the student write fractions for each region. Start by asking students to count the number of shaded parts and to write that number as the numerator of a fraction. Then have the student count the total number of parts and write that number in the denominator. After the student has written fractions for both regions, ask him or her to compare the shaded areas using the terms greater than, less than, or equal to. Finally, have the student use the table at the top of the page to select the symbol that compares the two fractions.

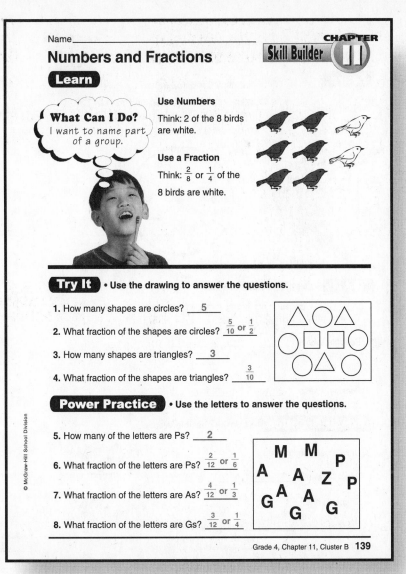

Name_____

Numbers and Fractions

Skill Builder

Learn

What Can I Do?
I want to name part of a group.

Use Numbers
Think: 2 of the 8 birds are white.

Use a Fraction
Think: $\frac{2}{8}$ or $\frac{1}{4}$ of the 8 birds are white.

Try It • Use the drawing to answer the questions.

1. How many shapes are circles? ___5___

2. What fraction of the shapes are circles? $\frac{5}{10}$ or $\frac{1}{2}$

3. How many shapes are triangles? ___3___

4. What fraction of the shapes are triangles? $\frac{3}{10}$

Power Practice • Use the letters to answer the questions.

5. How many of the letters are Ps? ___2___

6. What fraction of the letters are Ps? $\frac{2}{12}$ or $\frac{1}{6}$

7. What fraction of the letters are As? $\frac{4}{12}$ or $\frac{1}{3}$

8. What fraction of the letters are Gs? $\frac{3}{12}$ or $\frac{1}{4}$

M M
A P
A A Z P
G A G
G

© McGraw-Hill School Division

Grade 4, Chapter 11, Cluster B **139**

WHAT IF THE STUDENT CAN'T

Write a Fraction for a Part of a Group

• Show a group of coins. Ask students to count the coins and to write the number as the denominator of a fraction. Then ask them to count the number of pennies and to write the number as the numerator of the fraction. Have the students read the fraction and ask them to tell what the fraction shows. Repeat for other coins in the group and for other groups of coins as needed.

Complete the Power Practice

• Use a group with only two different letters. For example: A A A B B B.

• Ask: *What fraction of the letters are Bs?* Have students write a verbal fraction: The fraction of the letters that are Bs = the number of Bs / the total number of letters.

• Ask students to count the number of letters. Ask them to count the number of Bs. Have them write the fraction of the letters that are Bs. Tell them to use their word fraction to help them.

USING THE LESSON

Lesson Goal

• Use a number and a fraction to name part of a group.

What the Student Needs to Know

• Write a fraction for a part of a group.

Getting Started

Use ten two-color counters.

• Lay the counters on a flat surface and ask students to write a fraction for the number of counters that are each color.

• Repeat for other numbers of the two-color counters.

What Can I Do?

Read the question and the response. Then read and discuss the examples. Ask:

• *How many of the birds are black?* (6)

• *What fraction of the birds are black?* ($\frac{6}{8}$ or $\frac{3}{4}$)

• *In what two ways can you describe the part of the group of birds that are black?* (Use the number 6 or the fraction $\frac{6}{8}$.)

Try It

• Ask students to count the total number of shapes. (10)

• Ask them how they will use the total number of shapes to write fractions. (It will be the denominator of the fractions.)

Power Practice

• Ask students to count the total number of letters. (12)

• Have students complete the practice, then ask volunteers to explain how they solved each problem.

USING THE LESSON

Lesson Goal
- List possible events.

What the Student Needs to Know
- Identify different events.
- Write a list.

Getting Started
Ask students to make the following lists:
- List all of the even numbers between 1 and 15. (2, 4, 6, 8, 10, 12, 14)
- List all of the multiples of three that are less than 20. (3, 6, 9, 12, 15, 18)
- Have students show the different ways they listed the numbers.

What Can I Do?
Read the question and the response. Then read and discuss the examples. Ask:
- *There are six sections on the spinner. Why aren't there six possible events?* (The event $5 is on the spinner three times. The event $10 is on the spinner twice.)
- *What is a possible event for a spinner?* (A possible event is what can happen if the spinner is spun.)

Try It
Read the directions with the students. Ask:
- *How many possible events are there for Exercise 1? How do you know?* (There are four different numbers on the cards so there are four possible events.)
- *How many possible events are there for Exercise 2?* (2)

Power Practice
- Remind students that each thing that can happen is listed only once when naming possible events.
- Have students complete the practice items. Then review each answer.

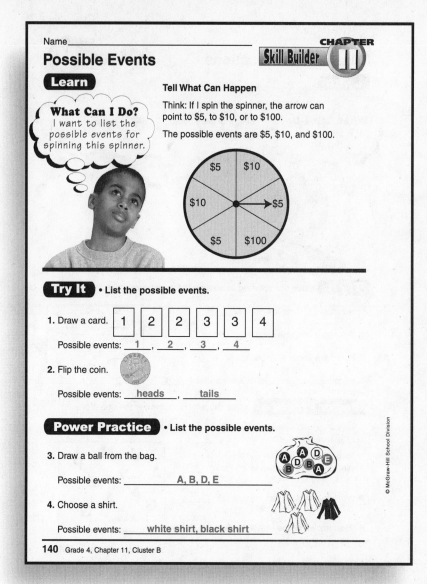

Name_____

CHAPTER
Skill Builder 11

Possible Events

Learn

What Can I Do? I want to list the possible events for spinning this spinner.

Tell What Can Happen

Think: If I spin the spinner, the arrow can point to $5, to $10, or to $100.

The possible events are $5, $10, and $100.

Spinner sections: $5, $10, $10, $5, $5, $100

Try It • List the possible events.

1. Draw a card. [1] [2] [2] [3] [3] [4]

   Possible events: __1__, __2__, __3__, __4__

2. Flip the coin.

   Possible events: __heads__, __tails__

Power Practice • List the possible events.

3. Draw a ball from the bag. (A A D B A E D B A)

   Possible events: _____ A, B, D, E _____

4. Choose a shirt.

   Possible events: _____ white shirt, black shirt _____

140 Grade 4, Chapter 11, Cluster B

© McGraw-Hill School Division

WHAT IF THE STUDENT CAN'T

Identify Different Events
- Encourage students to look at each event one by one. Have them list each event the first time they see it then not write it again. When they have looked at each event they will have listed all of the possible events. They can then check to be sure no event is on the list more than once.

Write a List
- Ask students to name some ways a list can be written. Possible formats include writing items in a column and writing items in a row with commas between each item.

Complete the Power Practice
- Start with events that have two possible outcomes such as flipping a coin, tossing a bottle cap, or spinning a spinner in two sections. Ask the student what results are possible.
- Then move on to situations with three or more unique events possible. For example drawing one of these cards: A, B, or C.
- Finally present more complex situations. For example: A bag with 1 blue, 3 red, 2 green, and 5 yellow marbles.

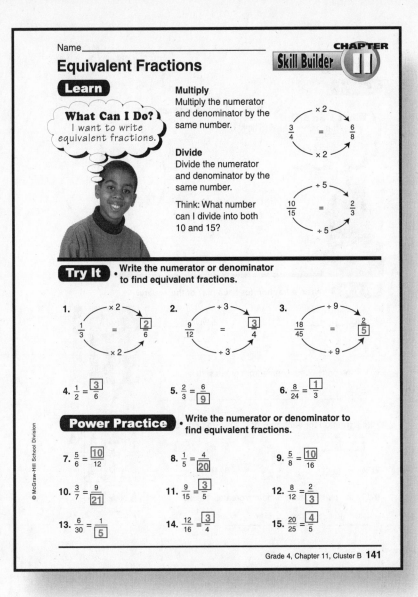

Learn

What Can I Do?
I want to write equivalent fractions.

Multiply
Multiply the numerator and denominator by the same number.

$$\frac{3}{4} = \frac{6}{8}$$
×2 ... ×2

Divide
Divide the numerator and denominator by the same number.

Think: What number can I divide into both 10 and 15?

$$\frac{10}{15} = \frac{2}{3}$$
÷5 ... ÷5

Try It • Write the numerator or denominator to find equivalent fractions.

1. $\frac{1}{3} = \frac{2}{6}$ ×2 ... ×2

2. $\frac{9}{12} = \frac{3}{4}$ ÷3 ... ÷3

3. $\frac{18}{45} = \frac{2}{5}$ ÷9 ... ÷9

4. $\frac{1}{2} = \frac{3}{6}$

5. $\frac{2}{3} = \frac{6}{9}$

6. $\frac{8}{24} = \frac{1}{3}$

Power Practice • Write the numerator or denominator to find equivalent fractions.

7. $\frac{5}{6} = \frac{10}{12}$

8. $\frac{1}{5} = \frac{4}{20}$

9. $\frac{5}{8} = \frac{10}{16}$

10. $\frac{3}{7} = \frac{9}{21}$

11. $\frac{9}{15} = \frac{3}{5}$

12. $\frac{8}{12} = \frac{2}{3}$

13. $\frac{6}{30} = \frac{1}{5}$

14. $\frac{12}{16} = \frac{3}{4}$

15. $\frac{20}{25} = \frac{4}{5}$

© McGraw-Hill School Division

Grade 4, Chapter 11, Cluster B **141**

WHAT IF THE STUDENT CAN'T

Multiply by a One-Digit Number
- Use flash cards to determine which multiplication facts the student does not know. Then provide daily practice with these facts.
- Review multiplication by a one-digit number using manipulatives. Have the student rename and record his or her actions in writing.

Divide by a One-Digit Number
- Use flash cards to determine which division facts the student does not know. Then provide daily practice with these facts.
- Review division by a one-digit number using manipulatives. Have the student rename and record his or her actions in writing.

Complete the Power Practice
- Provide additional examples like those in Exercises 1–3.
- For any problems the student missed have the student talk through his or her selection of a number by which to multiply or divide.

USING THE LESSON

Lesson Goal
- Write equivalent fractions.

What the Student Needs to Know
- Multiply by a one-digit number.
- Divide by a one-digit number.

Getting Started
Present some multiplication and division facts and ask students to name the products or quotients. For example:
- 6×5 (30)
- 8×5 (40)
- 5×3 (15)
- 9×3 (27)
- $12 \div 4$ (3)
- $16 \div 4$ (4)
- $18 \div 6$ (3)
- $36 \div 6$ (6)

What Can I Do?
Read the question and the response. Then read and discuss the examples. Ask:
- *How can you show that $\frac{3}{4} = \frac{6}{8}$ using a drawing?* (Possible answer or student drawing: Use two same-size rectangles. Divide one rectangle into 4 equal sections and color 3 of them. Divide the other rectangle into 8 equal sections and color 6 of them.)

Try It
- For exercises 4–6 ask students if they will multiply or divide to find equivalent fractions.
- Have students complete 1–6. Then have volunteers explain how to find equivalent fractions for items 4–6.

Power Practice
- Ask students how they can decide what number to multiply or divide by for each exercise. (Look at the relationship between the numerators if both numerators are given and between the denominators if both denominators are given.)

USING THE LESSON

Lesson Goal
• Order fractions from greatest to least.

What the Student Needs to Know
• Write a fraction for a part of a region.
• Write a fraction for a part of a set.

Getting Started
Ask students to write each set of numbers in order from greatest to least.
• 7, 11, 5, 3, 8 (3, 5, 7, 8, 11)
• 2, 8, 3, 6, 1 (1, 2, 3, 6, 8)

What Can I Do?
Read the question and the response. Then read and discuss the examples. Ask:

• *How does the drawing help you order the fractions from greatest to least?* (The greatest fraction will be the fraction for the letter with the greatest number of sections on the spinner.)

• *How can you use the numerators of the fractions to order the fractions?* (Since the denominators are the same, the fraction with the greatest numerator is the greatest fraction. You can order the fractions by ordering the numerators.)

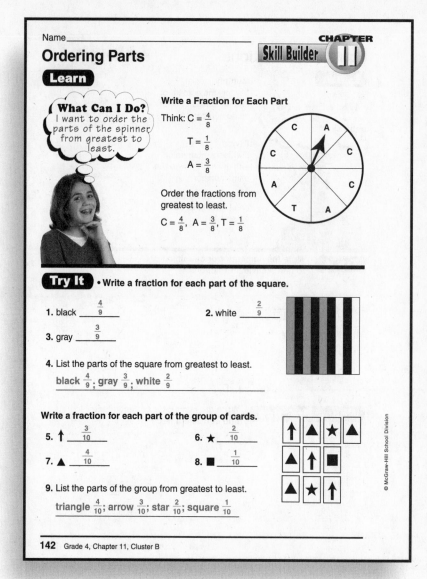

WHAT IF THE STUDENT CAN'T

Write a Fraction for a Part of a Region

• Show a rectangle separated into 8 equal sections. Color 5 of the sections red.

• Ask students to count the total number of sections and to write the number as the denominator of the fraction.

• Have students count the number of red sections and write the number as the numerator of the fraction.

• Write a verbal fraction for the part of the rectangle that is white: the number of white sections / the total number of sections. Then have students write the fraction for the part of the rectangle that is white.

Write a Fraction for a Part of a Set

• Show a set of cards each with a single shape drawn on the card. Use 1 card with a heart shape, 3 cards with 1 rectangle on each, 2 cards with 1 diamond on each, and 4 cards with 1 circle on each.

• Ask students to count the number of cards and to write the number as the denominator of the fraction.

• Have students count the number of cards with a rectangle and write the number as the numerator of the fraction.

Name_____

Power Practice • Write a fraction for each part of the rectangle.

10. A $\frac{2}{12}$ 11. U $\frac{3}{12}$

12. T $\frac{1}{12}$ 13. H $\frac{6}{12}$

H	U	A
U	H	H
T	A	H
U	H	H

14. List the parts of the rectangle from greatest to least.

H $\frac{6}{12}$; U $\frac{3}{12}$; A $\frac{2}{12}$; T $\frac{1}{12}$

Write a fraction for each part of the group of hats.

15. top hat $\frac{3}{14}$

16. baseball hat $\frac{2}{14}$

17. sun hat $\frac{5}{14}$

18. western hat $\frac{4}{14}$

19. List the parts of the group of hats in order from greatest to least.

sun hat $\frac{5}{14}$; western hat $\frac{4}{14}$; top hat $\frac{3}{14}$; baseball hat $\frac{2}{14}$

Write a fraction for the parts of the circle.

20. white $\frac{3}{9}$ 21. gray $\frac{1}{9}$

22. black $\frac{5}{9}$

23. List the parts of the circle from greatest to least.

black $\frac{5}{9}$; white $\frac{3}{9}$; gray $\frac{1}{9}$

Grade 4, Chapter 11, Cluster B **143**

USING THE LESSON

Try It

- Ask students how many equal sections the square has. (9)
- Ask the students how they will use the total number of equal sections to write fractions. (The total number of sections will be the denominator of the fraction for each color.)
- Ask students how many cards there are in all. (10)
- Remind students that since, in each exercise, all of the denominators are the same they can order the numerators to list the fractions in order.

Power Practice

- Ask the students how many equal sections the rectangle has. (12)
- Ask the students how many hats there are in all. (14)
- Ask the students how many equal parts the circle has. (9)
- Have students complete the exercises. Then ask volunteers to explain how they ordered the parts from greatest to least.

WHAT IF THE STUDENT CAN'T

- Have students write a fraction for the part of the set of cards that has each of the other shapes.

Complete the Power Practice

- Be sure the student is able to write fractions for sets and fractions for regions.

- List fractions with common denominators and remind the student that since the fractions have the same denominator he or she can order the fractions by ordering the numerators. Then have the students write the fractions in order.

CHALLENGE

Lesson Goal
• Find fractional parts of sets.

Introducing the Challenge
• Explain that students will solve riddles by using a fraction of the letters in one word to make another word.

• Read the first example. Ask students how many letters the answer to the riddle has. (4) Have students answer the riddle.

• Ask how many letters the answer to the second riddle has. (4) Have students name the vegetable that is $\frac{4}{8}$ of pheasant.

Fractions of Words

Solve each riddle using a fraction of a word.

Examples:

You have plenty of money if you are $\frac{4}{7}$ of ost<u>rich</u>.

The name of a vegetable is $\frac{4}{8}$ of <u>pheas</u>ant.

> Think: The numerator tells me how many letters are in the answers to the riddle.

Solve each riddle. Write the word.

1. The name of an insect is $\frac{3}{8}$ of elephant. <u>ant</u>

2. A musical instrument is $\frac{4}{6}$ of hornet. <u>horn</u>

3. You use $\frac{4}{5}$ of horse to water a garden. <u>hose</u>

4. You work to earn $\frac{5}{6}$ of monkey. <u>money</u>

5. The liquid that you cry is $\frac{4}{8}$ of anteater. <u>tear</u>

6. What a bell did is $\frac{4}{9}$ of orangutan. <u>rang</u>

7. $\frac{3}{6}$ of kitten is a number. <u>ten</u>

8. You open the door with $\frac{3}{6}$ of turkey. <u>key</u>

These riddles are harder. The letters that make up the answer may not be in order.

9. ♥ is the symbol for $\frac{5}{7}$ of hamster. <u>heart</u>

10. $\frac{6}{9}$ of bumblebee is a kind of gum. <u>bubble</u>

11. $\frac{3}{7}$ of dolphin is how a rabbit moves. <u>hop</u>

12. $\frac{3}{6}$ of jaguar is a carpet. <u>rug</u>

Name_____

Get ready to write your own riddles by answering these questions.

13. What fraction of frog is fog? $\frac{3}{4}$

14. What fraction of bluebird is bride? $\frac{5}{8}$

15. What fraction of camel is lace? $\frac{4}{5}$

16. What fraction of seagull is age? $\frac{3}{7}$

17. What fraction of porcupine is pine? $\frac{4}{9}$

18. What fraction of jackrabbit is crab? $\frac{4}{10}$

Write three riddles. Give your riddles to a classmate to solve.

19. _____ Answers will vary. _____

_____

_____

20. _____

_____

_____

21. _____

_____

_____

CHALLENGE

Using the Challenge

- Be sure students understand that the numerator tells the number of letters in the answer to the riddle.

- Point out that in the first set of exercises the letters that make up the answer to the riddle are in order within the word. In the second set of exercises, the letters that make up the answer are not in order.

- Work through Exercise 13 with the students. Have them write a word fraction for the problem: fog/frog. Then have them count the letters and write the fraction $\frac{3}{4}$.

- Tell students to use the riddles on the previous page as guides for writing their own riddles.

CHALLENGE

Lesson Goal
- Draw a complete figure using a fractional part of the figure.

Introducing the Challenge
- Read the directions and point out the example. Ask students how many of the shapes were used to make the star. (5)
- Ask students how the fraction tells them the number of shapes to use to draw the figure. (The denominator of the fraction is the number of shapes needed to draw the figure.)

Name_____

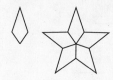

Draw the Whole

Each shape is part of a whole figure. Draw the whole figure.

Example: The shape is $\frac{1}{5}$ of a star. Draw the star.

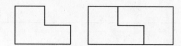

1. The shape is $\frac{1}{2}$ of a rectangle. Draw the rectangle.

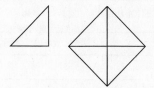

2. The shape is $\frac{1}{4}$ of a square. Draw the square.

Name_____

3. The shape is $\frac{1}{6}$ of a hexagon. Draw the hexagon.

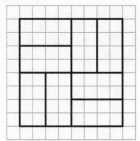

4. The shape is $\frac{1}{8}$ of a square. Draw the square.

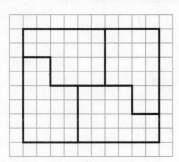

Possible answer given.

5. The shape is $\frac{1}{4}$ of a rectangle. Draw the rectangle.

Possible answer given.

© McGraw-Hill School Division

Using the Challenge

- For each exercise, ask students how many of the shapes they will use to draw the figure.
- Students may want to trace and cut out each shape and then draw around the shape to sketch the complete figure.

Name_____

 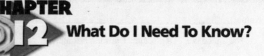
Factors

Find all of the factors of each number.

1. 8 _____

2. 12 _____

3. 18 _____

Common Factors

List the common factors for each pair of numbers.

4. 8 and 12 _____

5. 12 and 18 _____

6. 8 and 18 _____

Greatest Common Factor

Name the greatest common factor for each pair of numbers.

7. 8 and 12 _____

8. 18 and 12 _____

9. 8 and 18 _____

Simplest Form Fractions and Mixed Numbers

Write each as a fraction or mixed number in simplest form.

10. $\frac{9}{12}$ _____

11. $\frac{15}{18}$ _____

12. $\frac{5}{4}$ _____

13. $\frac{7}{3}$ _____

Least Common Multiple

Find the least common multiple for each pair of numbers.

14. 3 and 5 _____   **15.** 2 and 6 _____   **16.** 8 and 3 _____

Equivalent Fractions

Circle all of the fractions that are equivalent to the first fraction given.

17. $\frac{3}{4}$ | $\frac{12}{16}$ $\frac{9}{12}$ $\frac{8}{10}$ $\frac{6}{8}$

18. $\frac{20}{30}$ | $\frac{15}{18}$ $\frac{10}{15}$ $\frac{4}{5}$ $\frac{2}{3}$

19. $\frac{8}{10}$ | $\frac{4}{5}$ $\frac{12}{18}$ $\frac{16}{20}$ $\frac{20}{28}$

Common Denominator

Circle the number that is a common denominator for the two fractions.

20. $\frac{1}{2}$ and $\frac{2}{3}$ 4   5   6   7   8

21. $\frac{1}{4}$ and $\frac{1}{3}$ 7   9   10   12   14

22. $\frac{3}{8}$ and $\frac{3}{4}$ 6   8   12   14   18

Whole Number Properties

Complete each number sentence. Write *identity*, *commutative* or *associative* to name the property used.

23. _____ + (5 + 3) = (7 + 5) + 3 _____

24. 0 + _____ = 4 _____

25. 9 + 6 = _____ + 9 _____

CHAPTER 12 PRE-CHAPTER ASSESSMENT

Assessment Goal

This two-page assessment covers skills identified as necessary for success in Chapter 12 Fraction Operations. The first page assesses the major prerequisite skills for Cluster A. The second page assesses the major prerequisite skills for Cluster B. When the Cluster A and Cluster B prerequisite skills overlap, the skill(s) will be covered in only one section.

Getting Started

- Allow students time to look over the two pages of the assessment. Point out the labels that identify the skills covered.
- Have students find math vocabulary terms used in the assessment. List vocabulary terms on the board as students identify them. If necessary, review the meanings of all essential math vocabulary.

Introducing the Assessment

- Explain to students that these pages will help you know if they are ready to start a new chapter in their math textbooks.
- Students who have transferred from another school may not have been introduced to some of these skills. Encourage students to do their best and assure them you will help them learn any needed skills.

Cluster A Challenge

Those students who demonstrate mastery of the skills on this page will not need to use the reteaching worksheets. Instead, these students can do the Cluster A Challenge found on pages 156–157.

Name_____

Factors

Find all of the factors of each number.

1. 8   <u>1, 2, 4, 8</u>

2. 12   <u>1, 2, 3, 4, 6, 12</u>

3. 18   <u>1, 2, 3, 6, 9, 18</u>

Common Factors

List the common factors for each pair of numbers.

4. 8 and 12   <u>1, 2, 4</u>

5. 12 and 18   <u>1, 2, 3, 6</u>

6. 8 and 18   <u>1, 2</u>

Greatest Common Factor

Name the greatest common factor for each pair of numbers.

7. 8 and 12   <u>4</u>

8. 18 and 12   <u>6</u>

9. 8 and 18   <u>2</u>

Simplest Form Fractions and Mixed Numbers

Write each as a fraction or mixed number in simplest form.

10. $\frac{9}{12}$ $\frac{3}{4}$ _____

11. $\frac{15}{18}$ $\frac{5}{6}$ _____

12. $\frac{5}{4}$ $1\frac{1}{4}$ _____

13. $\frac{7}{3}$ $2\frac{1}{3}$ _____

147A Use with Grade 4, Chapter 12, Cluster A

CLUSTER A PREREQUISITE SKILLS

The skills listed in this chart are those identified as major prerequisite skills for students' success in the lessons in Cluster A of the chapter. Each skill is covered by one or more assessment items as shown in the middle column. The right column provides the page number for the lessons in this book that reteach the cluster A prerequisite skills.

Skill Name	Assessment Items	Lesson Pages
Factors, Common Factors, Greatest Common Factor	1-9	148-149
Simplest Form Fractions and Mixed Numbers	10-13	150

Name_____

Least Common Multiple

Find the least common multiple for each pair of numbers.

14. 3 and 5 ___15___   **15.** 2 and 6 ___6___   **16.** 8 and 3 ___24___

Equivalent Fractions

Circle all of the fractions that are equivalent to the first fraction given.

17. $\frac{3}{4}$ | $\left(\frac{12}{16}\right)$ $\left(\frac{9}{12}\right)$ $\frac{8}{10}$ $\left(\frac{6}{8}\right)$

18. $\frac{20}{30}$ | $\frac{15}{18}$ $\left(\frac{10}{15}\right)$ $\frac{4}{5}$ $\left(\frac{2}{3}\right)$

19. $\frac{8}{10}$ | $\left(\frac{4}{5}\right)$ $\frac{12}{18}$ $\left(\frac{16}{20}\right)$ $\frac{20}{28}$

Common Denominator

Circle the number that is a common denominator for the two fractions.

20. $\frac{1}{2}$ and $\frac{2}{3}$ 4   5   ⑥   7   8

21. $\frac{1}{4}$ and $\frac{1}{3}$ 7   9   10   ⑫   14

22. $\frac{3}{8}$ and $\frac{3}{4}$ 6   ⑧   12   14   18

Whole Number Properties

Complete each number sentence. Write *identity*, *commutative* or *associative* to name the property used.

23. ___7___ + (5 + 3) = (7 + 5) + 3 ___associative___

24. 0 + ___4___ = 4 ___identity___

25. 9 + 6 = ___6___ + 9 ___commutative___

CLUSTER B PREREQUISITE SKILLS

The skills listed in this chart are those identified as major prerequisite skills for students' success in the lessons in Cluster B of the chapter. Each skill is covered by one or more assessment items as shown in the middle column. The right column provides the page numbers for the lessons in this book that reteach the Cluster B prerequisite skills

Skill Name	Assessment Items	Lesson Pages
Least Common Multiple	14-16	151
Equivalent Fractions	17-19	152
Common Denominator	20-22	153
Whole Number Properties	23-25	154-155

CHAPTER 12 PRE-CHAPTER ASSESSMENT

Alternative Assessment Strategies

- Oral administration of the assessment is appropriate for younger students or those whose native language is not English. Read the skills title and directions one section at a time. Check students' understanding by asking them to tell you how they will do the first exercise in the group.

- For some skill types you may wish to use group administration. In this technique, a small group or pair of students complete the assessment together. Through their discussion, you will be able to decide if supplementary reteaching materials are needed.

Intervention Materials

If students are not successful with the prerequisite skills assessed on these pages, reteaching lessons have been created to help them make the transition into the chapter.

Item correlation charts showing the skills lessons suitable for reteaching the prerequisite skills are found beneath the reproductions of each page of the assessment.

Cluster B Challenge
Those students who demonstrate mastery of the skills on this page will not need to use the reteaching worksheets. Instead, these students can do the Cluster B Challenge found on pages 158–159.

USING THE LESSON

Lesson Goal

- Find the greatest common factor of two numbers.

What the Student Needs to Know

- Find the factors of a number.
- Find the common factors of two numbers.
- Find the greatest number in a set.

Getting Started

Ask students to think of as many pairs of numbers as they can that have the following numbers as a product.

- 8 (1 x 8, 2 x 4)
- 12 (1 x 12, 2 x 6, 3 x 4)
- 18 (1 x 18, 2 x 9, 3 x 6)
- 19 (1 x 19)
- 20 (1 x 20, 2 x 10, 4 x 5)
- 25 (1 x 25, 5 x 5)

What Can I Do?

Read the question and the response. Then read and discuss the examples. Ask:

- *How can you find the factors of 16?* (Find pairs of numbers that have 16 as their product.)
- *Why is it important to list the factors of the two numbers in order?* (When the factors are listed in order it is easier to compare the factors of the two numbers and to locate common factors.)
- *How can you find the common factors of 16 and 24?* (Look for numbers that are listed as factors for both 16 and 24.)
- *How can you tell that 4 is not the greatest common factor of 16 and 24?* (There is another number, 8, that is greater than 4 and is a factor of both 16 and 24.)

Name_____

Factors, Common Factors, Greatest Common Factor

Learn

What Can I Do?
I want to find the greatest common factor of two numbers.

What is the greatest common factor of 16 and 24?

Think: I will look for pairs of numbers that can be multiplied together to make the number.

List the Factors
The factors of 16 are 1, 2, 4, 8, 16.
The factors of 24 are 1, 2, 3, 4, 6, 8, 12, 24.

Find the Common Factors
1, 2, 4, and 8 are factors of both 16 and 24.

Find the Greatest Common Factor
8 is the greatest factor of both 16 and 24.

Try It • List the factors of each number.

1. 12   _1, 2, 3, 4, 6, 12_   2. 8   _1, 2, 4, 8_

3. 18   _1, 2, 3, 6, 9, 18_   4. 9   _1, 3, 9_

Find the common factors of each pair of numbers.

5. 8 and 12   6. 9 and 18   7. 12 and 18

   _1, 2, 4_   _1, 3, 9_   _1, 2, 3, 6_

Name the greatest common factor of each pair of numbers.

8. 8 and 12   9. 9 and 18   10. 12 and 18

   _4_   _9_   _6_

WHAT IF THE STUDENT CAN'T

Find the Factors of a Number

- Have students think of pairs of numbers that have the number to be factored as a product. Remind them that numbers that are multiplied together are called factors.
- Tell students to start with one and go through the numbers in order, 1, 2, 3, 4, …For each number, they should decide if it can divide evenly into the number for which they are finding factors.

Find the Common Factors of Two Numbers

- Check that students are finding all of the factors of the two numbers.
- Have students compare the factors of the two numbers one-by-one. Tell students to cross off any factors that are not common to both numbers and to circle and draw lines connecting the factors that are common to both numbers.

Name_____

Power Practice • List the factors of each number.

11. 15 <u>1, 3, 5, 15</u>   12. 6 <u>1, 2, 3, 6</u>

13. 10 <u>1, 2, 5, 10</u>   14. 20 <u>1, 2, 4, 5, 10, 20</u>

15. 14 <u>1, 2, 7, 14</u>   16. 27 <u>1, 3, 9, 27</u>

Find the common factors for each pair of numbers.

17. 6 and 15   18. 10 and 20   19. 14 and 27

<u>1, 3</u>   <u>1, 2, 5, 10</u>   <u>1</u>

20. 15 and 27   21. 14 and 6   22. 15 and 14

<u>1, 3</u>   <u>1, 2</u>   <u>1</u>

Name the greatest common factor for each pair of numbers.

23. 6 and 15   24. 10 and 20   25. 14 and 27

<u>3</u>   <u>10</u>   <u>1</u>

26. 15 and 27   27. 14 and 6   28. 15 and 14

<u>3</u>   <u>2</u>   <u>1</u>

Grade 4, Chapter 12, Cluster A **149**

USING THE LESSON

Try It

- Tell students that each number will have at least two factors. Ask students to name the two factors. (1 and the number itself)

- Point out that 2 is listed as a factor of 12. Ask students what number times 2 equals 12. (6) Elicit from the students that this number must also be a factor of 12.

- Have students complete the exercises. Then have volunteers explain how they found the greatest common factor for exercises 8–10.

- Encourage students to share their methods for finding factors.

Power Practice

- Ask students if every pair of numbers will have a common factor. Then have them explain their reasoning. (Each number has at least two factors, one and itself. So, each pair of numbers will have at least one common factor, 1.)

- Have students complete the exercises. Then review the answers and ask volunteers to explain how they found the greatest common factors for exercises 23–28.

WHAT IF THE STUDENT CAN'T

Find the Greatest Number in a Set

- Have students locate each number in the set on a number line. Explain that the number farthest to the right on the number line is the greatest number. Ask students to use the number line to name the greatest number in the set.

- Review comparing pairs of numbers. Name two numbers such as 15 and 21. Have students compare the numbers saying: 21 is greater than 15 or 15 is less than 21.

Complete the Power Practice

- Work through finding factors, finding common factors, and finding greatest common factors with the student to determine what help the student needs. Then provide reteaching and review in those areas.

Lesson Goal
- Write fractions and mixed numbers in simplest form.

What the Student Needs to Know
- Recall division facts.
- Find common factors.

Getting Started
- Present some division facts and have students name the quotients.
- Ask students to find the common factors for 6 and 8. (1 and 2)

What Can I Do?
Read the question and the response. Then read and discuss the examples. Ask:

- *How can you tell if a fraction is in simplest form?* (If the fraction is in simplest form, the numerator and denominator have only 1 as a common factor.)
- *How can you tell if a fraction can be written as a mixed number?* (If the numerator is greater than the denominator, the fraction can be written as a mixed number.)

Try It
- Ask: *In Exercise 1, will dividing by 3 give a fraction in simplest form? How do you know?* (Yes, 3 is the greatest common factor of 15 and 21.)

Power Practice
- Have students explain the difference between simplifying a fraction and writing it in simplest form. (Sometimes when a fraction is simplified by dividing, the new fraction can also be simplified. So for example $\frac{8}{20}$ can be simplified to $\frac{4}{10}$, but in simplest form $\frac{8}{20} = \frac{2}{5}$.)
- Tell students to be sure their answers are in simplest form.

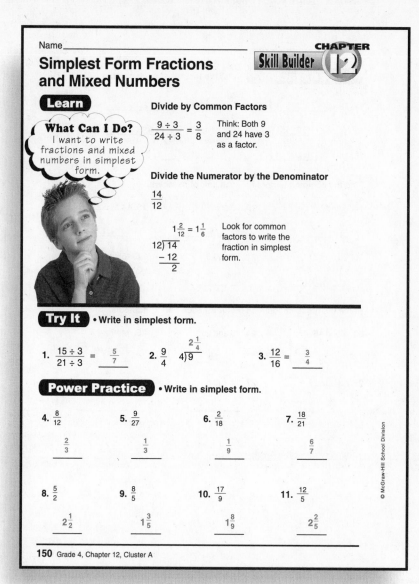

Name_____

Skill Builder | CHAPTER **12**

Simplest Form Fractions and Mixed Numbers

Learn

What Can I Do?
I want to write fractions and mixed numbers in simplest form.

Divide by Common Factors

$$\frac{9 \div 3}{24 \div 3} = \frac{3}{8}$$

Think: Both 9 and 24 have 3 as a factor.

Divide the Numerator by the Denominator

$$\frac{14}{12}$$

$$1\frac{2}{12} = 1\frac{1}{6}$$

$$12\overline{)14}$$
$$\underline{-12}$$
$$2$$

Look for common factors to write the fraction in simplest form.

Try It • Write in simplest form.

1. $\dfrac{15 \div 3}{21 \div 3} = \dfrac{5}{7}$

2. $\dfrac{9}{4}$ $4\overline{)9}^{\,2\frac{1}{4}}$

3. $\dfrac{12}{16} = \dfrac{3}{4}$

Power Practice • Write in simplest form.

4. $\dfrac{8}{12}$ $\dfrac{2}{3}$

5. $\dfrac{9}{27}$ $\dfrac{1}{3}$

6. $\dfrac{2}{18}$ $\dfrac{1}{9}$

7. $\dfrac{18}{21}$ $\dfrac{6}{7}$

8. $\dfrac{5}{2}$ $2\frac{1}{2}$

9. $\dfrac{8}{5}$ $1\frac{3}{5}$

10. $\dfrac{17}{9}$ $1\frac{8}{9}$

11. $\dfrac{12}{5}$ $2\frac{2}{5}$

150 Grade 4, Chapter 12, Cluster A

© McGraw-Hill School Division

WHAT IF THE STUDENT CAN'T

Recall Division Facts
- Remind students that they can use counters to model any division facts they are unsure of.
- Demonstrate how to divide on a number line using repeated subtraction. Tell students they can use this technique when they cannot recall a division fact.
- Have pairs of students work together to practice division facts using manipulatives, flash cards, or number lines.

Find Common Factors
- Ask students to explain what a common factor is. (A number that divides into both numbers in a pair)
- Ask students what divisibility rules they know that can help them find common factors. (Students will probably recall divisibility rules for 5 and 10. They may also recall others.)

Complete the Power Practice
- Discuss each incorrect answer. Isolate problem areas by having the student explain his or her reasoning step by step for each problem.

Least Common Multiple

Skill Builder CHAPTER 12

Learn

What Can I Do?
I want to find the least common multiple of two numbers.

List the Multiples

What is the least common multiple of 6 and 4?

Multiply by	1	2	3	4	5	6	7	8	9
Multiples of 6	6	(12)	18	(24)	30	(36)	42	48	54
Multiples of 4	4	8	(12)	16	20	(24)	28	32	(36)

Think: 12, 24, and 36 are multiples of both 6 and 4.
12 is the least number that is a multiple of both 6 and 4.

Try It • List multiples.

1. List some multiples of 2. _____ Possible answers: 2, 4, 6, 8, 10, 12

2. List some multiples of 8. _____ Possible answers: 8, 16, 24, 32, 40, 48

3. List some multiples of 3. _____ Possible answers: 3, 6, 9, 12, 15, 18, 21, 24

Find the least common multiple of each pair of numbers.

4. 2 and 8 __8__ 5. 2 and 3 __6__ 6. 3 and 8 __24__

Power Practice • Find the least common multiple of each pair of numbers.

7. 3 and 9 __9__ 8. 5 and 2 __10__ 9. 4 and 8 __8__

10. 6 and 12 __12__ 11. 3 and 4 __12__ 12. 4 and 10 __20__

WHAT IF THE STUDENT CAN'T

Find Multiples

- Point out that multiples of a number can be found by skip counting by the number.

- Tell students that a multiple is a product of the number multiplied by any other number. Remind them that to find multiples in order they can multiply the number by 1, 2, 3, 4, 5, and so on.

- Provide practice with multiplication facts for any students who have not yet mastered them.

Find the Least Number in a Group of Numbers

- Tell students to draw a number line and then locate each number on the line. Remind them that the least number is the number that is farthest left on the number line.

- Review ordering numbers. Have students compare the digits in the greatest place first, then the digits in the next place, and so on.

Complete the Power Practice

- Discuss each incorrect answer. Have the student explain how he or she selected the least common multiple for each pair of numbers.

USING THE LESSON

Lesson Goal

- Find the least common multiple (LCM) of two numbers.

What the Student Needs to Know

- Find multiples.

- Find the least number in a group of numbers.

Getting Started

- Have students skip count by 2, 3, 4, 5, and 10.

What Can I Do?

Read the question and the response. Then read and discuss the examples. Ask:

- *How were the multiples of 6 found?* (6 was multiplied by each of the numbers 1 through 9.)

- *How were the multiples of 4 found?* (4 was multiplied by each of the numbers 1 through 9.)

- *How do you know that 12 is the least common multiple of 4 and 6?* (The numbers that are multiples of both 4 and 6 are circled on the chart. 12 is the least of the circled numbers.)

Try It

- Ask: *Can the least common multiple of two numbers be one of the two numbers?* (Yes, for example: the least common multiple of 3 and 6 is 6.)

Power Practice

- Remind students that they can list multiples to help them find the least common multiple.

- Have students share their methods for finding the least common multiples.

Lesson Goal
• Find equivalent fractions.

What the Student Needs to Know
• Find multiples.
• Find common factors.

Getting Started
• Present some multiplication facts and ask students to find the products.
• Present some division facts and ask students to find the quotients.

What Can I Do?
Read the question and the response. Then read and discuss the examples. Ask:

• *Is 6 the only number by which you can multiply the numerator and denominator of $\frac{5}{6}$ to find equivalent fractions? Explain.* (Equivalent fractions can be found by multiplying the numerator and denominator by any non-zero number.)

• *Is there more than one equivalent fraction for $\frac{20}{25}$?* (Only one equivalent fraction can be found by dividing, but other equivalent fractions can be found by multiplying the numerator and denominator of either $\frac{4}{5}$ or $\frac{20}{25}$ by the same number.)

Try It
• Ask students how they will decide which fractions in the list are equivalent to the first fraction. (Decide if the numerator and denominator of the first fraction can be multiplied or divided by some number to get each of the other fractions in the list. Or, decide if the numerator and denominator of each fraction in the list can be multiplied or divided by a number to get the first fraction.)

Power Practice
• Remind students that there may be more than one fraction in each list that is equivalent to the first fraction.

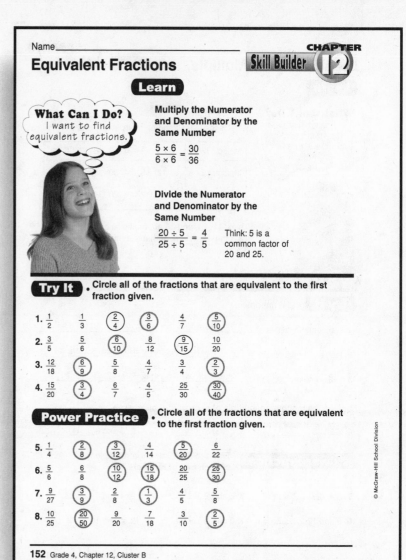

Name_____

Equivalent Fractions

Skill Builder **CHAPTER 12**

Learn

What Can I Do? I want to find equivalent fractions.

Multiply the Numerator and Denominator by the Same Number

$\frac{5 \times 6}{6 \times 6} = \frac{30}{36}$

Divide the Numerator and Denominator by the Same Number

$\frac{20 \div 5}{25 \div 5} = \frac{4}{5}$ Think: 5 is a common factor of 20 and 25.

Try It — Circle all of the fractions that are equivalent to the first fraction given.

1. $\frac{1}{2}$ $\frac{1}{3}$ ②$\frac{2}{4}$ ③$\frac{3}{6}$ $\frac{4}{7}$ ⑤$\frac{5}{10}$

2. $\frac{3}{5}$ $\frac{5}{6}$ ⑥$\frac{6}{10}$ $\frac{8}{12}$ ⑨$\frac{9}{15}$ $\frac{10}{20}$

3. $\frac{12}{18}$ ⑥$\frac{6}{9}$ $\frac{5}{8}$ $\frac{4}{7}$ $\frac{3}{4}$ ②$\frac{2}{3}$

4. $\frac{15}{20}$ ③$\frac{3}{4}$ $\frac{6}{7}$ $\frac{4}{5}$ $\frac{25}{30}$ ㉚$\frac{30}{40}$

Power Practice — Circle all of the fractions that are equivalent to the first fraction given.

5. $\frac{1}{4}$ ②$\frac{2}{8}$ ③$\frac{3}{12}$ $\frac{4}{14}$ ⑤$\frac{5}{20}$ $\frac{6}{22}$

6. $\frac{5}{6}$ $\frac{6}{8}$ ⑩$\frac{10}{12}$ ⑮$\frac{15}{18}$ $\frac{20}{25}$ ㉕$\frac{25}{30}$

7. $\frac{9}{27}$ ③$\frac{3}{9}$ $\frac{2}{8}$ ①$\frac{1}{3}$ $\frac{4}{5}$ $\frac{5}{8}$

8. $\frac{10}{25}$ ⑳$\frac{20}{50}$ $\frac{9}{20}$ $\frac{7}{18}$ $\frac{3}{10}$ ②$\frac{2}{5}$

152 Grade 4, Chapter 12, Cluster B

© McGraw-Hill School Division

WHAT IF THE STUDENT CAN'T

Find Multiples
• Remind students that multiples of a number can be found by skip counting by that number.
• Have students make a table like the one below and complete it to find multiples of various numbers.

	1	2	3	4	5	6	7
× 3							
× 4							

Find Common Factors
• Remind students that numbers that can be divided into a given number are factors of the number. Students may find factors by trying to divide each number in order or by using number properties.
• Encourage students to list factors for each of the two numbers and then circle factors that are the same for both numbers.

Complete the Power Practice
• For each problem, discuss each fraction in the list to determine if the numerator and denominator can be multiplied or divided by the same number to make the first fraction in the list.

Common Denominator

Learn

What Can I Do?
I want to find a common denominator for two fractions.

Find the Least Common Multiple of the Two Denominators

Find a common denominator for $\frac{1}{6}$ and $\frac{3}{4}$.

Multiply by	1	2	3	4	5	6
Multiples of 6	6	(12)	18	24	30	36
Multiples of 4	4	8	(12)	16	20	24

The least common multiple of 6 and 4 is 12.
A common denominator for $\frac{1}{6}$ and $\frac{3}{4}$ is 12.

Try It • Find a common denominator for each pair of fractions.
Answers may vary. Possible answers are given.

1. $\frac{2}{3}$ and $\frac{1}{2}$ ___6___

Multiples of 3 __3, 6, 9, 12__

Multiples of 2 __2, 4, 6, 8__

2. $\frac{1}{9}$ and $\frac{5}{6}$ ___18___

Multiples of 9 __9, 18, 27, 36__

Multiples of 6 __6, 12, 18, 24__

3. $\frac{1}{4}$ and $\frac{3}{8}$ ___8___

4. $\frac{1}{3}$ and $\frac{3}{5}$ ___15___

Power Practice • Circle the number that is a common denominator for the two fractions.

5. $\frac{1}{6}$ and $\frac{2}{3}$ 2   3   4   5   (6)

6. $\frac{3}{4}$ and $\frac{1}{3}$ 4   6   8   (12)   14

7. $\frac{4}{5}$ and $\frac{1}{2}$ 4   5   (10)   15   25

8. $\frac{1}{2}$ and $\frac{5}{8}$ 10   (8)   6   4   2

Grade 4, Chapter 12, Cluster B   **153**

WHAT IF THE STUDENT CAN'T

Find the Common Multiples for Two Numbers

- Remind students that they can use a number line or skip counting to find multiples of each of the two numbers. Tell them to write down the multiples as they count.

- Students should recall that they can find multiples by finding the product of a number and each of the digits 1, 2, 3, 4, and so on. It may help students to list the factors and the products in a table.

Complete the Power Practice

- Discuss each incorrect answer. Have the students circle the denominators. Explain that it is the denominators for which they need to find common multiples.

- Have students find the multiples for each denominator and circle the common denominators.

- Students can then look at the answers to determine which of the common denominators is on the list.

USING THE LESSON

Lesson Goal
- Find the common denominator for two fractions.

What the Student Needs to Know
- Find the common multiples for two numbers.

Getting Started
Ask students to write equivalent fractions by finding the missing numerator for each fraction.

- $\frac{1}{6} = \frac{m}{12}$ ($m = 2$)
- $\frac{3}{4} = \frac{r}{12}$ ($r = 9$)
- $\frac{2}{3} = \frac{w}{6}$ ($w = 4$)
- $\frac{1}{2} = \frac{h}{6}$ ($h = 3$)
- $\frac{2}{9} = \frac{d}{18}$ ($d = 4$)
- $\frac{1}{5} = \frac{p}{15}$ ($p = 3$)

What Can I Do?
Read the question and the response. Then read and discuss the examples. Ask:

- *What is another common denominator for $\frac{1}{6}$ and $\frac{3}{4}$?* (24)

- *What is the least common denominator for $\frac{1}{6}$ and $\frac{3}{4}$?* (12)

Try It
- Tell students that the least common denominator for a pair of fractions is the least common multiple of the two denominators.

- Have students complete the exercises. Then ask volunteers to explain how they found the common denominator for Exercises 3 and 4.

Power Practice
- Have students complete the practice. Then review each answer.

- Ask students to share their methods for choosing the common denominator for the two fractions in each exercise.

Lesson Goal
- Recognize and use properties of whole numbers.

What the Student Needs to Know
- Recall addition facts.
- Find the sum for more than two addends.
- Group addends using grouping symbols.

Getting Started
Ask students to find the following sums.
- 0 + 7 (7)
- 2 + 3 + 4 (9)
- 6 + 8 (14)
- 8 + 6 (14)
- 9 + 0 (9)
- 8 + 3 + 1 (12)
- 4 + 6 + 7 (17)

What Can I Do?
Read the question and the response. Then read and discuss the examples. Ask:
- *Why is "identity property" a good name for the property that says the sum of any number and 0 is the number?* (Possible answer: Because the number stays the same. It is identical to itself.)
- *Why is "commutative property" a good name for the order property?* (Possible answer: Because the numbers can be moved or exchanged and the sum is the same.)
- *Why is "associative property" a good name for the grouping property?* (Possible answer: Because it does not matter how the numbers are put together or partnered, the sum is the same.)

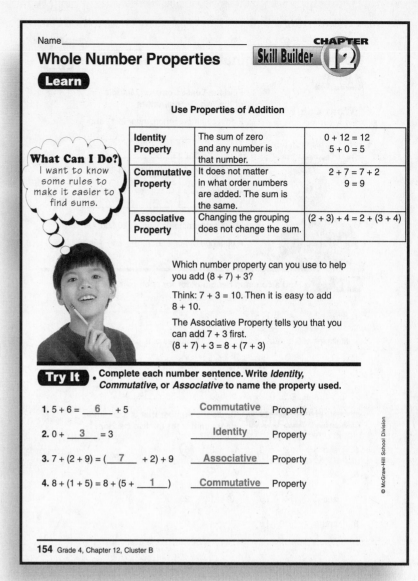

Name_____

Whole Number Properties
Skill Builder CHAPTER 12

Learn

Use Properties of Addition

Identity Property	The sum of zero and any number is that number.	0 + 12 = 12 5 + 0 = 5
Commutative Property	It does not matter in what order numbers are added. The sum is the same.	2 + 7 = 7 + 2 9 = 9
Associative Property	Changing the grouping does not change the sum.	(2 + 3) + 4 = 2 + (3 + 4)

What Can I Do?
I want to know some rules to make it easier to find sums.

Which number property can you use to help you add (8 + 7) + 3?

Think: 7 + 3 = 10. Then it is easy to add 8 + 10.

The Associative Property tells you that you can add 7 + 3 first.
(8 + 7) + 3 = 8 + (7 + 3)

Try It • Complete each number sentence. Write *Identity*, *Commutative*, or *Associative* to name the property used.

1. 5 + 6 = ___6___ + 5   _Commutative_ Property

2. 0 + ___3___ = 3   _Identity_ Property

3. 7 + (2 + 9) = (___7___ + 2) + 9   _Associative_ Property

4. 8 + (1 + 5) = 8 + (5 + ___1___)   _Commutative_ Property

154 Grade 4, Chapter 12, Cluster B

WHAT IF THE STUDENT CAN'T

Recall Addition Facts
- Remind students that they can use counters or a number line to model any addition facts they cannot recall.
- Ask students to record any facts they are having difficulty remembering. Have them use their lists to help them learn the facts and to help them recall the sums.
- Have pairs of students work together with flash cards to master all of the addition facts.

Find the Sum for More Than Two Addends
- Use an example such as: 2 + 5 + 4 + 7. Explain to students that they know how to find the sum of two addends. Demonstrate how they can find the sum of two addends and then add that sum to the next addend. Show the students that they will be using their ability to add two addends to find the sum of more than two addends.

Name_____

Find each sum.

5. $7 + 0 =$ __7__   **6.** $5 + (5 + 9) =$ __19__   **7.** $9 + 4 =$ __13__

8. $4 + 9 =$ __13__   **9.** $(6 + 8) + 2 =$ __16__   **10.** $0 + 23 =$ __23__

Power Practice   Complete each number sentence.
• Write *Identity*, *Commutative*, or *Associative* to name the property used.

		Property
11. __6__ $+ 0 = 6$		Identity
12. $(7 + 6) + 3 = 7 + ($ __6__ $+ 3)$		Associative
13. __0__ $+ 2 = 2$		Identity
14. $9 + 7 = 7 +$ __9__		Commutative

Find each sum.

15. $(9 + 4) + 4 =$ __17__   **16.** $0 + 15 =$ __15__

17. $8 + (2 + 5) =$ __15__   **18.** $(8 + 7) + 2 =$ __17__

19. $8 + (2 + 9) =$ __19__   **20.** $5 + 0 =$ __5__

© McGraw-Hill School Division

© McGraw-Hill School Division

USING THE LESSON

Try It

Help students connect the properties and their names. Ask:

• *What property says that the order of the numbers can change?* (Commutative property)

• *What is the name of the zero property?* (Identity property)

• *What property says you can change the grouping of the addends?* (Associative property)

Power Practice

• Say each word and ask students to describe the property that it names.

Grouping (Associative property)

Order (Commutative property)

Zero (Identity property)

• Review Exercises 15–20 with the students. Ask volunteers to explain how they solved each problem and what properties they used.

WHAT IF THE STUDENT CAN'T

Group Addends Using Grouping Symbols

• Show an example such as: $4 + (3 + 4)$. Remind students that the grouping symbols tell them which sums to find first. Ask students to find the sum of $3 + 4$. Then instruct them to find the sum for $4 + 7$.

• When students are comfortable with 3 addends, provide additional practice with more complex problems such as: $(1 + 5) + (3 + 4)$.

Complete the Power Practice

• Discuss each incorrect answer. Have students use the words *grouping*, *order*, and *zero* to describe the properties. Then direct them to the top of page 154 to find the name of the property if they are unable to recall it.

CHALLENGE

Lesson Goal
- Completely factor a number.

Introducing the Challenge
- Ask students to name some pairs of numbers that have a product of 48. Point out that the pairs of numbers are factors of 48. (Possible answers: 2 x 24, 3 x 16, 4 x 12, 6 x 8)

Name_____

Factor Trees

This is a **factor tree.** 48 is factored until each number can be divided only by itself and by 1.

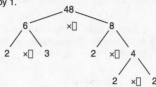

Complete these two factor trees for 36.

1.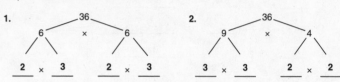

2.

3. What do you notice about the final factors in each tree for Exercises 1–2?

They are the same: 2, 2, 3, 3.

4. Draw another factor tree for 36.
   Hint: Other factor pairs for 36 are 12 and 3, 18 and 2.

Possible Answer:

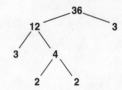

Draw factor trees for each number. Start by finding two factors that have the number as their product.

5.

54
× ☐

Possible Answer:

54
6 — 9
3 2   3 3

6.

63
× ☐

Possible Answer:

63
7   9
3 3

7.

72
× ☐

Possible Answer:

72
9   8
3 3   4 2
2 2

8. Choose your own number.

☐
× ☐

Answers will vary.

CHALLENGE

Using the Challenge

- Ask students to describe how each branch of the factor tree in the example is formed.
- Tell students that they can use any pair of factors that have a product of 48 as the first branches of their factor tree.
- Have students make another factor tree for 48 starting with a different pair of factors that have a product of 48.
- Ask students how they will know when they have finished their factor tree. (Each of the end numbers will be divisible by only itself and 1.)

CHALLENGE

Lesson Goal
- Make an equivalent fraction table.
- Use the table to find equivalent fractions.

Introducing the Challenge
- Ask students how they can find equivalent fractions for $\frac{15}{30}$. (Multiply or divide both the numerator and denominator by the same number.)

Equivalent Fraction Table

Make an equivalent fraction table. Multiply the numerator and denominator of each fraction along the side by the numbers across the top of the table.

1. Write equivalent fractions to complete the table.

	2	3	4	5	6	7	8	9
$\frac{1}{2}$	$\frac{2}{4}$	$\frac{3}{6}$	$\frac{4}{8}$	$\frac{5}{10}$	$\frac{6}{12}$	$\frac{7}{14}$	$\frac{8}{16}$	$\frac{9}{18}$
$\frac{1}{3}$	$\frac{2}{6}$	$\frac{3}{9}$	$\frac{4}{12}$	$\frac{5}{15}$	$\frac{6}{18}$	$\frac{7}{21}$	$\frac{8}{24}$	$\frac{9}{27}$
$\frac{1}{4}$	$\frac{2}{8}$	$\frac{3}{12}$	$\frac{4}{16}$	$\frac{5}{20}$	$\frac{6}{24}$	$\frac{7}{28}$	$\frac{8}{32}$	$\frac{9}{36}$
$\frac{1}{5}$	$\frac{2}{10}$	$\frac{3}{15}$	$\frac{4}{20}$	$\frac{5}{25}$	$\frac{6}{30}$	$\frac{7}{35}$	$\frac{8}{40}$	$\frac{9}{45}$
$\frac{1}{6}$	$\frac{2}{12}$	$\frac{3}{18}$	$\frac{4}{24}$	$\frac{5}{30}$	$\frac{6}{36}$	$\frac{7}{42}$	$\frac{8}{48}$	$\frac{9}{54}$
$\frac{1}{7}$	$\frac{2}{14}$	$\frac{3}{21}$	$\frac{4}{28}$	$\frac{5}{35}$	$\frac{6}{42}$	$\frac{7}{49}$	$\frac{8}{56}$	$\frac{9}{63}$
$\frac{1}{8}$	$\frac{2}{16}$	$\frac{3}{24}$	$\frac{4}{32}$	$\frac{5}{40}$	$\frac{6}{48}$	$\frac{7}{56}$	$\frac{8}{64}$	$\frac{9}{72}$
$\frac{1}{9}$	$\frac{2}{18}$	$\frac{3}{27}$	$\frac{4}{36}$	$\frac{5}{45}$	$\frac{6}{54}$	$\frac{7}{63}$	$\frac{8}{72}$	$\frac{9}{81}$

Use your table to write each fraction in simplest form.

2. $\frac{7}{56}$ $\frac{1}{8}$ _____

3. $\frac{5}{15}$ $\frac{1}{3}$ _____

4. $\frac{6}{30}$ $\frac{1}{5}$ _____

5. $\frac{8}{48}$ $\frac{1}{6}$ _____

6. $\frac{4}{36}$ $\frac{1}{9}$ _____

7. $\frac{7}{28}$ $\frac{1}{4}$ _____

8. Explain how you can use your table to find a fraction equivalent to $\frac{2}{3}$ that has a denominator of 18.

Look for a fraction equivalent to $\frac{1}{3}$ that has a denominator of 18.

Then multiply its numerator by 2. _____

_____

_____

Write the numerator to make equivalent fractions.
Use your table to help you.

9. $\frac{3}{4} = \frac{\boxed{18}}{24}$

10. $\frac{4}{9} = \frac{\boxed{32}}{72}$

11. $\frac{2}{5} = \frac{\boxed{14}}{35}$

12. $\frac{5}{6} = \frac{\boxed{15}}{18}$

13. $\frac{4}{7} = \frac{\boxed{12}}{21}$

14. $\frac{7}{8} = \frac{\boxed{49}}{56}$

15. $\frac{2}{3} = \frac{\boxed{18}}{27}$

16. $\frac{4}{5} = \frac{\boxed{32}}{40}$

CHALLENGE

Using the Challenge

- Instruct students to complete the table by multiplying both the numerator and the denominator of each fraction by each of the numbers in the top row.

- Ask students to explain how they will find the simplest form for the fraction $\frac{7}{56}$. (Find $\frac{7}{56}$ in their table. Follow the row across to the fraction on the far left. That is the simplest form of the fraction.)

- Have volunteers share their explanations for Exercise 8. Students can then use the methods described to find equivalent fractions for exercises 9–16.

Whole Number Place Value

Use the number 526,891. Write the value of each digit.

1. 2 _____   **2.** 8 _____

3. 9 _____   **4.** 5 _____

Simplest Form Fractions

Write each fraction in simplest form.

5. $\frac{8}{10}$ _____   **6.** $\frac{70}{100}$ _____   **7.** $\frac{42}{100}$ _____

Write Numerals

Write each number.

8. Forty-five thousand sixty-seven _____

9. Two thousand, three hundred ten _____

Write Number Words

Write each number in words.

10. 809,112 _____

11. 5,044 _____

Equivalent Fractions

Find the numerator to write equivalent fractions.

12. $\frac{1}{4} = \frac{}{100}$ **13.** $\frac{3}{5} = \frac{}{10}$ **14.** $\frac{1}{2} = \frac{}{100}$

Name_____

Simplest Form Mixed Numbers

Write each mixed number in simplest form.

15. $1\frac{5}{10}$ _____   **16.** $2\frac{35}{100}$ _____   **17.** $4\frac{300}{1000}$ _____

Compare and Order Whole Numbers

Compare. Write >, <, or =.

18. 721 _____ 803   **19.** 474 _____ 465   **20.** 2,910 _____ 2,955

Order from least to greatest.

21. 351, 305, 315, 350 _____

Round Whole Numbers

Round each number to its greatest place.

22. 44 _____   **23.** 6,732 _____

Round to the Nearest Dollar

Round to the nearest dollar.

24. $4.75 _____   **25.** $15.15 _____

Assessment Goal

This two-page assessment covers skills identified as necessary for success in Chapter 13 Relate Fractions and Decimals. The first page assesses the major prerequisite skills for Cluster A. The second page assesses the major prerequisite skills for Cluster B. When the Cluster A and Cluster B prerequisite skills overlap, the skill(s) will be covered in only one section.

Getting Started

- Allow students time to look over the two pages of the assessment. Point out the labels that identify the skills covered.

- Have students find math vocabulary terms used in the assessment. List vocabulary terms on the board as students identify them. If necessary, review the meanings of all essential math vocabulary.

Introducing the Assessment

- Explain to students that these pages will help you know if they are ready to start a new chapter in their math textbooks.

- Students who have transferred from another school may not have been introduced to some of these skills. Encourage students to do their best and assure them you will help them learn any needed skills.

Cluster A Challenge

Those students who demonstrate mastery of the skills on this page will not need to use the reteaching worksheets. Instead, these students can do the Cluster A Challenge found on pages 170–171.

Name_____

CHAPTER 13 What Do I Need To Know?

Whole Number Place Value

Use the number 526,891. Write the value of each digit.

1. 2 _____20,000_____   2. 8 _____800_____

3. 9 _____90_____   4. 5 _____500,000_____

Simplest Form Fractions

Write each fraction in simplest form.

5. $\frac{8}{10}$ ___$\frac{4}{5}$___   6. $\frac{70}{100}$ ___$\frac{7}{10}$___   7. $\frac{42}{100}$ ___$\frac{21}{50}$___

Write Numerals

Write each number.

8. Forty-five thousand sixty-seven _____45,067_____

9. Two thousand, three hundred ten _____2,310_____

Write Number Words

Write each number in words.

10. 809,112 ___eight hundred nine thousand, one hundred twelve___

11. 5,044 ___five thousand forty-four___

Equivalent Fractions

Find the numerator to write equivalent fractions.

12. $\frac{1}{4} = \frac{25}{100}$ 13. $\frac{3}{5} = \frac{6}{10}$ 14. $\frac{1}{2} = \frac{50}{100}$

159A Use with Grade 4, Chapter 13, Cluster A

CLUSTER A PREREQUISITE SKILLS

The skills listed in this chart are those identified as major prerequisite skills for students' success in the lessons in Cluster A of the chapter. Each skill is covered by one or more assessment items as shown in the middle column. The right column provides the page number for the lessons in this book that reteach the cluster A prerequisite skills.

Skill Name	Assessment Items	Lesson Pages
Whole Number Place Value	1-4	160-161
Simplest Form Fractions	5-7	162
Write Numerals	8-9	163
Write Number Words	10-11	164
Equivalent Fractions	12-14	165

Name_____

Simplest Form Mixed Numbers

Write each mixed number in simplest form.

15. $1\frac{5}{10}$ ___$1\frac{1}{2}$___   **16.** $2\frac{35}{100}$ ___$2\frac{7}{20}$___   **17.** $4\frac{300}{1000}$ ___$4\frac{3}{10}$___

Compare and Order Whole Numbers

Compare. Write >, <, or =.

18. 721 __<__ 803   **19.** 474 __>__ 465   **20.** 2,910 __<__ 2,955

Order from least to greatest.

21. 351, 305, 315, 350 _____ 305, 315, 350, 351

Round Whole Numbers

Round each number to its greatest place.

22. 44 ___40___   **23.** 6,732 ___7,000___

Round to the Nearest Dollar

Round to the nearest dollar.

24. $4.75 ___$5.00___   **25.** $15.15 ___$15.00___

Use with Grade 4, Chapter 13, Cluster B **159B**

CLUSTER B PREREQUISITE SKILLS

The skills listed in this chart are those identified as major prerequisite skills for students' success in the lessons in Cluster B of the chapter. Each skill is covered by one or more assessment items as shown in the middle column. The right column provides the page numbers for the lessons in this book that reteach the Cluster B prerequisite skills

Skill Name	Assessment Items	Lesson Pages
Simplest Form Mixed Numbers	15-17	166
Compare and Order Whole Numbers	18-21	167
Round Whole Numbers	22-23	168
Round to the Nearest Dollar	24-25	169

CHAPTER 13 PRE-CHAPTER ASSESSMENT

Alternative Assessment Strategies

- Oral administration of the assessment is appropriate for younger students or those whose native language is not English. Read the skills title and directions one section at a time. Check students' understanding by asking them to tell you how they will do the first exercise in the group.

- For some skill types you may wish to use group administration. In this technique, a small group or pair of students complete the assessment together. Through their discussion, you will be able to decide if supplementary reteaching materials are needed.

Intervention Materials

If students are not successful with the prerequisite skills assessed on these pages, reteaching lessons have been created to help them make the transition into the chapter.

Item correlation charts showing the skills lessons suitable for reteaching the prerequisite skills are found beneath the reproductions of each page of the assessment.

Cluster B Challenge

Those students who demonstrate mastery of the skills on this page will not need to use the reteaching worksheets. Instead, these students can do the Cluster B Challenge found on pages 172–173.

Lesson Goal
- For any digit in a number, write the name of the place and the value of the digit.

What the Student Needs to Know
- Recall that the value of each place is 10 times greater than the place to its right.
- Recall that a number can be written as the sum of the values of its digits.

Getting Started
Ask students to read each number.
- Eighty-two
- Four hundred sixty-seven
- Seven hundred three
- Two thousand, five hundred ninety-one
- Three thousand, eighty
- 45
- 623
- 1,412
- 6,004

What Can I Do?
Read the question and the response. Then read and discuss the examples. Ask:
- *How are the places on each side of the comma alike? How are they different?* (Each group of three digits shows hundreds, tens, and ones. The places to the left of the comma show thousands.)
- *What do the words hundred thousands above the number 4 in the place-value chart tell you?* (That the 4 is in the hundred thousands place and its value is 400,000.)
- *What is the value of 7 in the number 463,217?* (7)
- *What is the value of the 2 in the number 463,217?* (200)

Name_____

Whole Number Place Value

Skill Builder

Learn

Use a Place-Value Chart

What is the value of 6 in the number 463,217?

hundred thousands	ten thousands	one thousands	hundreds	tens	ones
4	6	3	2	1	7
4	0	0 ,	0	0	0
	6	0 ,	0	0	0
		3 ,	0	0	0
			2	0	0
				1	0
					7

I want to write the value of the digits in a number.

What Can I Do?

The 6 in 463,217 is in the ten thousands place.
The value of 6 in 463,217 is 60,000.

Try It Use the number 956,802. Write the name of the place each digit is in. Then write its value.

hundred thousands	ten thousands	one thousands	hundreds	tens	ones
9	5	6	8	0	2

		Place		Value
1.	8	hundreds		800
2.	9	hundred thousands		900,000
3.	5	ten thousands		50,000
4.	2	ones		2

WHAT IF THE STUDENT CAN'T

Recall That the Value of Each Place is 10 Times Greater than the Place to Its Right
Use place-value models:
- Show one and write the number. Show ten and write the number. Ask students to show how many ones are needed to make a ten. Show them that the digit 1 in the number 10 has a value ten times as great as the digit 1 in the number 1.
- Show a hundred model. Write the number. Ask students to show the number of tens needed to make 100. Ask them to explain how many times greater the value

of the digit 1 in 100 is than the value of the digit 1 in 10.
- Have students model the number of hundreds needed to make a thousand. Then have them describe the relationship between the value of the digit 1 in 100 and the value of the digit 1 in 1,000.
- Ask students to tell about the relationship between the value of the digit 1 in 1,000 and the value of the digit 1 in 10,000.
- Ask students to describe the relationship between the value of the digit 1 in 10,000 and the value of the digit 1 in 100,000.

Name _____

Power Practice • Use the number 716,325. Write the name of the place each digit is in. Then write its value.

hundred thousands	ten thousands	one thousands	hundreds	tens	ones
7	1	6	3	2	5

		Place	Value
5.	6	thousands	6,000
6.	2	tens	20
7.	7	hundred thousands	700,000
8.	5	ones	5
9.	1	ten thousands	10,000
10.	3	hundreds	300

Use the number 94,076. Write the value of each digit.

11.	6	6
12.	4	4,000
13.	9	90,000
14.	7	70

Try It

Before students begin, ask:

- *How can you find the place for each digit in the number?* (Read the words above the number in the place-value chart.)
- *How can you write the value for each digit in the number?* (Write the digit in its place and then write zeros in each place to the right of the digit.)

Power Practice

- Select several problems and ask volunteers to explain how they determined the place and the value for the digit.
- Ask students who did not use the place-value chart to explain how they found the place and the value.

WHAT IF THE STUDENT CAN'T

Recall that a Number Can Be Written as the Sum of the Values of Its Digits

- Show the number 2,483 using place-value models.
- Ask students to write the number shown by the thousands models. (2,000)
- Ask students to write the number shown by the hundreds models. (400)
- Ask students to write the number shown by the tens models. (80)
- Ask students to write the number shown by the ones models. (3)

- Ask students to write the number shown by the entire group of models. (2,483)

Complete the Power Practice

- Discuss each incorrect answer. Have the student write the number given in the direction line on a place-value chart. Then direct student attention to the location of each digit and its value.

USING THE LESSON

Lesson Goal
- Write fractions given in tenths or hundredths in simplest form.

What the Student Needs to Know
- Find common factors.
- Divide by a 1-digit or a 2-digit number.

Getting Started
Have students find the factors of these numbers:
- 10 (1, 2, 5, 10)
- 15 (1, 3, 5, 15)
- 50 (1, 2, 5, 10, 25, 50)
- 80 (1, 2, 4, 5, 8, 10, 16, 20, 40, 80)
- 88 (1, 2, 4, 8, 11, 22, 44, 88)

What Can I Do?
Read the question and the response. Then read and discuss the examples. Ask:
- *What is a common factor?* (A common factor is a number that is a factor of both numbers.)
- *How can you tell when a fraction is in simplest form?* (A fraction is in simplest form if the only common factor of the numerator and the denominator is 1.)
- *How could you find the simplest form fraction for $\frac{75}{100}$ in just one simplification?* (25 is the greatest common factor of both 75 and 100. Divide both the numerator and denominator of the fraction $\frac{75}{100}$ by 25. $\frac{75}{100} = \frac{3}{4}$)

Try It
- Remind students to check that all fractions are in simplest form.

Power Practice
- Point out that the factors of 100 are given at the top of the page.
- Ask students to explain how the factors of these two numbers can help them find the simplest form fractions for the exercises.
- Review each answer with the students.

Simplest Form Fractions

Learn

What Can I Do?
I want to write fractions given in tenths or hundredths in simplest form.

Divide by a Common Factor

Factors of 75: 1, 3, 5, 15, 25, 75

Factors of 100: 1, 2, 4, 5, 10, 20, 25, 50, 100

Look for a factor of 100 that is also a factor of the numerator.

$$\frac{75}{100} = \frac{75 \div 5}{100 \div 5} = \frac{15}{20}$$

Check to see if the fraction is in simplest form. If not, divide by a common factor.

$$\frac{15}{20} = \frac{15 \div 5}{20 \div 5} = \frac{3}{4}$$

Try It • Write each fraction in simplest form.

1. $\frac{5}{10} = \frac{5 \div 5}{10 \div 5} = \frac{1}{2}$

2. $\frac{30}{100} = \frac{30 \div 10}{100 \div 10} = \frac{3}{10}$

3. $\frac{40}{100} = \frac{40 \div 20}{100 \div 20} = \frac{2}{5}$

4. $\frac{22}{100} = \frac{22 \div 2}{100 \div 2} = \frac{11}{50}$

Power Practice • Write each fraction in simplest form.

5. $\frac{2}{10}$ $\frac{1}{5}$

6. $\frac{50}{100}$ $\frac{1}{2}$

7. $\frac{80}{100}$ $\frac{4}{5}$

8. $\frac{4}{100}$ $\frac{1}{25}$

9. $\frac{5}{100}$ $\frac{1}{20}$

10. $\frac{88}{100}$ $\frac{22}{25}$

11. $\frac{10}{100}$ $\frac{1}{10}$

12. $\frac{76}{100}$ $\frac{19}{25}$

© McGraw-Hill School Division

WHAT IF THE STUDENT CAN'T

Find Common Factors
- Show students how to find factors by looking for numbers that divide evenly into the given number.
- Ask students to find pairs of numbers that have the given number as a product.
- Have students list the factors of two numbers and then circle the factors that are the same for both numbers. Explain that these are the common factors. Ask students to identify the greatest common factor.

Divide by a 1-Digit or a 2-Digit Number
- Remind students that they can divide by repeated subtraction.
- Use place-value models to show dividing 100 by some of its factors (2, 4, 5, 10, 20, 25, 50, 100).

Complete the Power Practice
- Discuss each incorrect answer. Have the student find the factors for the numerator. Ask if the numerator and the denominator (10 or 100) have any common factors.

Name_____

Write Numerals

Learn

What Can I Do?
I want to write a number in place of words.

Write a Comma for the Word *Thousand*

Write the number for two hundred thousand, six hundred five.

Write the number before the word *thousand*.

Write a comma for the word *thousand*.

Write the rest of the number.

Think: Write 200. Then write a comma. Then write 605.

The number for two hundred thousand, six hundred five is 200,605.

Try It • Write each number.

1. twenty-six thousand, three hundred fifteen __2__ __6__ , __3__ __1__ __5__

2. five thousand, sixty-seven __5__ , __0__ __6__ __7__

3. six hundred nine thousand, three hundred __6__ __0__ __9__ , __3__ __0__ __0__

Power Practice • Write each number.

4. nine thousand, seven hundred fifty-three _____9,753_____

5. fourteen thousand, five hundred ten _____14,510_____

6. two hundred eight thousand, seventeen _____208,017_____

7. fifty-one thousand, six hundred fifty-one _____51,651_____

8. eight thousand, eighty _____8,080_____

Grade 4, Chapter 13, Cluster A **163**

WHAT IF THE STUDENT CAN'T

Read a Number Written in Words

- Begin with 1-digit numbers. Have students read the words and write the number. Then move to 2-digit numbers and so on.

- Explain that if students can read 1-digit, 2-digit, and 3-digit numbers, they can read any number. Show students that they read a number, read the comma as the period, or group name, and then read another number.

Apply Place Value

- Show a place-value chart. Point out that numbers are separated into periods and that the periods are separated by commas. Explain that when numbers are written in words the word for the period name tells when to write the comma. Illustrate using the number fifteen thousand, seven hundred twelve.

Complete the Power Practice

- Discuss each incorrect answer. Have students read the words and then read the number they have written and listen for any differences.

USING THE LESSON

Lesson Goal

- Write a numeral for words.

What the Student Needs to Know

- Read a number written in words.
- Apply place value.

Getting Started

Ask students to write each number.

- Five (5)
- Seventeen (17)
- Twenty-six (26)
- Six hundred fifteen (615)
- Two hundred two (202)

What Can I Do?

Read the question and the response. Have students read the words two hundred thousand, six hundred five. Ask:

- *What is the number for the words before "thousand"?* (200)

- *What do you write for the word "thousand"?* (a comma)

- *What is the number for the words after the word "thousand"?* (605)

- *What are the three parts of the number?* (the number to the left of the word thousand, the word thousand, the number to the right of the word thousand)

Try It

- Have students read the words for each number.

- Point out that the comma is written in each answer. Ask students how many digits the thousands can have. (1, 2, or 3)

- Ask how many digits the number after the comma can have. (It must have 3 digits.)

Power Practice

- Remind students to write the number before the word *thousand*, write a comma for *thousand* and then write the number after the word *thousand*.

USING THE LESSON

Lesson Goal
- Write a number in words.

What the Student Needs to Know
- Read a number.
- Understand and use place value.

Getting Started
Have students write the words for these numbers.
- 1 (one)
- 8 (eight)
- 10 (ten)
- 13 (thirteen)
- 20 (twenty)
- 55 (fifty-five)

What Can I Do?
Read the question and the response. Then have students read the number 78,295. Ask:
- *How many thousand are there?* (78)
- *What signals you to write the word "thousand"?* (the comma)
- *What is the number after the comma?* (295)
- *What are the three parts of the number?* (the number before the comma, 78; the comma; and the number after the comma, 295)

Try It
- Have students read each number and identify the parts of the number.
- Ask students to name the word or words that are missing in each answer.
- Have the students write the words. Review responses.

Power Practice
- Remind students to write the number to the left of the comma, the word *thousand*, and then the number to the right of the comma.

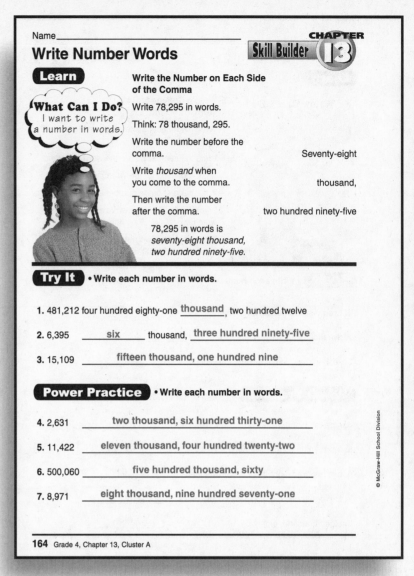

WHAT IF THE STUDENT CAN'T

Read a Number
- Have students begin by reading 1-digit and 2-digit numbers. Then read 3-digit numbers and so on.
- Ask students how they read the comma in a number. (Say *thousands*.)
- Point out that if students can read numbers through hundreds they can read any number. They can read the number on the left of the comma, then say *thousand*, and then read the number on the right of the comma.

Understand and Use Place Value
- Write numbers on a place-value chart. Illustrate how numbers are separated into periods and how the periods are separated by commas.
- Use place-value models to show the relationships among the values of the digits in each places.

Complete the Power Practice
- Discuss each incorrect answer. Have students read the number and then compare what they read to the words they wrote.

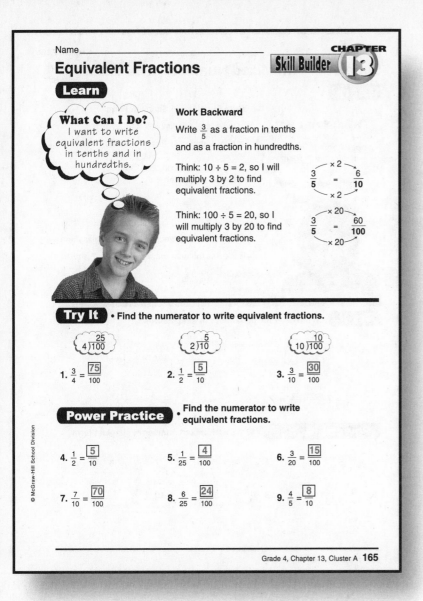

Name _____

Equivalent Fractions

CHAPTER 13

Learn

What Can I Do?
I want to write equivalent fractions in tenths and in hundredths.

Work Backward

Write $\frac{3}{5}$ as a fraction in tenths and as a fraction in hundredths.

Think: $10 \div 5 = 2$, so I will multiply 3 by 2 to find equivalent fractions.

$$\frac{3}{5} \overset{\times 2}{\underset{\times 2}{=}} \frac{6}{10}$$

Think: $100 \div 5 = 20$, so I will multiply 3 by 20 to find equivalent fractions.

$$\frac{3}{5} \overset{\times 20}{\underset{\times 20}{=}} \frac{60}{100}$$

Try It • Find the numerator to write equivalent fractions.

$4\overline{)100}^{\;25}$

$2\overline{)10}^{\;5}$

$10\overline{)100}^{\;10}$

1. $\frac{3}{4} = \frac{75}{100}$

2. $\frac{1}{2} = \frac{5}{10}$

3. $\frac{3}{10} = \frac{30}{100}$

Power Practice • Find the numerator to write equivalent fractions.

4. $\frac{1}{2} = \frac{5}{10}$

5. $\frac{1}{25} = \frac{4}{100}$

6. $\frac{3}{20} = \frac{15}{100}$

7. $\frac{7}{10} = \frac{70}{100}$

8. $\frac{6}{25} = \frac{24}{100}$

9. $\frac{4}{5} = \frac{8}{10}$

© McGraw-Hill School Division

Grade 4, Chapter 13, Cluster A **165**

WHAT IF THE STUDENT CAN'T

Find Equivalent Fractions

- Ask students to draw a rectangle and separate it into 5 equal sections. Then have them color 2 of the sections and write a fraction for the colored part of the rectangle.

- Have the students divide the rectangle into 10 equal sections. Ask them how many sections are colored. Have them write the equivalent fraction.

- Show students that the numerator and denominator of the equivalent fraction are twice those of the original fraction.

- Ask students to find equivalent fractions for $\frac{2}{5}$ by multiplying by 3, 4, 5, and 10.

Complete the Power Practice

- Discuss each incorrect answer. Have students divide the denominators. Then ask them to tell by what number they will multiply the numerator and denominator.

Lesson Goal
- Write equivalent fractions in tenths and hundredths.

What the Student Needs to Know
- Find equivalent fractions.

Getting Started
Have students find each quotient.
- $10 \div 2$ (5)
- $10 \div 5$ (2)
- $100 \div 10$ (10)
- $100 \div 25$ (4)
- $100 \div 20$ (5)
- $100 \div 5$ (20)

What Can I Do?
Read the question and the response. Then read and discuss the examples. Ask:

- *Why are the numerator and denominator of $\frac{3}{5}$ multiplied by 2 to find an equivalent fraction with a denominator of 10?* (The denominators are 5 and 10. 10 is 2 times 5, so the numerator and denominator of $\frac{3}{5}$ are multiplied by 2 to find equivalent fractions.)

- *How can you figure out what number to multiply the numerator and denominator of $\frac{3}{5}$ by to write a fraction with a denominator of 100?* (Divide 100 by 5 to find the number that can be multiplied by 5 to get 100.)

Try It
- For each exercise, ask students what number they will multiply the numerator and denominator by to find a fraction with the given denominator.

Power Practice
- Ask students to explain how they will decide what number they are going to multiply by. (Divide the denominators.)

- Select some exercises and ask volunteers to show how they selected the number to multiply by and how they found the equivalent fraction.

Grade 4, Chapter 13, Cluster A **165**

USING THE LESSON

Lesson Goal
• Write mixed numbers in simplest form.

What the Student Needs to Know
• Find common factors.
• Write a fraction in simplest form.

Getting Started
Ask students to find the factors of these numbers:
• 10 (1, 2, 5, 10)
• 100 (1, 2, 4, 5, 10, 20, 25, 50, 100)
• 1,000 (1, 2, 4, 5, 10, 20, 25, 40, 50, 100, 200, 250, 500, 1000)

What Can I Do?
Read the question and the response. Then read and discuss the examples. Ask:
• *How do you know that the fraction $\frac{700}{1000}$ is not in simplest form?* (700 and 1,000 have common factors, for example 100.)
• *Suppose you simplified $\frac{700}{1000}$ like this:*

$\frac{700}{1000} = \frac{70}{100}$

Is the fraction in simplest form? (No) *How can you write the fraction in simplest form?* (Simplify again. Divide the numerator and denominator by 10.)
• *How can you choose the greatest possible number to divide by?* (Divide by the greatest common factor of the numerator and denominator.)

Try It
• Ask students to explain how each divisor was chosen.

Power Practice
• Remind students to look for common denominators and to check that their answers are in simplest form.

Name_____

Simplest Form Mixed Numbers  Skill Builder CHAPTER 13

Learn

What Can I Do?
I want to write some special mixed numbers in simplest form.

Write Fractions in Simplest Form
To write $3\frac{700}{1,000}$ in simplest form, look for common factors.

Think: 700 and 1,000 both have 100 as a factor.

$3\frac{700}{1,000} = 3\frac{700 \div 100}{1,000 \div 100} = 3\frac{7}{10}$

Check to see that fractions are in simplest form.

Think: 1 is the only common factor for 7 and 10.

So, $3\frac{700}{1,000} = 3\frac{7}{10}$

Try It • Write each mixed number in simplest form.

1. $4\frac{5}{10} = 4\frac{5 \div 5}{10 \div 5} = 4\frac{1}{2}$

2. $3\frac{60}{100} = 3\frac{60 \div 20}{100 \div 20} = 3\frac{3}{5}$

3. $7\frac{900}{1,000} = 7\frac{900 \div 100}{1,000 \div 100} = 7\frac{9}{10}$

4. $1\frac{55}{100} = 1\frac{55 \div 5}{100 \div 5} = 1\frac{11}{20}$

Power Practice • Write each mixed number in simplest form.

5. $5\frac{2}{10}$ $5\frac{1}{5}$

6. $2\frac{50}{100}$ $2\frac{1}{2}$

7. $8\frac{300}{1,000}$ $8\frac{3}{10}$

8. $1\frac{25}{100}$ $1\frac{1}{4}$

9. $9\frac{750}{1,000}$ $9\frac{3}{4}$

10. $1\frac{65}{100}$ $1\frac{13}{20}$

© McGraw-Hill School Division

166 Grade 4, Chapter 13, Cluster B

WHAT IF THE STUDENT CAN'T

Find Common Factors
• Have students list the factors of each of the two numbers. Then have them cross off any factors that are not common to both numbers.
• Tell students that the factors both numbers have in common are called common factors. Have them identify the greatest common factor.

Write a Fraction in Simplest Form
• Remind students that the numerator and denominator of a fraction in simplest form have only 1 as a common factor.

• Have students find the factors of the numerator and denominator. Ask them to circle any factors that are common to both numbers. Explain that if there is a common factor other than one, the fraction is not in simplest form.

Complete the Power Practice
• Discuss each incorrect answer. Have students explain how they simplified the fraction and how they know the fraction is in simplest form.

Compare and Order Whole Numbers

Learn

What Can I Do?
I want to decide which mountain is higher.

Compare Digits from Left to Right

Gold Mountain	5,821 ft
Silver Mountain	5,281 ft

Thousands digits are the same.   **5,**821 **5,**281

Hundreds digits are different.   5,**8**21 5,**2**81

Compare hundreds digits.

Think: 8 is greater than 2,
so, 5,**8**21 is greater than 5,**2**81.   5,821 > 5,281

Try It • Compare. Write >, <, or =.

1. 648 _<_ 736
2. 493 _>_ 475
3. 8,421 _>_ 8,403

4. 147 _>_ 143
5. 5,573 _<_ 6,313
6. 2,783 _<_ 2,873

Power Practice • Compare. Write >, <, or =.

7. 462 _<_ 484
8. 379 _>_ 377
9. 7,372 _>_ 7,274

10. 3,936 _<_ 4,046
11. 1,006 _>_ 1,004
12. 935 _>_ 888

Write the numbers in order from least to greatest.

13. 246, 372, 272, 346

_246, 272, 346, 372_

14. 1,562; 2,652; 1,625

_1,562; 1,625; 2,652_

Grade 4, Chapter 13, Cluster B **167**

© McGraw-Hill School Division

WHAT IF THE STUDENT CAN'T

Identify and Use Inequality Symbols

- Ask students to compare 36 and 45 by telling you which is greater. (45 is greater than 36.) Introduce the greater than sign. Have students write the inequality. (45 > 36)

- Ask students to compare 36 and 45 by telling you which is less. (36 is less than 45.) Introduce the less than sign. Have students write the inequality. (36 < 45)

- Tell students to think of the inequality signs as arrows. Ask them which number the arrows point to in each inequality. (36) Help them make the generalization that

the "arrow" points to the lesser number.

Complete the Power Practice

- Discuss each incorrect answer. Guide students through the comparison of the numbers starting with the digit in the greatest place.

- Have students express the inequality verbally. Ask them which symbol they will use to show the inequality.

Lesson Goal
- Compare and order whole numbers.

What the Student Needs to Know
- Identify and use inequality symbols.

Getting Started
Ask students to read these inequalities. You may wish to have students use number lines to illustrate the inequalities.

- 7 > 5 (Seven is greater than five.)
- 52 < 55 (Fifty-two is less than fifty-five.)
- 256 = 256 (Two hundred fifty-six equals two hundred fifty-six)

What Can I Do?
Read the question and the response. Then read and discuss the examples. Ask:

- *If the hundreds digits in the example were the same, what digits would you compare next?* (tens)

- *If one number has three digits and the other number has four digits, which number is greater? How do you know?* (The 4-digit number is greater. It has a digit in the thousands place. The greatest place in a 3-digit number is the hundreds place.)

Try It
- Have student look at Exercise 1. Ask students what digits they will compare first. (The hundreds digits.)

- Ask students how the bold digits can help them compare the numbers. (The bold digits are the first digits that are different.)

Power Practice
- Remind students to start comparing at the greatest place.

- Ask volunteers to explain how to put numbers in order for Exercises 13 and 14.

USING THE LESSON

Lesson Goal
• Round whole numbers.

What the Student Needs to Know
• Recall place value.

Getting Started
Tell students that they will be rounding to the nearest ten, hundred, or thousand. Ask them to skip count.
• by 10 to 100
• by 100 to 1,000
• by 1000 to 10,000

Explain that when they round, their answer will be a multiple of 10, 100, or 1000.

What Can I Do?
Read the question and the response. Then read and discuss the examples. Ask:
• *How do you know what place to round 87 to?* (The 8 is in the tens place. That is the greatest place, so round to the nearest ten.)
• *How do you know what digit to use to round a number?* (Use the digit to the right of the greatest digit.)

Try It
• Ask students to name the greatest place for each number.
• Ask them to explain why one digit is bold in each number. (That is the digit they use to decide whether to round the number up or down.)

Power Practice
• Remind students to round to the greatest place.
• Tell them to look at the digit to the right of the greatest place.
• Ask them to name the digits that will tell them to round down. (0, 1, 2, 3, 4)
• Ask them to name the digits that will tell them to round up. (5, 6, 7, 8, 9)

Name_____

Round Whole Numbers

Learn

What Can I Do?
I want to round whole numbers.

Round to the Greatest Place

Round 87 to the nearest ten.
Look at the ones digit.
If it is 5 or greater, round up.
If it is less than 5, round down.
Think: 7 is greater than 5. Round up.
    87 → 90

Round 416 to the nearest hundred.
Look at the tens digit.
Think: 1 is less than 5.
Round down.
    416 → 400

Round 5,392 to the nearest thousand.
Look at the hundreds digit.
    5,392 → 5,000

Try It • Round each number to its greatest place.

1. 842 __8__00   2. 65 __7__0   3. 7,662 __8__,000

4. 21 __20__   5. 9,287 __9,000__   6. 485 __500__

Power Practice • Round each number to its greatest place.

7. 92 __90__   8. 538 __500__   9. 1,626 __2,000__

10. 279 __300__   11. 3,206 __3,000__   12. 58 __60__

168 Grade 4, Chapter 13, Cluster B

© McGraw-Hill School Division

WHAT IF THE STUDENT CAN'T

Recall Place Value
Use a place-value chart.
• Show a number such as 3,629 and ask students to name the value of the greatest place.
• Show a number such as 4,693 and have students identify the place of each digit you name. Ask questions like "What place is 6 in?"
• Show a number such as 832. Ask students to identify the digit in a place you name. For example, ask "What digit is in the tens place?"

Complete the Power Practice
• Discuss each incorrect answer. Have students identify the place to which they will round.
• Ask students to name the digit they will use to round the number and to explain how they will use it to round the number.

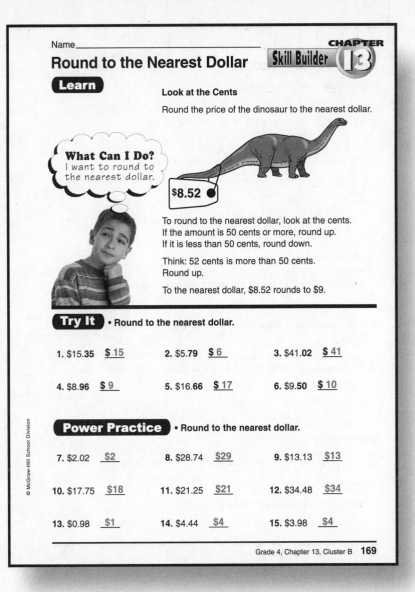

Name_____

Round to the Nearest Dollar

Learn

Look at the Cents

Round the price of the dinosaur to the nearest dollar.

What Can I Do?
I want to round to the nearest dollar.

$8.52

To round to the nearest dollar, look at the cents.
If the amount is 50 cents or more, round up.
If it is less than 50 cents, round down.

Think: 52 cents is more than 50 cents.
Round up.

To the nearest dollar, $8.52 rounds to $9.

Try It • Round to the nearest dollar.

1. $15.35 $15
2. $5.79 $6
3. $41.02 $41

4. $8.96 $9
5. $16.66 $17
6. $9.50 $10

Power Practice • Round to the nearest dollar.

7. $2.02 $2
8. $28.74 $29
9. $13.13 $13

10. $17.75 $18
11. $21.25 $21
12. $34.48 $34

13. $0.98 $1
14. $4.44 $4
15. $3.98 $4

Grade 4, Chapter 13, Cluster B **169**

© McGraw-Hill School Division

WHAT IF THE STUDENT CAN'T

Recall Money Notation

• Use play money. Show some money amounts. Then show the notation for each amount. Check to be sure that students understand that dollars are written to the left of the decimal point and cents are written to the right. Emphasize the importance of including the dollar sign. Ask students how they would write an amount with no dollars, for example sixty cents. ($0.60).

Decide If a Whole Number is Greater Than or Less Than 50

• Show a number line from 1 to 100. Have students locate

50 on the number line. Then have them locate other whole numbers and determine whether each number is greater than or less than 50. Ask students if each number is closer to 0 or closer to 100.

Complete the Power Practice

• Discuss each incorrect answer. Ask students to name the two dollars the amount in each exercise is between. Then have students point out the cents and determine if the amount is greater than 50 cents or less than 50 cents.

Lesson Goal

• Round to the nearest dollar.

What the Student Needs to Know

• Recall money notation.

• Decide if a whole number is greater than or less than 50.

Getting Started

Ask students what two dollar amounts each of these amounts is between.

• $4.76 ($4 and $5)

• $9.98 ($9 and $10)

• $14.49 ($14 and $15)

• $0.66 ($0 and $1)

• $36.12 ($36 and $37)

What Can I Do?

Read the question and the response. Then read and discuss the examples. Ask:

• *What two dollar amounts is $8.52 between?* ($8 and $9)

• *What number can you use to decide which dollar amount $8.52 is closest to?* (52 cents)

• *How can you use 52 cents to decide whether to round down to $8 or up to $9?* (If the number of cents is 50 or more, round up. Round $8.52 to $9.)

Try It

• Ask students what numbers they will use to decide whether to round up or down. (The cents, which are shown in bold)

• For each exercise, have students tell what two dollars the amount is between.

Power Practice

• Remind students to think about what two dollar amounts each number is between.

• Ask a volunteer to review how to round to the nearest dollar.

Grade 4, Chapter 13, Cluster B **169**

CHALLENGE

Lesson Goal
- Use place-value concepts.

Introducing the Challenge
- Provide small pieces of paper or tell students to cut a sheet of notebook paper into 10 pieces. Have the students write the digits 0–9 on each piece.

CHALLENGE CHAPTER 13

Place-Value Puzzles

Make number cards like these.

1	3	5	7	9

2	4	6	8	0

Use the cards for 2, 5, 7, 4.

1. How many different numbers can you make with 5 in the hundreds place?

   _____6_____

2. How many different numbers can you make with 5 in the ones place?

   _____6_____

3. Predict how many different numbers you can make with 2 in the thousands place. Then check your prediction.

   _____6_____

Use the digits 9, 2, 5, 7, and 4.

4. How many numbers can you make with 5 in the hundreds place?

   _____24_____

5. How many of those numbers have 7 in the tens place?

   _____6_____

Name_____

Find each number.

6. I have 7 in the ten thousands place, 8 in the tens place, 4 in the thousands place, 3 in the ones place, and 0 in the hundreds place. What number am I?

       74,083

7. I have a 3 in the hundred thousands place and a 9 in the ten thousands place. Each of the other digits is one less than the digit to its left. What number am I?

       398,765

8. I have 5 digits. They are all odd numbers. The greatest digit is in my ones place, and the least digit is in my ten thousands place. My thousands digit is 4 less than my hundreds digit. What number am I?

       13,759

9. The sum of the digits in my thousands place and hundreds place is 15. The sum of the digits in my tens place and ones place is 11. Each digit is one less than the digit to its left. What number am I?

       8,765

10. Write a *What Number Am I?* riddle. Give your riddle to a classmate to solve.

       Answers will vary.

_____

_____

_____

_____

CHALLENGE

Using the Challenge

- You may want to have students work in pairs.
- Have students separate the cards for 2, 5, 7, and 4. Tell them to arrange these cards to answer Exercises 1–3. Encourage them to work in an organized way, perhaps making all of the numbers with 7 in the thousands place first, then the numbers with 2 in the thousands place, and so on. Remind students to record each arrangement.
- For the *What Number Am I?* riddles, tell students they may use their cards to model each number. They may want to draw a place-value chart to help them.

CHALLENGE

Lesson Goal

- Estimate by rounding money amounts.

Introducing the Challenge

- Ask students to give examples of situations in which rounding money amounts could help them decide if they have enough money.

Do I Have Enough Money?

Use these items.

Round the prices to answer each question.

1. Brenda has $40. If she buys a day pack, will she have at least $1.00 left to take the bus home? Tell how you know.

   <u>No; the day pack would have to cost $39 or less—it costs $39.69</u>

   _____

2. Will wants to buy a travel kit and a tire patch kit. He has $20. Does he have enough money? Show your thinking.

   Yes. $14 + $5 = $19

   _____

   _____

Name_____

3. Jose bought 2 items. He spent $63.88. What did he buy?

a day pack and a mountain climbing video

4. Abby wants to buy three gifts. She has $45. What can she buy?

Possible answer: National Parks calendar,

Best Hikes guide, biking T-shirt: $12 + $14 + $17 = $43.

5. Is $32 enough to buy 3 pairs of hiking socks? How do you know?

Yes. Possible answer: Each pair of socks costs less

than $10, and $10 × 3 = $30.

6. Mason earns $6 an hour. How many hours would he have to work to earn enough to buy a headlight and a taillight for his mountain bike?

6 hours

7. Jennifer says that when you are shopping, you should always round prices up to be sure you have enough money. Do you agree or disagree? Give an example to back up your answer.

Possible answer: Agree. If you have $29 you will not have

enough to buy a $12.29 calendar and a $17.29 T-shirt even

though the rounded sum is $12 + $17 = $29.

8. Write a problem that can be solved using the prices of the items shown. Exchange problems with a classmate to solve.

Answers will vary.

_____

_____

Using the Challenge

- Explain that to solve these problems students will round money amounts. For some problems they will also need to make calculations using the rounded numbers

- Many of these problems are multi-step problems. Encourage students to write down the rounded numbers and the results of their calculations as they work through the problem.

Add Whole Numbers

Find each sum.

1. 38
   + 25

2. 482
   + 153

3. 3,604
   + 2,277

Add Money

Find each sum.

4. $1.52
   + 0.18

5. $22.90
   + 17.19

6. $35.53
   + 6.04

Equivalent Decimals

Circle the decimal that is equivalent to the first decimal given.

7. 0.6   **a.** 6   **b.** 0.60   **c.** 0.06

8. 3.24   **a.** 3.240   **b.** 3.024   **c.** 0.324

9. 0.50   **a.** 0.05   **b.** 0.005   **c.** 0.500

Estimate Sums

Estimate each sum to the nearest ten.

10. 17 + 54 _____   11. 81 + 28 _____

Estimate each sum to the nearest hundred.

12. 637 + 282 _____   13. 195 + 444 _____

Name_____

Subtract Whole Numbers

Find each difference.

14.	862 − 415	15.	1,208 − 533	16.	5,553 − 2,351

Subtract Money

Find each difference.

17.	$5.29 − 3.55	18.	$47.30 − 14.12	19.	$21.85 − 3.02

Add to Check Subtraction

Add to check each subtraction. Write *correct* or *incorrect* for each problem.

20.	418 − 144 + ____ 374	21.	8,105 − 2,366 + _____ 5,739

_____   _____

Estimate Differences

Estimate each difference to the nearest hundred.

22. 477− 261 _____   **23.** 618 − 103 _____

Estimate each difference to the nearest thousand.

24. 4,627− 1,511   **25.** 8,294 − 3,889

_____   _____

CHAPTER 14 PRE-CHAPTER ASSESSMENT

Assessment Goal

This two-page assessment covers skills identified as necessary for success in Chapter 14 Decimal Operations. The first page assesses the major prerequisite skills for Cluster A. The second page assesses the major prerequisite skills for Cluster B. When the Cluster A and Cluster B prerequisite skills overlap, the skill(s) will be covered in only one section.

Getting Started

- Allow students time to look over the two pages of the assessment. Point out the labels that identify the skills covered.
- Have students find math vocabulary terms used in the assessment. List vocabulary terms on the board as students identify them. If necessary, review the meanings of all essential math vocabulary.

Introducing the Assessment

- Explain to students that these pages will help you know if they are ready to start a new chapter in their math textbooks.
- Students who have transferred from another school may not have been introduced to some of these skills. Encourage students to do their best and assure them you will help them learn any needed skills.

Cluster A Challenge

Those students who demonstrate mastery of the skills on this page will not need to use the reteaching worksheets. Instead, these students can do the Cluster A Challenge found on pages 184–185.

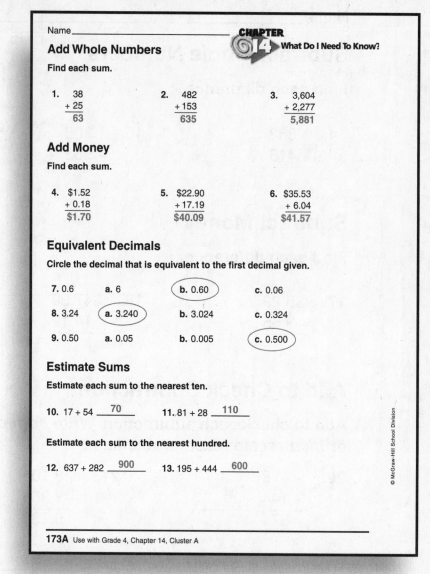

Name_____

CHAPTER 14 What Do I Need To Know?

Add Whole Numbers

Find each sum.

1. 38
   + 25
   ——
    63

2. 482
   + 153
   ——
    635

3. 3,604
   + 2,277
   ——
    5,881

Add Money

Find each sum.

4. $1.52
   + 0.18
   ——
    $1.70

5. $22.90
   + 17.19
   ——
    $40.09

6. $35.53
   + 6.04
   ——
    $41.57

Equivalent Decimals

Circle the decimal that is equivalent to the first decimal given.

7. 0.6   **a.** 6   (**b.** 0.60)   **c.** 0.06

8. 3.24   (**a.** 3.240)   **b.** 3.024   **c.** 0.324

9. 0.50   **a.** 0.05   **b.** 0.005   (**c.** 0.500)

Estimate Sums

Estimate each sum to the nearest ten.

10. 17 + 54 ___70___   11. 81 + 28 ___110___

Estimate each sum to the nearest hundred.

12. 637 + 282 ___900___   13. 195 + 444 ___600___

173A Use with Grade 4, Chapter 14, Cluster A

© McGraw-Hill School Division

CLUSTER A PREREQUISITE SKILLS

The skills listed in this chart are those identified as major prerequisite skills for students' success in the lessons in Cluster A of the chapter. Each skill is covered by one or more assessment items as shown in the middle column. The right column provides the page number for the lessons in this book that reteach the cluster A prerequisite skills.

Skill Name	Assessment Items	Lesson Pages
Add Whole Numbers	1-3	174
Add Money	4-6	175
Equivalent Decimals	7-9	176
Estimate Sums to the Nearest Ten	10-11	177
Estimate Sums to the Nearest Hundred	12-13	178

Name_____

Subtract Whole Numbers

Find each difference.

14.   862
    – 415
    ‾‾‾‾‾
     447

15. 1,208
    – 533
    ‾‾‾‾‾
     675

16. 5,553
    – 2,351
    ‾‾‾‾‾‾
     3,202

Subtract Money

Find each difference.

17. $5.29
    – 3.55
    ‾‾‾‾‾
    $1.74

18. $47.30
    – 14.12
    ‾‾‾‾‾‾
    $33.18

19. $21.85
    – 3.02
    ‾‾‾‾‾‾
    $18.83

Add to Check Subtraction

Add to check each subtraction. Write *correct* or *incorrect* for each problem.

20.   418   144
    – 144 + 374
    ‾‾‾‾‾   ‾‾‾‾‾
     374   518

        incorrect

21. 8,105   2,366
   – 2,366 + 5,739
   ‾‾‾‾‾‾   ‾‾‾‾‾‾
    5,739   8,105

        correct

Estimate Differences

Estimate each difference to the nearest hundred.

22. 477– 261 ___200___   23. 618 – 103 ___500___

Estimate each difference to the nearest thousand.

24. 4,627– 1,511   25. 8,294 – 3,889
      ___3,000___   ___4,000___

© McGraw-Hill School Division

Use with Grade 4, Chapter 14, Cluster B **173B**

CLUSTER B PREREQUISITE SKILLS

The skills listed in this chart are those identified as major prerequisite skills for students' success in the lessons in Cluster B of the chapter. Each skill is covered by one or more assessment items as shown in the middle column. The right column provides the page numbers for the lessons in this book that reteach the Cluster B prerequisite skills

Skill Name	Assessment Items	Lesson Pages
Subtract Whole Numbers	14-16	179
Subtract Money	17-19	180
Add to Check Subtraction	20-21	181
Estimate Differences to the Nearest Hundred	22-23	182
Estimate Differences to the Nearest Thousand	24-25	183

Alternative Assessment Strategies

- Oral administration of the assessment is appropriate for younger students or those whose native language is not English. Read the skills title and directions one section at a time. Check students' understanding by asking them to tell you how they will do the first exercise in the group.

- For some skill types you may wish to use group administration. In this technique, a small group or pair of students complete the assessment together. Through their discussion, you will be able to decide if supplementary reteaching materials are needed.

Intervention Materials

If students are not successful with the prerequisite skills assessed on these pages, reteaching lessons have been created to help them make the transition into the chapter.

Item correlation charts showing the skills lessons suitable for reteaching the prerequisite skills are found beneath the reproductions of each page of the assessment.

Cluster B Challenge

Those students who demonstrate mastery of the skills on this page will not need to use the reteaching worksheets. Instead, these students can do the Cluster B Challenge found on pages 186–187.

Lesson Goal
- Add whole numbers.

What the Student Needs to Know
- Recall addition facts.
- Regroup numbers.

Getting Started
Ask students to find these sums.
- 6 + 7 (13)
- 3 + 8 (11)
- 5 + 7 (12)
- 9 + 5 (14)
- 8 + 6 (14)

What Can I Do?
Read the question and the response. Then read and discuss the example. Ask:

- *How do you line up the digits in the two numbers so you can add them?* (Line up the digits from right to left, starting with the ones.)

- *When you add the ones digit in the example, what does the digit 1 written above the tens digits show?* (that 13 ones have been regrouped to 1 ten and 3 ones)

- *Why is there no digit above the hundreds digits in the solution of the problem?* (The sum of the tens digits is 2. No regrouping is needed.)

Try It
- Tell students to rewrite each problem so the digits are lined up and ready to add. The first problem is done for them.

- Ask students how they will determine whether regrouping is needed as they add. (If a sum has two digits, regrouping is needed.)

Power Practice
- Encourage students to rewrite the problems so the digits are lined up correctly and they are ready to add.

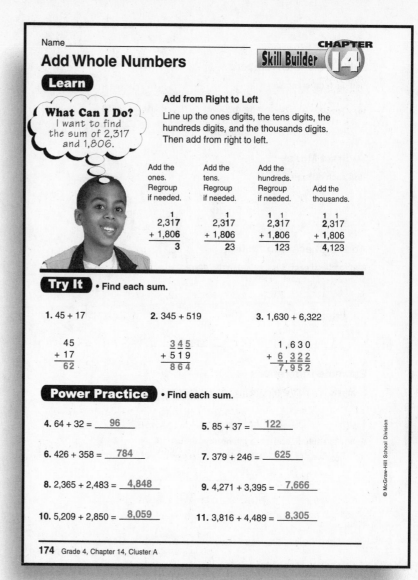

Name _____

Add Whole Numbers

Learn

What Can I Do? I want to find the sum of 2,317 and 1,806.

Add from Right to Left

Line up the ones digits, the tens digits, the hundreds digits, and the thousands digits. Then add from right to left.

Add the ones. Regroup if needed.	Add the tens. Regroup if needed.	Add the hundreds. Regroup if needed.	Add the thousands.
1 2,317 + 1,806 3	1 2,317 + 1,806 23	1 1 2,317 + 1,806 123	1 1 2,317 + 1,806 4,123

Try It • Find each sum.

1. 45 + 17

$$\begin{array}{r} 45 \\ + 17 \\ \hline 62 \end{array}$$

2. 345 + 519

$$\begin{array}{r} 345 \\ + 519 \\ \hline 864 \end{array}$$

3. 1,630 + 6,322

$$\begin{array}{r} 1,630 \\ + 6,322 \\ \hline 7,952 \end{array}$$

Power Practice • Find each sum.

4. 64 + 32 = __96__

5. 85 + 37 = __122__

6. 426 + 358 = __784__

7. 379 + 246 = __625__

8. 2,365 + 2,483 = __4,848__

9. 4,271 + 3,395 = __7,666__

10. 5,209 + 2,850 = __8,059__

11. 3,816 + 4,489 = __8,305__

174 Grade 4, Chapter 14, Cluster A

© McGraw-Hill School Division

WHAT IF THE STUDENT CAN'T

Recall Addition Facts
- Review ways that students can find sums they do not remember. For instance, students can use counters, draw pictures, count on a number line, or add or subtract from sums they do recall.

- Have students make a list of facts they do not know or make flash cards for the facts. Persuade students to test themselves regularly until they know the facts.

Regroup Numbers
- Provide place-value models and ask students to solve a two-digit addition problem such as 26 + 38. Illustrate how to regroup ones as tens. Have students record their work as they solve the problem.

- Have students complete additional 2-digit additions, then have them try 3-digit addition.

Complete the Power Practice
- Discuss each incorrect answer. Check to see that the digits are correctly aligned. Then ask students to show how they solved the problem step by step.

Name_____

Add Money

Learn

What Can I Do?
I want to find the cost of a $28.69 kite and a $3.19 roll of string.

Remember the Dollar Sign and Decimal Point

Add money the way you add whole numbers. Just remember to write the dollar sign and the decimal point in the answer.

Line up the digits and the decimal points.	Add from right to left.	Write the dollar sign and the decimal point in the answer.
$28.69 + 3.19	¹ ¹ $28.69 + 3.19 —— 31 88	¹ ¹ $28.69 + 3.19 —— $31.88

The kite and the string will cost $31.88.

Try It • Find each sum.

1. $2.40 + $5.55

$2.40
+ 5.55
———
$7.95

2. $22.93 + $16.44

$22.93
+ 16.44
———
$39.37

3. $52.77 + $3.15

$52.77
+ 3.15
———
$55.92

Power Practice • Find each sum.

4. $8.12 + $1.85 = __$9.97__

5. $6.09 + $5.89 = __$11.98__

6. $14.95 + $14.24 = __$29.19__

7. $13.25 + $12.87 = __$26.12__

8. $17.88 + $2.08 = __$19.96__

9. $24.07 + $8.15 = __$32.22__

10. $29.35 + $19.40 = __$48.75__

11. $38.75 + $22.98 = __$61.73__

© McGraw-Hill School Division

Grade 4, Chapter 14, Cluster A **175**

WHAT IF THE STUDENT CAN'T

Add Whole Numbers

- Assess student skill starting with basic facts.
- Proceed to addition of 2-digit numbers with regrouping. Have students use place-value models if necessary.
- Continue with addition of 3-digit and 4-digit numbers.
- Be sure that students align digits properly and that they know how to record regrouping as they add.

Complete the Power Practice

- Discuss each incorrect answer. Have students model the exercise using play money if necessary.
- Check to see that students have correctly aligned the money amounts.
- Prompt students who have forgotten to place the dollar sign and decimal point in the answer to do so.

USING THE LESSON

Lesson Goal
- Add money.

What the Student Needs to Know
- Add whole numbers.

Getting Started
Ask students to find each sum.
- 9 + 8 (17)
- 18 + 5 (23)
- 15 + 16 (31)
- 57 + 68 (125)
- 49 + 151 (200)
- 142 + 284 (426)

What Can I Do?
Read the question and the response. Then read and discuss the example. Ask:
- *How do you line up the digits to add money amounts?* (Line up the decimal points and the digits on each side of the decimal point.)
- *How is adding money like adding whole numbers? How is it different?* (You use the same rules and methods to add money as to add whole numbers. You write a dollar sign and a decimal point in the answer.)

Try It
- Have students finish writing each problem in vertical form so the digits are aligned and ready to add. The first exercise has been done for the students.
- Remind students to write the dollar sign and the decimal point in their answers.

Power Practice
- Tell students to write each problem in vertical form first, so the decimal points and the digits are lined up and ready to add.
- Remind students to write the dollar sign and the decimal point in their answers.

Lesson Goal
- Write equivalent decimals.

What the Student Needs to Know
- Identify the decimal with the greatest number of places.

Getting Started
Tell students to write > or < to compare each pair of decimals.
- 8.5 ___ 7.8 (>)
- 1.25 ___ 1.52 (<)
- 0.66 ___ 0.73 (<)
- 4.015 ___ 4.111 (<)

What Can I Do?
Read the question and the response. Then read and discuss the examples. Ask:
- *What does it mean if two decimals are equivalent?* (The two decimals have the same value.)
- *Does adding zeros to the right side of a decimal number change its value?* (No.)
- *Name two decimals equivalent to 0.8.* (Possible answers: 0.80, 0.800)
- *Can 0.8 be written as an equivalent decimal in thousandths? If so, how? If not, why not?* (Yes. 0.800)
- *Can 0.392 be written as an equivalent decimal in tenths? If so, how? If not, why not?* (No; 0.392 has three decimal places. The digits in the hundredths and thousandths place are not zeros so they cannot be dropped.)

Try It
- Have students read the first decimal for Exercises 1 and 2 aloud. Suggest that they read the other decimals to themselves.
- Ask students how many decimal places each number in exercises 3–6 will have. (3)

Power Practice
- Students should look for the decimal with the greatest number of places as they do exercise 9.

Name_____

Equivalent Decimals

Learn

What Can I Do?
I want to write a group of decimals with the same number of decimal places.

Use Zeros

Write each of these decimals with the same number of decimal places: 0.8, 0.65, 0.392

Write zeros so all of the decimals are in the thousandths.

ones		tenths	hundredths	thousandths
0	.	8	0	0
0	.	6	5	0
0	.	3	9	2

Try It • Circle the decimal that is equivalent to the first decimal given.

1. 0.9 | 9. (0.90) 0.09
2. 1.52 | (1.520) 1.052 0.152

Write each of these decimals in thousandths.

3. 0.25   4. 1.7   5. 6.3   6. 0.19
   0.250   1.700   6.300   0.190

Power Practice • Circle all of the decimals that are equivalent to the first decimal given.

7. 0.400 | 0.04 (0.40) (0.4) 4.00
8. 3.670 | (3.67) 0.367 36.70 3.067

Write all of these numbers with the same number of decimal places.

9. 0.13   1.6   0.257   0.130, 1.600, 0.257

WHAT IF THE STUDENT CAN'T

Identify the Decimal with the Greatest Number of Places
- Show numbers on a place-value chart.
- Write some decimal numbers on the chalkboard. Ask students how many decimal places each number has. Be sure students understand that the digits to the left of the decimal point are not counted when determining the number of decimal places. The number of decimal places includes only the number of places to the right of the decimal point.

Complete the Power Practice
- Discuss each incorrect answer. Writing each decimal on a place-value chart may help students visualize equivalent decimals.

Estimate Sums to the Nearest Ten

Skill Builder CHAPTER **14**

Learn

What Can I Do?
I want to know about how far it is from Bradford to New Port.

Estimate to the Nearest Ten

Look at the ones digit to round each number to the nearest ten.

73 miles	65 miles
Bradford	Westfield	New Port

Think: If the ones digit is less than 5, round down. If the ones digit is 5 or more, round up.

$$
\begin{array}{r}
73 \\
+\ 65 \\
\end{array}
\quad
\begin{array}{l}
\text{rounds to} \\
\text{rounds to}
\end{array}
\quad
\begin{array}{r}
70 \\
+\ 70 \\
\hline
140
\end{array}
\quad
\begin{array}{l}
\text{Add the} \\
\text{rounded} \\
\text{numbers.}
\end{array}
$$

It is about 140 miles from Bradford to New Port.

Try It • Estimate each sum to the nearest ten.

1. $\begin{array}{r} 41 \\ +58 \end{array} \rightarrow \begin{array}{r} 40 \\ +60 \\ \hline 100 \end{array}$

2. $\begin{array}{r} 19 \\ +64 \end{array} \rightarrow \begin{array}{r} 2\,0 \\ +6\,0 \\ \hline 8\,0 \end{array}$

3. $\begin{array}{r} 33 \\ +82 \end{array} \rightarrow \begin{array}{r} 3\,0 \\ +8\,0 \\ \hline 110 \end{array}$

Power Practice • Estimate each sum to the nearest ten.

4. 86 + 35 ___130___

5. 71 + 29 ___100___

6. 18 + 33 ___50___

7. 27 + 59 ___90___

8. 46 + 17 ___70___

9. 52 + 12 ___60___

10. 66 + 72 ___140___

11. 75 + 14 ___90___

12. 28 + 55 ___90___

13. 54 + 95 ___150___

14. 85 + 65 ___160___

15. 67 + 91 ___160___

© McGraw-Hill School Division

Grade 4, Chapter 14, Cluster A **177**

WHAT IF THE STUDENT CAN'T

Round to the Nearest Ten

Use a number line with multiples of 10 labeled.

- Have the student locate 47 on the number line.
- Ask what two tens 47 is between. (40 and 50)
- Ask which ten 47 is nearest to on the number line. (50)
- Have the student complete this sentence: 47 rounded to the nearest ten is ___. (50)
- Repeat for other examples.
- Show an example such as 35. Ask students how they would round the number. Explain that it is equally close to two tens, but numbers with 5 in the ones place are rounded up.
- Conclude by asking students to name the ones digits for numbers that are rounded down to the nearest ten (0, 1, 2, 3, 4). Then ask them to name the ones digits for numbers that are rounded up to the nearest ten. (5, 6, 7, 8, 9)

Complete the Power Practice

- Discuss each incorrect answer. Ask students to explain their rounding methods.

USING THE LESSON

Lesson Goal

- Estimate sums to the nearest ten.

What the Student Needs to Know

- Round to the nearest ten.

Getting Started

- Have students count by tens.
- Have students use mental math to multiply 10 by each of the digits 1–9.
- Explain that when they round to the nearest ten, the rounded number will be a multiple of 10.

What Can I Do?

Read the question and the response. Then read and discuss the example. Ask:

- *How can you find the distance from Bradford to New Port?* (Find the sum of the two distances given on the map.)
- *What word tells you an exact answer is not needed?* (about)
- *Explain how to round 73 to the nearest ten.* (Look at the ones digit, 3. Think: "3 is less than 5, so 73 rounds down to 70.")
- *Explain how to round 65 to the nearest ten.* (The ones digit is 5, so 65 rounds up to 70.)

Try It

- Remind students that they will round each addend to the nearest ten. Then add the rounded numbers.
- Have a volunteer explain how to round 41 to the nearest ten and how to round 58 to the nearest ten.
- Ask: *Which ones digits round down?* (1, 2, 3, 4) Ask: *Which ones digits round up?* (5, 6, 7, 8, 9)

Power Practice

- Ask students to name the steps they will use to estimate each sum. (Round each number to the nearest ten. Find the sum of the rounded numbers.)

Grade 4, Chapter 14, Cluster A **177**

Lesson Goal

- Estimate sums to the nearest hundred.

What the Student Needs to Know

- Round to the nearest hundred.

Getting Started

- Have students count by hundreds from 0 to 1,000.
- Ask students to use mental math to multiply 100 by each of the digits 1–9.
- Explain to students that when they round to the nearest hundred, the rounded number will be a multiple of 100.

What Can I Do?

Read the question and the response. Then read and discuss the example. Ask:

- *How can you find the number of tickets sold?* (Find the sum of the number of adult tickets plus the number of child tickets.)
- *How do you know you do not need to find an exact answer?* (You are finding *about* how many tickets were sold.)
- *What digit do you look at to round a number to the nearest hundred?* (the digit in the tens place)
- *Explain how to round 489 to the nearest hundred.* (The tens digit is 8, so 489 rounds up to 500.)
- *Explain how to round 135 to the nearest hundred.* (The tens digit is 3; 135 rounds down to 100.)

Try It

- Ask: *How many zeros will each of the rounded addends have?* (2)
- Ask students how they know what digit to look at to round to the nearest hundred. (Look at the tens place digit. The tens digit is bold in these exercises.)

Power Practice

- Remind students to round each addend to the nearest hundred and then to add to estimate the sum.

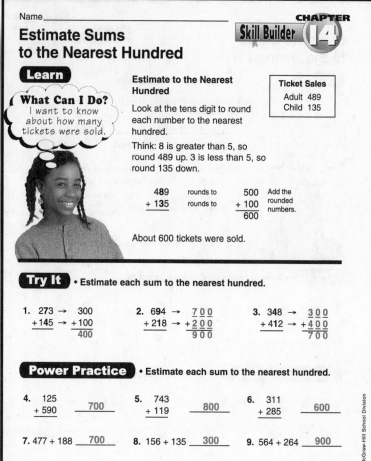

Name_____

Estimate Sums to the Nearest Hundred

Learn

What Can I Do?
I want to know about how many tickets were sold.

Estimate to the Nearest Hundred

Look at the tens digit to round each number to the nearest hundred.

Think: 8 is greater than 5, so round 489 up. 3 is less than 5, so round 135 down.

Ticket Sales	
Adult	489
Child	135

$$\begin{array}{r} 489 \\ + 135 \\ \end{array}$$ rounds to / rounds to $$\begin{array}{r} 500 \\ + 100 \\ \hline 600 \end{array}$$ Add the rounded numbers.

About 600 tickets were sold.

Try It • Estimate each sum to the nearest hundred.

1. $\begin{array}{r} 273 \\ +145 \end{array} \rightarrow \begin{array}{r} 300 \\ +100 \\ \hline 400 \end{array}$

2. $\begin{array}{r} 694 \\ +218 \end{array} \rightarrow \begin{array}{r} 7\,0\,0 \\ +2\,0\,0 \\ \hline 9\,0\,0 \end{array}$

3. $\begin{array}{r} 348 \\ +412 \end{array} \rightarrow \begin{array}{r} 3\,0\,0 \\ +4\,0\,0 \\ \hline 7\,0\,0 \end{array}$

Power Practice • Estimate each sum to the nearest hundred.

4. $\begin{array}{r} 125 \\ +590 \end{array}$ ___700___

5. $\begin{array}{r} 743 \\ +119 \end{array}$ ___800___

6. $\begin{array}{r} 311 \\ +285 \end{array}$ ___600___

7. 477 + 188 ___700___

8. 156 + 135 ___300___

9. 564 + 264 ___900___

10. 635 + 217 ___800___

11. 452 + 501 ___1,000___

12. 345 + 264 ___600___

178 Grade 4, Chapter 14, Cluster A

WHAT IF THE STUDENT CAN'T

Round to the Nearest Hundred.

Use a number line between 300 and 400 with hundreds numbered and tens marked.

- Have students estimate the location of 323 on the number line.
- Ask them what two hundreds 323 is between. (300 and 400)
- Ask them which hundred 323 is nearest to. (300)
- Have the students complete this sentence. 323 rounded to the nearest hundred is ___. (300)

- Repeat for other examples between 300 and 400.
- Ask students to name the tens digits for numbers that round down to 300. (0, 1, 2, 3, 4).
- Ask students to name the tens digits for numbers that round up to 400. (5, 6, 7, 8, 9)

Complete the Power Practice

- Discuss each incorrect answer. Ask students to explain their rounding methods.

Name_____

Subtract Whole Numbers

Learn

What Can I Do?
I want to subtract 853 from 7,509.

Subtract from Right to Left
Line up the ones digits, the tens digits, and hundreds digits. Then subtract from right to left.

Regroup tens as ones if needed. Subtract the ones.	Regroup hundreds as tens if needed. Subtract the tens.	Regroup thousands as hundreds if needed. Subtract hundreds.	Subtract thousands.
7,509 − 853 **6**	4 10 7,5̸0̸9 − 853 **56**	14 6 4̸10 7,5̸0̸9 − 853 **656**	14 6 4̸10 7,5̸0̸9 − 853 **6,656**

Try It • Find each difference.

1. 85 − 29

   85
− 29
   56

2. 232 − 166

   232
− 166
    66

3. 4,286 − 1,354

  4,286
− 1,354
  2,932

Power Practice • Find each difference.

4. 75 − 38 = __37__

5. 94 − 49 = __45__

6. 63 − 47 = __16__

7. 571 − 219 = __352__

8. 684 − 326 = __358__

9. 481 − 275 = __206__

10. 7,308 − 255 = __7,053__

11. 5,094 − 2,846 = __2,248__

12. 6,715 − 4,649 = __2,066__

13. 9,856 − 3,947 = __5,909__

14. 5,006 − 3,228 = __1,778__

15. 3,564 − 2,695 = __869__

Grade 4, Chapter 14, Cluster B **179**

WHAT IF THE STUDENT CAN'T

Recall Subtraction Facts

- Review ways that students can find subtraction facts that they do not remember. Possible methods include: using counters, drawing pictures, and counting back on a number line.

- Have students make a list of subtraction facts they are having difficulty remembering. Tell students to keep these lists handy and to test themselves on a fact or two during idle minutes in their day.

Regroup Numbers

- Provide place-value blocks and ask students to solve a two-digit subtraction problem such as 41 − 25. Show them that 5 ones cannot be subtracted from 1 one, so they must regroup. Review the way to regroup 4 tens and 1 one as 3 tens and 11 ones. Have students record their work as they solve the problem.

- Have students complete additional 2-digit examples. Then have them try 3-digit examples.

Complete the Power Practice

- Discuss each incorrect answer. Have students check that they have aligned the digits correctly. Then ask them to show the subtraction step by step.

USING THE LESSON

Lesson Goal
- Subtract whole numbers.

What the Student Needs to Know
- Recall subtraction facts.
- Regroup numbers.

Getting Started
Have students find these differences.
- 9 − 3 (6)
- 10 − 5 (5)
- 14 − 8 (6)
- 15 − 9 (6)
- 12 − 3 (9)
- 11 − 9 (2)

What Can I Do?
Read the question and the response. Then read and discuss the example. Ask:

- *How can place value help you line up the digits in the two numbers?* (Line up the digits in each place. Start with the ones digits and line the digits up from right to left.)

- *Why are the 5 and the 0 crossed off in the second step? Why are 4 and 10 written above the crossed-off numbers?* (5 hundreds and 0 tens are regrouped as 4 hundreds and 10 tens.)

- *What regrouping is shown in the third step?* (7 thousands and 4 hundreds are regrouped as 6 thousands and 14 hundreds.)

Try It
- Ask students how they will decide if regrouping is needed before they can subtract. (If there are not enough ones, tens, or hundreds to subtract, regroup.)

Power Practice
- Tell students to rewrite each problem so the digits are lined up and ready to subtract.

Lesson Goal
• Subtract money.

What the Student Needs to Know
• Subtract whole numbers.

Getting Started
Have students find these differences.
• 14 – 9 (5)
• 28 – 15 (13)
• 43 – 39 (4)
• 206 – 188 (18)
• 437 – 152 (285)

What Can I Do?
Read the question and the response. Then read and discuss the example. Ask:

• *How do you know that you need to subtract to solve the problem?* (To find how much more you need, you subtract the amount you have from the amount you need.)

• *How is subtracting money different from subtracting whole numbers?* (You need to put a dollar sign and decimal point in the answer.)

• *How do you know where to put the dollar sign and decimal point in the answer?* (Put the dollar sign before the first digit. Line the decimal point in the answer up with the decimal points in the problem.)

Try It
• Remind students to write the dollar sign and the decimal point in their answers.

Power Practice
• Ask students how they can set up the problems so that it will be easier to subtract. (Write them in vertical form, lining up the digits and the decimal points.)

• Remind students to write the dollar sign and the decimal point in each answer.

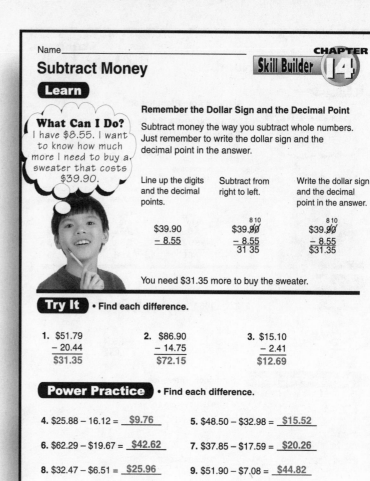

180 Grade 4, Chapter 14, Cluster B

WHAT IF THE STUDENT CAN'T

Subtract Whole Numbers
• Review subtraction facts to be sure the student is confident of them.

• Systematically assess student weakness starting with subtraction of 2-digit numbers with no regrouping, for example 87 – 52.

• Next review 2-digit subtraction with regrouping, for example 61 – 45. You may want to have the student use place-value models to show the problem. Explain how to regroup and have the student record the regrouping.

• When the student is confident with 2-digit subtraction, continue with 3-digit problems. Start with subtractions that require one regrouping (817 – 675) and move to subtractions that require more than one regrouping (562 – 285).

Complete the Power Practice
• Discuss each incorrect answer. You may want to have the student model the problem using play money.

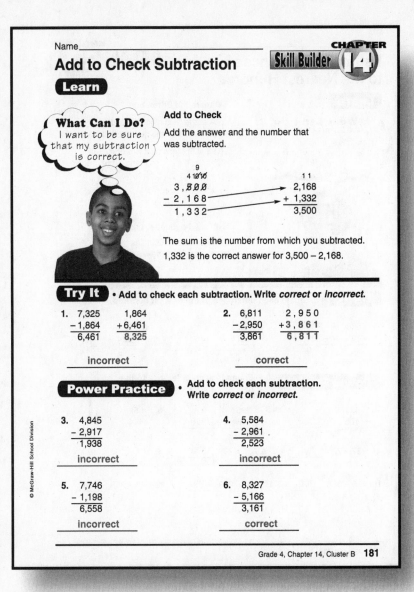

Name_____

Add to Check Subtraction

Learn

What Can I Do?
I want to be sure that my subtraction is correct.

Add to Check

Add the answer and the number that was subtracted.

$$
\begin{array}{r}
\overset{9}{4}\,\overset{}{12}\,\overset{}{10}\,\overset{}{10}\\
3,\cancel{5}\cancel{0}\cancel{0}\\
-\ 2,168\\
\hline
1,332
\end{array}
\longrightarrow
\begin{array}{r}
11\\
2,168\\
+\ 1,332\\
\hline
3,500
\end{array}
$$

The sum is the number from which you subtracted.
1,332 is the correct answer for 3,500 − 2,168.

Try It • Add to check each subtraction. Write *correct* or *incorrect*.

1.
$$
\begin{array}{r}
7,325\\
-\ 1,864\\
\hline
6,461
\end{array}
\qquad
\begin{array}{r}
1,864\\
+\ 6,461\\
\hline
8,325
\end{array}
$$

incorrect

2.
$$
\begin{array}{r}
6,811\\
-\ 2,950\\
\hline
3,861
\end{array}
\qquad
\begin{array}{r}
2,950\\
+\ 3,861\\
\hline
6,811
\end{array}
$$

correct

Power Practice • Add to check each subtraction.
Write *correct* or *incorrect*.

3.
$$
\begin{array}{r}
4,845\\
-\ 2,917\\
\hline
1,938
\end{array}
$$

incorrect

4.
$$
\begin{array}{r}
5,584\\
-\ 2,961\\
\hline
2,523
\end{array}
$$

incorrect

5.
$$
\begin{array}{r}
7,746\\
-\ 1,198\\
\hline
6,558
\end{array}
$$

incorrect

6.
$$
\begin{array}{r}
8,327\\
-\ 5,166\\
\hline
3,161
\end{array}
$$

correct

© McGraw-Hill School Division

Grade 4, Chapter 14, Cluster B **181**

WHAT IF THE STUDENT CAN'T

Add Whole Numbers
- Assess student skill, beginning with basic facts.
- Proceed to addition of 2-digit numbers with regrouping. You may want to have students use place-value models.
- Continue with addition of 3-digit and 4-digit numbers.
- Be sure that students align digits properly and that they know how to record regrouping as they add.

Compare Whole Numbers
- Remind students to start with the greatest place digit and compare numbers from left to right.

- Ask students to tell if pairs of numbers are *equal* or *not equal*. For example: 34 ___ 43 (not equal); 156 ___ 156 (equal); 3627 ___ 3617 (not equal).

Complete the Power Practice
- Discuss each incorrect answer. Be sure students chose the correct numbers to add and that they lined the digits up correctly. Then have them describe their thinking as they rework each problem.

Lesson Goal
- Add to check subtraction.

What the Student Needs to Know
- Add whole numbers.
- Compare whole numbers.

Getting Started
Ask students to name the three other facts that make up the fact family for each fact given.
- 8 + 6 = 14 (6 + 8 = 14, 14 − 6 = 8, 14 − 8 = 6)
- 9 − 5 = 4 (9 − 4 = 5, 4 + 5 = 9, 5 + 4 = 9)
- 12 − 7 = 5 (12 − 5 = 7, 7 + 5 = 12, 5 + 7 = 12)

What Can I Do?
Read the question and the response. Then read and discuss the example. Ask:
- *What numbers do you add to check a subtraction problem?* (The answer and the number that is being subtracted.)
- *Why can you use addition to check subtraction?* (Addition and subtraction are inverse operations.)
- *What can you do if the check shows that the subtraction is incorrect?* (Redo the subtraction, then check again.)

Try It
- Ask students how they will know if the answer to the subtraction problem is correct or incorrect. (If the sum for the check is equal to the number you are subtracting from, the answer to the subtraction is correct. If the sum for the check is not equal to the number you are subtracting from, the answer is incorrect.)

Power Practice
- Ask students to name the two numbers they will add to check each subtraction.
- Remind the students to write *correct* or *incorrect* on the line provided for each answer.

USING THE LESSON

Lesson Goal
- Estimate differences to the nearest hundred.

What the Student Needs to Know
- Round to the nearest hundred.

Getting Started
- Have students count by hundreds from 0 to 1,000.
- Ask students to use mental math to multiply 100 by each of the digits 1–9.
- Explain to students that when they round to the nearest hundred, the rounded number will be a multiple of 100.

What Can I Do?
Read the question and the response. Then read and discuss the example. Ask:

- *How can you find how many more miles Jeff flew?* (Subtract the number of miles Cindy flew from the number of miles Jeff flew.)

- *How do you know that you do not need an exact answer?* (You want to find *about* how many more miles Jeff flew.)

- *Explain how to round 874 to the nearest hundred.* (The tens digit is 7, so 874 rounds up to 900.)

- *Explain how to round 366 to the nearest hundred.* (The tens digit is 6, so 366 rounds up to 400.)

Try It
- Ask students how many zeros each addend has when rounded to the nearest hundred. (2)
- Ask students how many zeros each estimated difference has. (2)
- Ask students how they will decide what digit to look at to round to the nearest hundred. (Look at the tens-place digit. The tens-place digit is bold in these exercises.)

Power Practice
- Remind students to round to the nearest hundred. Then estimate each difference.

182 Grade 4, Chapter 14, Cluster B

Estimate Differences to the Nearest Hundred

Learn

What Can I Do?
Jeff flew 874 miles. Cindy flew 366 miles. I want to know about how many more miles Jeff flew.

Estimate the Difference

Look at the tens digit to round each number to the nearest hundred.

Think: If the tens digit is 5 or more, round up. If it is less than 5, round down.

$$\begin{array}{r} 874 \rightarrow 900 \\ +366 \rightarrow -400 \\ \hline 500 \end{array}$$

Subtract the rounded numbers.

Jeff flew about 500 miles more than Cindy flew.

Try It • Estimate each difference to the nearest hundred.

1. $\begin{array}{r} 658 \rightarrow 700 \\ -193 \rightarrow -200 \\ \hline 500 \end{array}$

2. $\begin{array}{r} 564 \rightarrow \underline{600} \\ -372 \rightarrow \underline{-400} \\ \hline \underline{200} \end{array}$

3. $\begin{array}{r} 833 \rightarrow \underline{800} \\ -524 \rightarrow \underline{-500} \\ \hline \underline{300} \end{array}$

Power Practice • Estimate each difference to the nearest hundred.

4. $\begin{array}{r} 421 \\ -106 \end{array}$ 300

5. $\begin{array}{r} 895 \\ -638 \end{array}$ 300

6. $\begin{array}{r} 552 \\ -444 \end{array}$ 200

7. 937 – 725   200

8. 781 – 293   500

9. 502 – 188   300

10. 456 – 308   200

11. 751 – 209   600

12. 649 – 253   300

182 Grade 4, Chapter 14, Cluster B

© McGraw-Hill School Division

WHAT IF THE STUDENT CAN'T

Round to the Nearest Hundred.

Use a number line showing 200 to 300 with the hundreds numbered and the tens marked.

- Have students estimate the location of 268 on the number line.
- Ask them what two hundreds 268 is between. (200 and 300)
- Ask them which hundred 268 is nearest to. (300)
- Have the students complete this sentence. 268 rounded to the nearest hundred is ___. (300)

- Repeat for other examples between 200 and 300.
- Ask students to name the tens digits for numbers that round down to 200. (0, 1, 2, 3, 4).
- Ask students to name the tens digits for numbers that round up to 300. (5, 6, 7, 8, 9)

Complete the Power Practice
- Discuss each incorrect answer. Ask students to explain how they rounded the numbers.

Name_____

Estimate Differences to the Nearest Thousand

Learn

What Can I Do?
The Thompson ranch is 1,889 acres. The Washington ranch is 4,217 acres. I want to know about how many acres larger the Washington ranch is.

Estimate the Difference

Round each number to the nearest thousand. Look at the digit in the hundreds place.

$$
\begin{array}{r}
4,217 \to 4,000 \\
-\ 1,889 \to -2,000 \\
\hline
2,000
\end{array}
$$

Think: 2 is less than 5, so round 4,217 down. 8 is more than 5, so round 1,889 up.

Subtract the rounded numbers.

The Washington ranch is about 2,000 acres larger.

Try It • Estimate each difference to the nearest thousand.

1.
$$
\begin{array}{r}
5,835 \to \underline{6,000} \\
-2,616 \to \underline{-3,000} \\
\hline
3,000
\end{array}
$$

2.
$$
\begin{array}{r}
9,147 \to \underline{9,000} \\
-6,029 \to \underline{-6,000} \\
\hline
3,000
\end{array}
$$

3.
$$
\begin{array}{r}
4,332 \to \underline{4,000} \\
-2,099 \to \underline{-2,000} \\
\hline
2,000
\end{array}
$$

4.
$$
\begin{array}{r}
8,765 \to \underline{9,000} \\
-4,668 \to \underline{-5,000} \\
\hline
4,000
\end{array}
$$

Power Practice • Estimate each difference to the nearest thousand.

5. 7,254 − 4,407 __3,000__

6. 6,821 − 1,940 __5,000__

7. 5,326 − 2,877 __2,000__

8. 6,555 − 3,009 __4,000__

© McGraw-Hill School Division

WHAT IF THE STUDENT CAN'T

Round to the Nearest Ten and Hundred

• Tell students that they can use what they know about rounding to the nearest ten and to the nearest hundred to round to the nearest thousand.

• Ask students to explain how to use the ones digit to round a number to the nearest ten. (If the ones digit is less than 5, round down. If the ones digit is 5 or greater, round up.)

• Ask students to explain how to use the tens digit to round a number to the nearest hundred. (If the tens digit is less than 5, round down. If the tens digit is 5 or greater, round up.)

• Ask students what digit they will look at to round a number to the nearest thousand. (the hundreds digit)

Complete the Power Practice

• Discuss each incorrect answer. Have students explain how they rounded each number in the problem.

USING THE LESSON

Lesson Goal

• Estimate differences to the nearest thousand.

What the Student Needs to Know

• Round to the nearest ten and hundred.

Getting Started

• Have students count by thousands from 0 to 10,000.

• Ask students to use mental math to multiply 1,000 by each of the digits 1–9.

• Explain to students that when they round to the nearest thousand the rounded number will be a multiple of 1,000.

What Can I Do?

Read the question and the response. Then read and discuss the example. Ask:

• *How can you find how many acres larger the Washington ranch is?* (Subtract the area of the Thompson ranch from the area of the Washington ranch.)

• *What digit do you look at to round a number to the nearest thousand?* (the hundreds digit)

• *Explain how to round 4,217 to the nearest thousand.* (The hundreds digit is 2, so 4,217 rounds down to 4,000.)

• *Explain how to round 1,889 to the nearest thousand.* (The hundreds digit is 8, so 1,889 rounds up to 2,000.)

Try It

• Ask students to tell what digit they will use to round 9,147 to the nearest thousand in exercise 2. (The hundreds digit, 1)

• Ask students to explain how they will round 6,029 to the nearest thousand. (The hundreds digit is 0, so 6,029 rounds down to 6,000.)

Power Practice

• Tell students to round each number to the nearest thousand, then subtract.

CHALLENGE

Lesson Goal

- Use whole number addition to solve a puzzle.

Introducing the Challenge

Ask students to find the number that will make a correct addition fact.

- $4 + \_\_\_ = 9$ (5)
- $\_\_\_ + 7 = 16$ (9)
- $6 + \_\_\_ = 12$ (6)
- $\_\_\_ + 3 = 11$ (8)

Name_____

Make the Sum

Make number cards like these.

Sample responses given.

Arrange number cards in the boxes to make the addition correct. Use each card only once.

1. What number plus 4 gives a sum of 9? ___5___

2. What number plus 3 gives a sum of 5? ___2___

3. Which of the numbers you have left can you put in the other boxes to make a true addition? __3 and 8__

Problems have more than one solution. A sample solution is given.

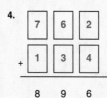

Arrange number cards in the boxes to make the addition correct. Use each card only once for each exercise.

4.
7	6	2
+ 1	3	4

8 9 6

5.
4 | 5 | 3

+ 2 | 2 | 7

6 8 0

© McGraw-Hill School Division

Name_____

Arrange number cards in the boxes to make the addition correct. Use each card only once for each exercise.

6.

	4	7	8
+	1	2	3
	6	0	1

7.

	6	8	3
+	2	5	4
	9	3	7

8.

	4	5	8
+	3	1	9
	7	7	7

9.

	4	2	5
+	3	7	6
	8	0	1

10.

	1	6	5
+	6	8	2
	8	4	7

11.

	5	9	3
+	2	7	4
	8	6	7

Using the Challenge

- Provide index cards or have students cut a sheet of paper into 10 pieces. Tell students to write one of the digits 0–9 on each piece of paper.

- Have the students complete problems 1–3. Then compare student responses. Point out that the puzzle has more than one correct answer.

- Tell students that the exercises may have more than one correct answer. Remind them that they should use each of their cards only once for each exercise.

CHALLENGE

Lesson Goal

- Use addition and subtraction of whole numbers to find pairs of mystery numbers.

Introducing the Challenge

- Ask students to choose two 3-digit numbers.
- Ask them to find the sum of the two numbers.
- Ask them to find the difference of the two numbers
- Tell students that in this challenge they will be given the sum and difference of two numbers. They will have to use these clues to decide which two numbers in the box are the mystery numbers.

CHALLENGE CHAPTER **14**

Sum and Difference Mysteries

Find the pair of mystery numbers.

Clues:
Their sum is 837.
Their difference is 215.

The suspects:

88	179	265
311	440	
526	616	783

1. To the nearest hundred, what is the sum of the two mystery numbers? __800__

2. To the nearest hundred, what is the difference of the two mystery numbers? __200__

3. Estimate to find pairs of numbers that have about the same sum as the mystery numbers. List the pairs.

   179 + 616 (200 + 600 = 800);

   265+ 526 (300 + 500 = 800); 311+ 526 (300 + 500 = 800)

4. Which of the pairs on your list have about the same difference as the mystery numbers?

   526 − 265 (500 − 300 = 200); 526 − 311 (500 − 300 = 200)

5. What are the mystery numbers? Add and subtract to prove you are correct.

   526 and 311; Proof: 526 + 311 = 837; 526 − 311 = 215

Name_____

Estimate to find each pair of mystery numbers.
Use the numbers from the previous page.

6. Clues: The sum is 528.   Proof: $\underline{440 + 88 = 528}$
The difference is 352. $\underline{440 - 88 = 352}$

Mystery numbers: $\underline{\quad 88 \text{ and } 440 \quad}$

7. Clues: The sum is 962.   Proof: $\underline{783 + 179 = 962}$
The difference is 604. $\underline{783 - 179 = 604}$

Mystery numbers: $\underline{\quad 783 \text{ and } 179 \quad}$

8. Clues: The sum is 966.   Proof: $\underline{526 + 440 = 966}$
The difference is 86. $\underline{526 - 440 = 86}$

Mystery numbers: $\underline{\quad 440 \text{ and } 526 \quad}$

9. Clues: The sum is 576.   Proof: $\underline{311 + 265 = 576}$
The difference is 46. $\underline{311 - 265 = 46}$

Mystery numbers: $\underline{\quad 311 \text{ and } 265 \quad}$

10. Write your own clues. Have a classmate find the mystery numbers using your clues.

Clues: The sum is: _____   Proof: _____

The difference is _____   _____

Mystery numbers: $\underline{\quad \text{Answers will vary.} \quad}$

CHALLENGE

Using the Challenge

- Work through problems 1–5 with the students. Then ask them to reiterate how to use estimation and the *Guess and Check* problem-solving strategy to find the mystery numbers.

- Ask student how they will prove that they have found the two mystery numbers. (Show that the sum and difference of the two numbers match the clues.)

- To make estimation easier, you may want to suggest that students round each of the numbers in the box to the nearest hundred and that they write the rounded number near the exact number.

- Students may want to exchange their own mystery number problems with classmates and try to solve them.